GCSE AQA

Chemistry

Complete Revision and Practice

If yo

Contents

Contents

The Periodic Table

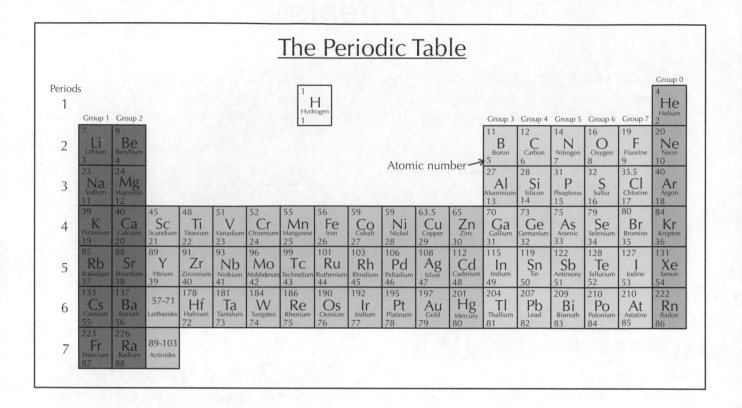

Published by CGP

From original material by Richard Parsons.

Editors:
Luke Antieul, Katherine Craig, Jane Sawers, Karen Wells.

Contributors:
Mike Bossart, Mike Dagless, Max Fishel, Sandy Gardner, Gemma Hallam, Sophie Watkins.

ISBN: 978 1 84762 661 5

With thanks to Barrie Crowther, Philip Dobson, Murray Hamilton and Glenn Rogers
for the proofreading.

With thanks to Jan Greenway, Laura Jakubowski and Laura Stoney for the copyright research.

Graph to show trend in atmospheric CO_2 concentration and global temperature on pages 49
and 70 based on data by EPICA Community Members 2004 and Siegenthaler et al 2005.

Groovy website: www.cgpbooks.co.uk

Printed by Elanders Ltd, Newcastle upon Tyne.
Jolly bits of clipart from CorelDRAW®

Photocopying – it's dull, grey and sometimes a bit naughty. Luckily, it's dead cheap, easy and quick to order
more copies of this book from CGP – just call us on 0870 750 1242. Phew!

The Scientific Process

You need to know a few things about how the world of science works.
First up is the scientific process — how a scientist's idea turns into a widely accepted theory.

Scientists come up with **hypotheses** — then **test** them

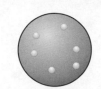

About 100 years ago, scientists hypothesised that atoms looked like this.

1) Scientists try to explain things. Everything.

2) They start by observing something they don't understand — it could be anything, e.g. planets in the sky, a person suffering from an illness, what matter is made of... anything.

3) Then, they come up with a hypothesis — a possible explanation for what they've observed.

4) The next step is to test whether the hypothesis might be right or not — this involves gathering evidence (i.e. data from investigations).

5) The scientist uses the hypothesis to make a prediction — a statement based on the hypothesis that can be tested. They then carry out an investigation.

6) If data from experiments or studies backs up the prediction, you're one step closer to figuring out if the hypothesis is true.

Investigations include lab experiments and studies.

Other scientists will **test** the hypothesis too

1) Other scientists will use the hypothesis to make their own predictions, and carry out their own experiments or studies.

2) They'll also try to reproduce the original investigations to check the results.

3) And if all the experiments in the world back up the hypothesis, then scientists start to think it's true.

4) However, if a scientist somewhere in the world does an experiment that doesn't fit with the hypothesis (and other scientists can reproduce these results), then the hypothesis is in trouble.

5) When this happens, scientists have to come up with a new hypothesis (maybe a modification of the old hypothesis, or maybe a completely new one).

After more evidence was gathered, scientists changed their hypothesis to this.

If **evidence** supports a hypothesis, it's **accepted** — for now

1) If pretty much every scientist in the world believes a hypothesis to be true because experiments back it up, then it usually goes in the textbooks for students to learn.

2) Accepted hypotheses are often referred to as theories.

Now we think it's more like this.

3) Our currently accepted theories are the ones that have survived this 'trial by evidence' — they've been tested many, many times over the years and survived (while the less good ones have been ditched).

4) However... they never, never become hard and fast, totally indisputable fact. You can never know... it'd only take one odd, totally inexplicable result, and the hypothesising and testing would start all over again.

You expect me to believe that — then show me the evidence...

If scientists think something is true, they need to produce evidence to convince others — it's all part of testing a hypothesis. One hypothesis might survive these tests, while others won't — it's how things progress. And along the way some hypotheses will be disproved — i.e. shown not to be true.

Your Data's Got To be Good

Evidence is the key to science — but not all evidence is equally good.
The way evidence is gathered can have a big effect on how trustworthy it is...

Lab experiments and studies are better than rumour

1) Results from experiments in laboratories are great. A lab is the easiest place to control variables so that they're all kept constant (except for the one you're investigating). This makes it easier to carry out a FAIR TEST.

2) For things that you can't investigate in the lab (e.g. climate) you conduct scientific studies. As many of the variables as possible are controlled, to make it a fair test.

3) Old wives' tales, rumours, hearsay, "what someone said", and so on, should be taken with a pinch of salt. Without any evidence they're NOT scientific — they're just opinions.

See page 7 for more about fair tests and variables.

The bigger the sample size the better

1) Data based on small samples isn't as good as data based on large samples. A sample should be representative of the whole population (i.e. it should share as many of the various characteristics in the population as possible) — a small sample can't do that as well.

2) The bigger the sample size the better, but scientists have to be realistic when choosing how big. For example, if you were studying how lifestyle affects people's weight it'd be great to study everyone in the UK (a huge sample), but it'd take ages and cost a lot of money. Studying a thousand people is more realistic.

If there's no evidence, there's no science...

You need to think carefully about where evidence has come from. If it's come from an experiment where the variables were controlled, then it's likely that you can trust the evidence. However, you also need to think about sample size — the bigger the sample, the better the results.

Your Data's Got To be Good

When it comes to evidence, <u>reliability</u> and <u>validity</u> are really important.

*Evidence needs to be **reliable** (**repeatable** and **reproducible**)*

Evidence is only <u>reliable</u> if it can be <u>repeated</u> (during an experiment) AND <u>other scientists can reproduce it too</u> (in other experiments). If it's not reliable, you can't believe it.

RELIABLE means that the data can be <u>repeated, and reproduced by others</u>.

<u>EXAMPLE:</u>

In 1989, two scientists claimed that they'd produced '<u>cold fusion</u>' (the energy source of the Sun — but without the big temperatures).

It was huge news — if true, it would have meant free energy for the world... forever.

However, other scientists just <u>couldn't reproduce the results</u> — so the results <u>weren't reliable</u>. And until they are, 'cold fusion' isn't going to be accepted as <u>fact</u>.

*Evidence also needs to be **valid***

VALID means that the data is <u>reliable</u> AND <u>answers the original question</u>.

<u>EXAMPLE: Do power lines cause cancer?</u>

Some studies have found that children who live near <u>overhead power lines</u> are more likely to develop <u>cancer</u>. What they'd actually found was a <u>correlation</u> (relationship) between the variables "<u>presence of power lines</u>" and "<u>incidence of cancer</u>" — they found that as one changed, so did the other.

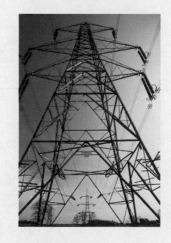

But this evidence is <u>not enough</u> to say that the power lines <u>cause</u> cancer, as other explanations might be possible.

For example, power lines are often near <u>busy roads</u>, so the areas tested could contain <u>different levels</u> of <u>pollution</u> from traffic.

So these studies don't show a definite link and so don't <u>answer the original question</u>.

RRR — Reliable means Repeatable and Reproducible...

By now you should have realised how <u>important</u> trustworthy <u>evidence</u> is. Unfortunately, you need to know loads more about fair tests and experiments — see pages 7-15.

Bias and How to Spot It

Scientific studies may <u>favour one side</u> of the argument for a number of reasons. This is called <u>bias</u>.

Scientific **evidence** can be **presented** in a **biased way**

1) People who want to make a point can sometimes <u>present data</u> in a <u>biased way</u>, e.g. they overemphasise a relationship in the data. (Sometimes <u>without knowing</u> they're doing it.)

2) And there are all sorts of reasons <u>why</u> people might <u>want</u> to do this — for example...

- They want to keep the <u>organisation</u> or <u>company</u> that's <u>funding the research</u> happy. (If the results aren't what they'd like they might not give them any more money to fund further research.)

- <u>Governments</u> might want to persuade voters, other governments, journalists, etc.

- <u>Companies</u> might want to 'big up' their products. Or make impressive safety claims.

- <u>Environmental campaigners</u> might want to persuade people to behave differently.

Things can affect **how seriously evidence** is **taken**

1) If an investigation is done by a team of <u>highly-regarded scientists</u> it's sometimes taken <u>more seriously</u> than evidence from <u>less well known scientists</u>.

2) But having experience, authority or a fancy qualification <u>doesn't</u> necessarily mean the evidence is <u>good</u> — the only way to tell is to look at the evidence scientifically (e.g. is it reliable, valid, etc.).

3) Also, some evidence might be <u>ignored</u> if it could create <u>political problems</u>, or <u>emphasised</u> if it <u>helps a particular cause</u>.

<u>EXAMPLE:</u>

Some governments were <u>pretty slow</u> to accept the fact that human activities are causing <u>global warming</u>, despite all the <u>evidence</u>.

This is because accepting it means they've got to <u>do something about it</u>, which <u>costs money</u> and could <u>hurt their economy</u>. This could <u>lose</u> them a lot of <u>votes</u>.

Trust me — I've got a BSc, PhD, PC, TV and a DVD...

We all tend to respect people bin authority, but you have to ignore that fact and <u>look at the evidence</u> (just because someone has got a massive list of letters after their name doesn't mean the evidence is good). Spotting biased evidence isn't the easiest thing in the world — ask yourself 'Does the scientist (or the person writing about it) stand to <u>gain something</u> (or lose something)?' If they do, it's possible that it <u>could be biased</u>.

Issues Created by Science

Scientific developments may not always <u>be for the best</u> — and here are a few reasons why.

Scientific developments are great, but they can raise issues

Scientific <u>knowledge is increased</u> by doing experiments. And this knowledge leads to <u>scientific developments</u>, e.g. new technologies or new advice. These developments can create <u>issues</u> though. For example:

Economic issues

Society <u>can't</u> always <u>afford</u> to do things scientists recommend (e.g. investing heavily in alternative energy sources) without <u>cutting back elsewhere</u>.

Social issues

Decisions based on scientific evidence affect <u>people</u> — e.g. should fossil fuels be taxed more highly (to invest in alternative energy)?

Should alcohol be banned (to prevent health problems)? <u>Would the effect on people's lifestyles be acceptable...</u>

Environmental issues

<u>Chemical fertilisers</u> may help us <u>produce more food</u> — but they also cause <u>environmental problems</u>.

Ethical issues

There are a lot of things that scientific developments have made possible, but <u>should we do them</u>? E.g. clone humans, develop better nuclear weapons.

Scientific developments aren't all good...

When you hear about a new development in science, think about whether it would have any issues or impacts. There will always be some, whether they're to do with the environment, people or money. Evaluating issues is the sort of thing that could come up in the exams, so get plenty of practice in now.

Science Has Limits

Science can give us amazing things — cures for diseases, space travel, heated toilet seats...
But science has its limitations — there are questions that it just can't answer.

Some questions are **unanswered** by science — so far

1) We don't understand everything. And we never will. We'll find out more, for sure
   — as more hypotheses are suggested, and more experiments are done.
   But there'll always be stuff we don't know.

   > EXAMPLES:
   > - Today we don't know as much as we'd like about the impacts of global warming.
   >   How much will sea level rise? And to what extent will weather patterns change?
   > - We also don't know anywhere near as much as we'd like about the Universe.
   >   Are there other life forms out there? And what is the Universe made of?

2) These are complicated questions. At the moment scientists don't all agree on the answers
   because there isn't enough reliable and valid evidence.

3) But eventually, we probably will be able to answer these questions once and for all...
   All we need is more evidence.

4) But by then there'll be loads of new questions to answer.

Other questions are **unanswerable** by science

1) Then there's the other type... questions that all the experiments in the world won't help us answer
   — the "Should we be doing this at all?" type questions. There are always two sides...

2) Think about new drugs which can be taken to boost your 'brain power'.

3) Different people have different opinions on them:

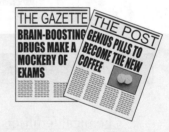

> Some people think they're good... Or at least no worse than
> taking vitamins or eating oily fish. They could let you keep thinking
> for longer, or improve your memory. It's thought that new drugs
> could allow people to think in ways that are beyond the powers of
> normal brains — in effect, to become geniuses...
>
> Other people say they're bad... taking them would give you an unfair advantage in exams, say.
> And perhaps people would be pressured into taking them so that they could work more effectively,
> and for longer hours.

4) The question of whether something is morally or ethically right or wrong can't be answered by
   more experiments — there is no "right" or "wrong" answer.

5) The best we can do is get a consensus from society — a judgement that most people are more or
   less happy to live by. Science can provide more information to help people make this judgement,
   and the judgement might change over time. But in the end it's up to people and their conscience.

Chips or rice? — totally unanswerable by science...

This is really important — science can't tell you whether you should or shouldn't do something.
That kind of thing is up to you and society to decide. There are tons of questions that science
might be able to answer in the future — like how much sea level might rise due to global warming
or what the Universe is made of. But these questions are unanswered by science so far.

Designing Investigations

You need to know all sorts about <u>investigations</u> for your <u>controlled assessment</u> and <u>your exams</u>. Investigations include <u>experiments</u> and <u>studies</u>. The next nine pages take you from start to finish. Enjoy.

Investigations *produce evidence* to *support* or *disprove* a *hypothesis*

1) Scientists <u>observe</u> things and come up with <u>hypotheses</u> to explain them (see page 1).

2) To figure out whether a hypothesis might be correct or not you need to do an <u>investigation</u> to <u>gather some evidence</u>.

3) The first step is to use the hypothesis to come up with a <u>prediction</u> — a statement about what you <u>think will happen</u> that you can <u>test</u>.

Sometimes the words 'hypothesis' and 'prediction' are used interchangeably.

4) For example, if your <u>hypothesis</u> is:

> "Spots are caused by picking your nose too much."

Then your <u>prediction</u> might be:

> "People who pick their nose more often will have more spots."

5) Investigations are used to see if there are <u>patterns</u> or <u>relationships between two variables</u>. For example, to see if there's a pattern or relationship between the variables 'having spots' and 'nose picking'.

6) The investigation has to be a <u>FAIR TEST</u> to make sure the evidence is <u>reliable</u> and <u>valid</u>...

See page 3 for more on reliability and validity.

To make an investigation a *fair test* you have to *control the variables*

1) In a lab experiment you usually <u>change one variable</u> and <u>measure</u> how it affects the <u>other variable</u>.

> EXAMPLE: you might change only the temperature of a chemical reaction and measure how this affects the rate of reaction.

2) To make it a fair test <u>everything else</u> that could affect the results should <u>stay the same</u> (otherwise you can't tell if the thing you're changing is causing the results or not — the data won't be reliable or valid).

> EXAMPLE continued: you need to keep the concentration of the reactants the same, otherwise you won't know if any change in the rate of reaction is caused by the change in temperature, or a difference in reactant concentration.

3) The variable you CHANGE is called the INDEPENDENT variable.
4) The variable you MEASURE is called the DEPENDENT variable.
5) The variables that you KEEP THE SAME are called CONTROL variables.

> EXAMPLE continued:
> Independent variable = temperature
> Dependent variable = rate of reaction
> Control variables = concentration of reactants, volume of reactants, etc.

Designing Investigations

There's a lot to think about when you're planning an investigation. Doing a <u>trial run</u> can make it easier to work out the best way to do an experiment though. Here's how...

Trial runs help figure out the range and interval of variable values

1) It's a good idea to do a <u>trial run</u> first — a <u>quick version</u> of your experiment.

2) Trial runs are used to figure out the <u>range</u> of variable values used in the proper experiment (the upper and lower limit). If you <u>don't</u> get a <u>change</u> in the dependent variable at the lower values in the trial run, you might <u>narrow</u> the range in the proper experiment. But if you still get a <u>big change</u> at the upper values you might <u>increase</u> the range.

> EXAMPLE continued:
> *   You might do a trial run with a range of 10-50 °C.
>   If there was no reaction at the lower end (e.g. 10-20 °C), you might narrow the range to 20-50 °C for the proper experiment.

3) And trial runs can be used to figure out the <u>interval</u> (gaps) between the values too. The intervals can't be too small (otherwise the experiment would take ages), or too big (otherwise you might miss something).

> EXAMPLE continued:
> *   If using 1 °C intervals doesn't give you much change in the rate of reaction each time you might decide to use 5 °C intervals, e.g. 20, 25, 30, 35, 40, 45, 50 °C...

4) Trial runs can also help you figure out <u>how many times</u> the experiment has to be <u>repeated</u> to get reliable results. E.g. if you repeat it three times and the <u>results</u> are all <u>similar</u>, then three repeats is enough.

You won't get a trial run at the exam, so get learning...

A trial run can also help you to spot any <u>problems</u> with your <u>method</u>. You don't want to find a load of issues when you're carrying out the real thing. For example, you might find an easier way to do something, or discover a way to do something that makes your results more accurate. And of course, as you've just learnt, trial runs help you work out the best range and interval of <u>variable values</u>.

Designing Investigations

You learnt on page 7 that to make a fair test, you have to control the variables. However, controlling all of the variables sometimes isn't as easy as it sounds — you might need to use a control group.

It can be **hard** to **control the variables** in a **study**

1) It's important that a study is a fair test, just like a lab experiment. It's a lot trickier to control the variables in a study than it is in a lab experiment though (see page 7).

2) Sometimes you can't control them all, but you can use a control group to help. This is a group of whatever you're studying (people, plants, lemmings, etc.) that's kept under the same conditions as the group in the experiment, but doesn't have anything done to it.

EXAMPLE:

- If you're studying the effect of pesticides on crop growth, pesticide is applied to one field but not to another field (the control field).

- Both fields are planted with the same crop, and are in the same area (so they get the same weather conditions).

- The control field is there to try and account for variables like the weather, which don't stay the same all the time, but could affect the results.

Investigations can be **hazardous**

1) A hazard is something that can potentially cause harm. Hazards include:

- Microorganisms, e.g. some bacteria can make you ill.
- Chemicals, e.g. sulfuric acid can burn your skin and alcohols catch fire easily.
- Fire, e.g. an unattended Bunsen burner is a fire hazard.
- Electricity, e.g. faulty electrical equipment could give you a shock.

You can find out about potential hazards by looking in textbooks, doing some internet research, or asking your teacher.

2) Scientists need to manage the risk of hazards by doing things to reduce them. For example:

- If you're working with sulfuric acid, always wear gloves and safety goggles. This will reduce the risk of the acid coming into contact with your skin and eyes.
- If you're using a Bunsen burner, stand it on a heat proof mat. This will reduce the risk of starting a fire.

The lab is a dangerous place...

There are plenty of things that can cause harm in the lab. When you're designing an investigation you need to think about how you can carry it out as safely as possible — even if it's just wearing a pair of safety goggles. That's not all you need to think about though... In a study, there might be some variables that are just impossible to control. This means you'll need to set up a control group.

Collecting Data

After designing your investigation to perfection, you'll need to <u>collect some data</u>.

Your data should be *reliable*, *accurate* and *precise*

1) To <u>improve</u> reliability you need to <u>repeat</u> the readings and calculate the <u>mean</u> (average). You need to repeat each reading at least <u>three times</u>.

2) To make sure your results are reliable you can cross check them by taking a <u>second set of readings</u> with <u>another instrument</u> (or a <u>different observer</u>).

3) Checking your results match with <u>secondary sources</u>, e.g. other studies, also increases the reliability of your data.

4) Your data also needs to be ACCURATE. Really accurate results are those that are <u>really close</u> to the <u>true answer</u>.

5) Your data also needs to be PRECISE. Precise results are ones where the data is <u>all really close</u> to the <u>mean</u> (i.e. not spread out).

Repeat	Data set 1	Data set 2
1	12	11
2	14	17
3	13	14
Mean	13	14

Data set 1 is more precise than data set 2.

Your *equipment* has to be *right for the job*

1) The measuring equipment you use has to be <u>sensitive enough</u> to measure the changes you're looking for. For example, if you need to measure changes of 1 ml you need to use a measuring cylinder that can measure in 1 ml steps — it'd be no good trying with one that only measures 10 ml steps.

2) The <u>smallest change</u> a measuring instrument can <u>detect</u> is called its RESOLUTION. E.g. some mass balances have a resolution of 1 g, some have a resolution of 0.1 g, and some are even more sensitive.

3) Also, equipment needs to be <u>calibrated</u> so that your data is <u>more accurate</u>. E.g. mass balances need to be set to zero before you start weighing things.

Reliability is really important in science...

Weirdly, data can be really <u>precise</u> but <u>not very accurate</u>, e.g. a fancy piece of lab equipment might give results that are precise, but if it's not calibrated properly those results won't be accurate.

Collecting Data

Errors and anomalous results can turn up in your data — but they don't have to lead to disaster.

You need to look out for errors and anomalous results

1) The results of your experiment will always vary a bit because of random errors — tiny differences caused by things like human errors in measuring.

2) You can reduce their effect by taking many readings and calculating the mean.

3) If the same error is made every time, it's called a SYSTEMATIC ERROR. For example, if you measured from the very end of your ruler instead of from the 0 cm mark every time, all your measurements would be a bit small.

Repeating the experiment in the exact same way and calculating an average won't correct a systematic error.

4) Just to make things more complicated, if a systematic error is caused by using equipment that isn't calibrated properly it's called a ZERO ERROR. For example, if a mass balance always reads 1 gram before you put anything on it, all your measurements will be 1 gram too heavy.

5) You can compensate for some systematic errors if you know about them though, e.g. if your mass balance always reads 1 gram before you put anything on it you can subtract 1 gram from all your results.

6) Sometimes you get a result that doesn't seem to fit in with the rest at all.

Park	Number of pigeons	Number of crazy tramps
A	28	1
B	42	2
C	1127	0

7) These results are called ANOMALOUS RESULTS.

8) You should investigate them and try to work out what happened. If you can work out what happened (e.g. you measured something totally wrong) you can ignore them when processing your results.

Zero error — sounds like a Bruce Willis film...

There are some errors that you just can't stop happening — these are called random errors. However, errors like zero errors can be avoided by making sure your equipment is set up properly to start with.

Processing and Presenting Data

After you've collected your data you'll have <u>loads of info</u> that you have to <u>make some kind of sense of</u>. You need to <u>process</u> and <u>present</u> it so you can look for <u>patterns</u> and <u>relationships</u> in it.

Data needs to be organised

1) Tables are dead useful for <u>organising data</u>.
2) When you draw a table <u>use a ruler</u>, make sure <u>each column</u> has a <u>heading</u> (including the <u>units</u>) and keep it neat and tidy.
3) Annoyingly, tables are about as useful as a chocolate teapot for showing <u>patterns</u> or <u>relationships</u> in data. You need to use some kind of graph for that.

You might have to process your data

1) When you've done repeats of an experiment you should always calculate the <u>mean</u> (average). To do this <u>ADD TOGETHER</u> all the data values and <u>DIVIDE</u> by the total number of values in the sample.
2) You might also need to calculate the <u>range</u> (how spread out the data is). To do this find the <u>LARGEST</u> number and <u>SUBTRACT</u> the <u>SMALLEST</u> number from it.

<u>EXAMPLE</u>   *Ignore anomalous results when calculating these.*

Test tube	Repeat 1 (g)	Repeat 2 (g)	Repeat 3 (g)	Mean (g)	Range (g)
A	28	37	32	(28 + 37 + 32) ÷ 3 = 32.3	37 − 28 = 9
B	47	51	60	(47 + 51 + 60) ÷ 3 = 52.7	60 − 47 = 13
C	68	72	70	(68 + 72 + 70) ÷ 3 = 70.0	72 − 68 = 4

If your data comes in categories, present it in a bar chart

1) If the independent variable is <u>categoric</u> (comes in distinct categories, e.g. blood types, metals) you should use a <u>bar chart</u> to display the data.
2) You also use them if the independent variable is <u>discrete</u> (the data can be counted in chunks, where there's no in-between value, e.g. number of people is discrete because you can't have half a person).
3) There are some <u>golden rules</u> you need to follow for <u>drawing</u> bar charts:

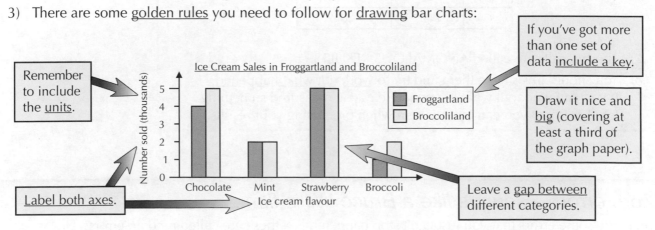

Remember to include the <u>units</u>.

Label both axes.

Ice Cream Sales in Froggartland and Broccoliland

Number sold (thousands)

Ice cream flavour

Chocolate · Mint · Strawberry · Broccoli

Froggartland
Broccoliland

If you've got more than one set of data <u>include a key</u>.

Draw it nice and <u>big</u> (covering at least a third of the graph paper).

Leave a <u>gap between</u> different categories.

Presenting Data

Scientists just <u>love</u> presenting data as <u>line graphs</u>...

*If your data is **continuous**, plot a **line graph***

1) If the independent variable is <u>continuous</u> (numerical data that can have any value within a range, e.g. length, volume, temperature) you should use a <u>line graph</u> to display the data.

2) Here are the <u>rules</u> for <u>drawing</u> line graphs:

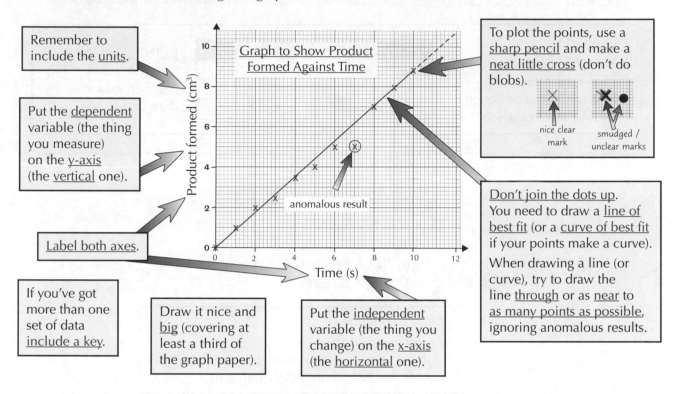

Remember to include the <u>units</u>.

Put the <u>dependent</u> variable (the thing you measure) on the <u>y-axis</u> (the <u>vertical</u> one).

<u>Label both axes</u>.

If you've got more than one set of data <u>include a key</u>.

Draw it nice and <u>big</u> (covering at least a third of the graph paper).

Put the <u>independent</u> variable (the thing you change) on the <u>x-axis</u> (the <u>horizontal</u> one).

Graph to Show Product Formed Against Time

Product formed (cm^3)

anomalous result

Time (s)

To plot the points, use a <u>sharp pencil</u> and make a <u>neat little cross</u> (don't do blobs).

nice clear mark

smudged / unclear marks

<u>Don't join the dots up</u>. You need to draw a <u>line of best fit</u> (or a <u>curve of best fit</u> if your points make a curve).

When drawing a line (or curve), try to draw the line <u>through</u> or as <u>near</u> to <u>as many points as possible</u>, ignoring anomalous results.

3) Line graphs are used to <u>show the relationship</u> between two variables (just like other graphs).

4) Data can show <u>three</u> different types of correlation (relationship):

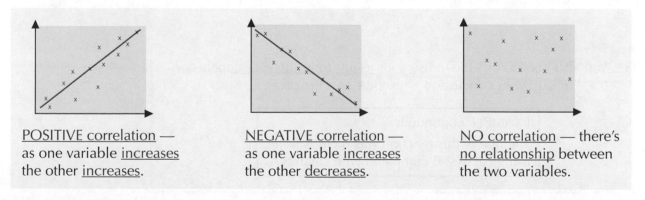

<u>POSITIVE correlation</u> — as one variable <u>increases</u> the other <u>increases</u>.

<u>NEGATIVE correlation</u> — as one variable <u>increases</u> the other <u>decreases</u>.

<u>NO correlation</u> — there's <u>no relationship</u> between the two variables.

5) You need to be able to describe the following relationships on line graphs too:

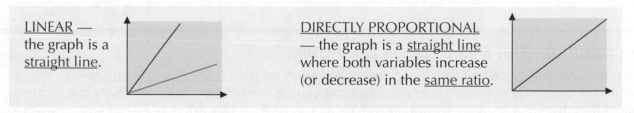

<u>LINEAR</u> — the graph is a <u>straight line</u>.

<u>DIRECTLY PROPORTIONAL</u> — the graph is a <u>straight line</u> where both variables increase (or decrease) in the <u>same ratio</u>.

Drawing Conclusions

You're nearly there now — the next step is to <u>draw a conclusion</u>. Here's what you need to do...

You can **only conclude** what the data shows and **NO MORE**

1) Drawing conclusions might seem pretty straightforward — you just <u>look at your data</u> and <u>say what pattern or relationship you see</u> between the dependent and independent variables.

EXAMPLE:

The table on the right shows the rate of a reaction in the presence of two different catalysts.

Catalyst	Rate of reaction (cm³/s)
A	13.5
B	19.5
No catalyst	5.5

CONCLUSION:
Catalyst <u>B</u> makes <u>this reaction</u> go faster than catalyst A.

2) But you've got to be really careful that your conclusion <u>matches the data</u> you've got and <u>doesn't go any further</u>.

EXAMPLE continued:

You <u>can't</u> conclude that catalyst B increases the rate of <u>any other reaction</u> more than catalyst A — the results might be completely different.

3) You also need to be able to <u>use your results</u> to <u>justify your conclusion</u> (i.e. back up your conclusion with some specific data).

EXAMPLE continued:

The rate of this reaction was 6 cm³/s faster using catalyst B compared with catalyst A.

I conclude that this page is a bit dull...

In the exams you could be given a <u>conclusion</u> and asked <u>whether some data supports it</u> — so make sure you understand <u>how far conclusions can go</u>. Remember, in a conclusion you can only say things that you can actually support with data. If you've got <u>no evidence</u>, it's just your <u>opinion</u>. <u>Correlation</u> and <u>cause</u> are also important in conclusions — luckily that's what the next page is about.

Drawing Conclusions

It's important that you understand the difference between <u>correlation</u> and <u>cause</u>. Take a bit of time to read over this page so that you don't make any mistakes when you're drawing conclusions.

Correlation DOES NOT mean cause

1) If two things are correlated (i.e. there's a relationship between them) it <u>doesn't</u> necessarily mean that a change in one variable is <u>causing</u> the change in the other — this is REALLY IMPORTANT, DON'T FORGET IT.

2) There are <u>three possible reasons</u> for a correlation:

1) Chance

1) Even though it might seem a bit weird, it's possible that two things show a correlation in a study purely because of <u>chance</u>.

2) For example, one study might find a correlation between people's hair colour and how good they are at frisbee. But other scientists don't get a correlation when they investigate it — the results of the first study are just a fluke.

2) Linked by a 3rd Variable

1) A lot of the time it may <u>look</u> as if a change in one variable is causing a change in the other, but it <u>isn't</u> — a <u>third variable links</u> the two things.

2) For example, there's a correlation between water temperature and shark attacks. This obviously isn't because warmer water makes sharks crazy. Instead, they're linked by a third variable — the number of people swimming (more people swim when the water's hotter, and with more people in the water you get more shark attacks).

3) Cause

1) Sometimes a change in one variable does <u>cause</u> a change in the other.

2) For example, there's a correlation between smoking and lung cancer. This is because chemicals in tobacco smoke cause lung cancer.

3) You can only conclude that a correlation is due to cause when you've <u>controlled all the variables</u> that could, just could, be affecting the result. (For the smoking example above this would include things like age and exposure to other things that cause cancer).

So remember, correlation and cause aren't the same thing...

If you've understood this page, you'll know that <u>cause</u> is <u>only one</u> of the reasons for a correlation in your results. If you didn't know that, you'd better go back and read the page again.

Controlled Assessment — Section 1

Controlled Assessment involves <u>doing an experiment</u> and <u>answering two question papers on it</u> under exam conditions. Luckily, the next two pages tell you all about the two question papers.

There are **two sections** in the **controlled assessment**

1) Planning

1) Before you do the Section 1 question paper you'll be given time to do some <u>research</u> into the topic that's been set — you'll need to develop a <u>hypothesis/prediction</u> and come up with <u>two</u> different methods to test it.

2) In your research, you should use a variety of <u>different sources</u> (e.g. the internet, textbooks etc.).

3) You'll need to be able to <u>outline both methods</u> and say which one is <u>best</u> (and why it's the best one) and describe your preferred method in <u>detail</u>.

4) You're allowed to write <u>notes</u> about your two methods on <u>one side of A4</u> and have them with you for both question papers.

In Section 1, you could be asked things like:

1) What your <u>hypothesis/prediction</u> is.

2) What variables you're going to <u>control</u> (and <u>how</u> you're going to control them).

3) What <u>measurements</u> you're going to take.

There's lots of help on all of these things on pages 7-15.

4) What <u>range</u> and <u>interval</u> of values you will use for the <u>independent variable</u>.

5) How you'd figure out the range and interval using a <u>trial run</u> (sometimes called a 'preliminary investigation' in the question papers). See page 8 for more.

6) How many times you're going to <u>repeat</u> the experiment — a minimum of <u>three</u> is a good idea.

7) What <u>equipment</u> you're going to use (and <u>why</u> that equipment is <u>right for the job</u>).

8) <u>How to carry out</u> the experiment, i.e. what you do first, what you do second...

9) What <u>hazards</u> are involved in doing the experiment, and <u>how to reduce them</u>.

10) What <u>table</u> you'll draw to put your results in.

When you've done the planning and completed the first question paper you'll actually <u>do the experiment</u>. Then you'll have to <u>present your data</u>. Make sure you use the <u>right type of graph</u>, and you <u>draw it properly</u> — see pages 12-13 for help. After that it's onto the Section 2 question paper...

Read all this through and you'll be ready to face Section 1...

That might be an Everest-sized list of stuff, but it's <u>all important</u>. No need to panic at the sight of it though — as long as you've <u>learnt everything</u> on the previous few pages, you should be fine.

Controlled Assessment — Section 2

One paper down. On to the second paper...

2) Drawing conclusions and evaluating

For the Section 2 question paper you have to do these things for <u>your experiment</u>:

1) <u>Analyse</u> and <u>draw conclusions</u> from your results. For this you need to <u>describe the relationship</u> between the variables in <u>detail</u> — see page 14 for how to do this.
E.g. 'I found that there is a relationship between picking your nose and having spots. The more often you pick your nose the more spots you'll have. For example, my results showed...'.

2) Say whether your results <u>back up the hypothesis/prediction</u>, and give reasons <u>why</u> or <u>why not</u>.
E.g. 'My results did not back up the prediction. The prediction was that picking your nose more has no effect on the number of spots you have. But I found the opposite to be true in my investigation'.

3) <u>Evaluate</u> your experiment.
For this you need to <u>suggest ways you could improve your experiment</u>.

- Comment on your <u>equipment</u> and <u>method</u>, e.g. could you have used more <u>accurate</u> equipment?

- Make sure you <u>explain how</u> the improvements would give you <u>better data</u> next time.

- <u>Refer to your results</u>. E.g. 'My data wasn't accurate enough because the mass balance I used only measured in 1 g steps. I could use a more sensitive one next time (e.g. a mass balance that measures in 0.5 g steps) to get more accurate data'.

You'll also be <u>given some secondary data</u> (data collected by someone else) from an experiment on the same topic and asked to <u>analyse it</u>. This just involves doing what you did for your data with the secondary data, e.g. draw conclusions from it.

And that's it for the controlled assessment...

You don't need to learn these two pages off by heart — they're just useful for when you're figuring out what you'll need to do in the two stages of your controlled assessment. Make sure you've read them through a couple of times — then you'll be familiar with what to expect in the papers. Everything you'll need to do in the planning and concluding stages has been covered on pages 7-15.

Atoms and Elements

Atoms are the building blocks of everything — and I mean everything.

Atoms have a small **nucleus** surrounded by **electrons**

There are quite a few different (and equally useful) models of the atom — but chemists tend to like this nuclear model best. You can use it to explain pretty much the whole of Chemistry... which is nice.

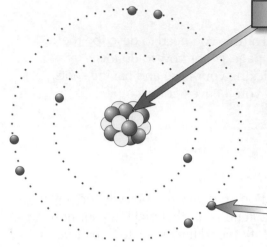

The Nucleus

1) It's in the middle of the atom.
2) It contains protons and neutrons.
3) Protons are positively charged.
4) Neutrons have no charge (they're neutral).
5) So the nucleus has a positive charge overall because of the protons.
6) But size-wise it's tiny compared to the rest of the atom.

The Electrons

1) Move around the nucleus.
2) They're negatively charged.
3) They're tiny, but they cover a lot of space.
4) They occupy shells around the nucleus.
5) These shells explain the whole of Chemistry.

Number of protons **equals** number of electrons

1) Atoms have no charge overall. They are neutral.
2) The charge on the electrons is the same size as the charge on the protons — but opposite.
3) This means the number of protons always equals the number of electrons in an atom.
4) If some electrons are added or removed, the atom becomes charged and is then an ion.

Elements consist of **one type** of atom only

1) Atoms can have different numbers of protons, neutrons and electrons. It's the number of protons in the nucleus that decides what type of atom it is.
2) For example, an atom with one proton in its nucleus is hydrogen and an atom with two protons is helium.
3) If a substance only contains one type of atom it's called an element.
4) There are about 100 different elements — quite a lot of everyday substances are elements:

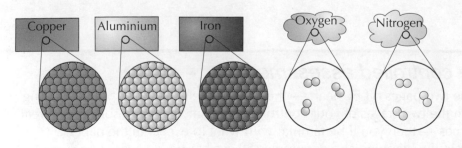

So all the atoms of a particular element (e.g. nitrogen) have the same number of protons...

...and different elements have atoms with different numbers of protons.

The Periodic Table

Chemistry would be <u>really messy</u> if it was all <u>big lists</u> of names and properties. So instead they've come up with a kind of <u>shorthand</u> for the names, and made a beautiful table to organise the elements — like a big <u>filing system</u>.

Atoms can be represented by **symbols**

Atoms of each element can be represented by a <u>one or two letter symbol</u> — it's a type of <u>shorthand</u> that saves you the bother of having to write the full name of the element.

Some make <u>perfect sense</u>, e.g.

| C = carbon | Li = lithium | Mg = magnesium |

Others seem to make about as much sense as an apple with a handle.

E.g.

| Na = sodium | Fe = iron | Pb = lead |

Most of these odd symbols actually come from the Latin names of the elements.

The **periodic table** puts **elements** with **similar properties together**

1) The periodic table is laid out so that elements with <u>similar properties</u> form <u>columns</u>.

2) These <u>vertical columns</u> are called <u>groups</u> and Roman numerals are often used for them.

3) All of the elements in a <u>group</u> have the <u>same number</u> of <u>electrons</u> in their <u>outer shell</u>.

4) This is why <u>elements</u> in the same group have <u>similar properties</u>. So, if you know the <u>properties</u> of <u>one element</u>, you can <u>predict</u> properties of <u>other elements</u> in that group.

5) For example, the <u>Group 1</u> elements are Li, Na, K, Rb, Cs and Fr. They're all <u>metals</u> and they <u>react the same way</u>. E.g. they all react with water to form an <u>alkaline solution</u> and <u>hydrogen gas</u>, and they all react with oxygen to form an <u>oxide</u>.

6) The elements in the final column (<u>Group 0</u>) are the noble gases. They all have <u>eight electrons</u> in their <u>outer shell</u>, apart from helium (which has two). This means that they're <u>stable</u> and <u>unreactive</u>.

The top number is the <u>mass number</u>. This is the total <u>number of protons and neutrons</u>.

So, if you want to find the number of neutrons in an atom, just subtract the atomic number from the mass number.

The bottom number is the <u>atomic number</u>. This is the <u>number of protons</u>, which conveniently also tells you the <u>number of electrons</u>.

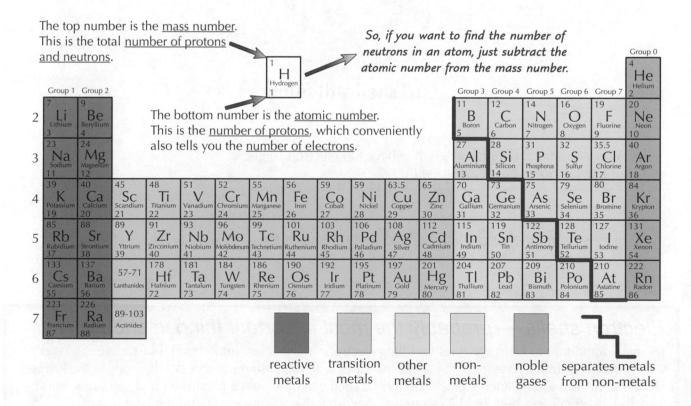

reactive metals | transition metals | other metals | non-metals | noble gases | separates metals from non-metals

Electron Shells

The fact that electrons occupy "shells" around the nucleus is what causes the whole of chemistry. Remember that, and watch how it applies to each bit of it. It's ace.

Electron shell **rules:**

1) Electrons always occupy <u>shells</u> (sometimes called <u>energy levels</u>).

2) The <u>lowest</u> energy levels are <u>always filled first</u> — these are the ones closest to the nucleus.

3) Only <u>a certain number</u> of electrons are allowed in each shell:

   • <u>1st shell</u> — 2

   • <u>2nd shell</u> — 8

   • <u>3rd shell</u> — 8

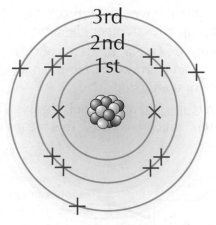

3rd shell still filling

4) Atoms are much <u>happier</u> when they have <u>full electron shells</u> — like the <u>noble gases</u> in <u>Group 0</u>.

5) In most atoms the <u>outer shell</u> is <u>not full</u> and this makes the atom want to <u>react</u> to fill it.

Electron shells — probably the most important thing in chemistry

It's really important to learn the rules for filling electron shells. It's so important I'll just leave this page with a quick reminder. Energy of the shells increases with increasing number (so shell one is the lowest). Fill the shell with lowest energy first. And the 1st shell can only hold a maximum of 2 electrons, but the 2nd and 3rd shells can both hold 8 electrons. Practise following these rules on the next page.

Electron Shells

You need to know the <u>electronic structures</u> for the first <u>20</u> elements
(things get a bit more complicated after that — luckily you don't have to worry about it).

*Follow the rules to **work out** electronic structures*

Electronic structures are not hard to work out.
For a quick example, take nitrogen. <u>Follow the steps...</u>

1) The periodic table tells us nitrogen has <u>seven</u> protons... so it must have <u>seven</u> electrons.

2) Follow the '<u>Electron Shell Rules</u>' above. The <u>first</u> shell can only take 2 electrons and the <u>second</u> shell can take a <u>maximum</u> of 8 electrons.

3) So the electronic structure for nitrogen <u>must</u> be <u>2, 5</u>. Easy peasy.

Now <u>you</u> try it for argon.

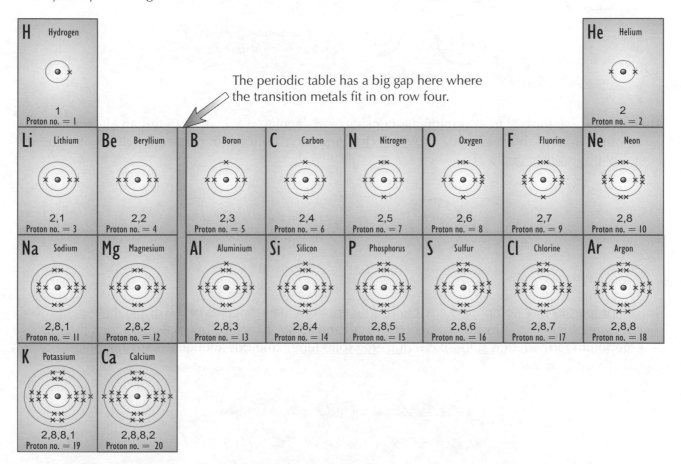

The periodic table has a big gap here where the transition metals fit in on row four.

Answer...

To calculate the electronic structure of argon, <u>follow the rules</u>. It's got 18 protons, so it <u>must</u> have 18 electrons. The first shell must have <u>2</u> electrons, the second shell must have <u>8</u>, and so the third shell must have <u>8</u> as well. It's as easy as <u>2, 8, 8</u>.

Each shell can only take a set number sof electrons

You need to know enough about electron shells to draw out that <u>whole diagram</u> at the bottom of the page without looking at it. Obviously, you don't have to learn each element separately, just <u>learn the pattern</u>. Cover the page: using a periodic table, find the atom with the electron structure 2, 8, 6.

Compounds

Life'd be oh so simple if you only had to worry about elements, even if there are a hundred or so of them. But you can mix and match elements to make lots of compounds, which complicates things no end.

Atoms *join together* to make *compounds*

1) When <u>different elements react</u>, atoms form <u>chemical bonds</u> with other atoms to form <u>compounds</u>. It's <u>usually difficult</u> to <u>separate</u> the two original elements out again.

2) <u>Making bonds</u> involves atoms giving away, taking or sharing <u>electrons</u>. Only the <u>electrons</u> are involved — it's nothing to do with the nuclei of the atoms at all.

3) A compound which is formed from a <u>metal</u> and a <u>non-metal</u> consists of <u>ions</u>. The <u>metal</u> atoms <u>lose</u> electrons to form <u>positive ions</u> and the non-metal atoms <u>gain</u> electrons to form <u>negative ions</u>. The <u>opposite charges</u> (positive and negative) of the ions mean that they're strongly <u>attracted</u> to each other. This is called <u>IONIC</u> bonding.

      E.g. NaCl

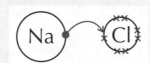

A sodium atom <u>gives</u> an electron to a chlorine atom.

4) A compound formed from <u>non-metals</u> consists of <u>molecules</u>. Each atom <u>shares</u> an <u>electron</u> with another atom — this is called a <u>COVALENT</u> bond. Each atom has to make enough covalent bonds to <u>fill up</u> its <u>outer shell</u>.

      E.g. HCl

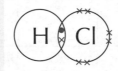

A hydrogen atom bonds with a chlorine atom by <u>sharing</u> an electron with it.

5) The <u>properties</u> of a compound are <u>totally different</u> from the properties of the <u>original elements</u>. For example, if iron (a lustrous magnetic metal) and sulfur (a nice yellow powder) react, the compound formed (<u>iron sulfide</u>) is a <u>dull grey solid lump</u>, and doesn't behave <u>anything like</u> either iron or sulfur.

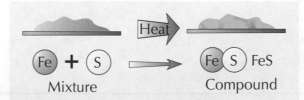

6) Compounds can be <u>small molecules</u> like water, or <u>great whopping lattices</u> like sodium chloride (when I say whopping I'm talking in atomic terms).

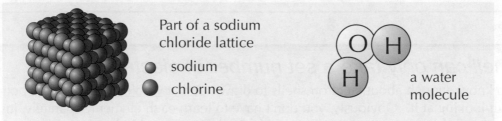

Part of a sodium chloride lattice
- sodium
- chlorine

a water molecule

Formulas and Reactions

Every compound has a <u>formula</u> — it tells you what it's made up of.

A *formula* shows what *atoms* are in a *compound*

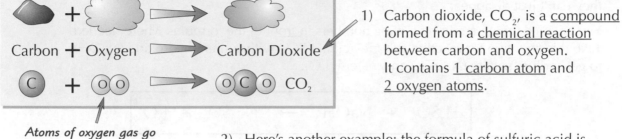

Atoms of oxygen gas go round in pairs (so it's O_2).

1) Carbon dioxide, CO_2, is a <u>compound</u> formed from a <u>chemical reaction</u> between carbon and oxygen. It contains <u>1 carbon atom</u> and <u>2 oxygen atoms</u>.

2) Here's another example: the formula of <u>sulfuric acid</u> is H_2SO_4. So, each molecule contains <u>2 hydrogen atoms</u>, <u>1 sulfur atom</u> and <u>4 oxygen atoms</u>.

3) There might be <u>brackets</u> in a formula, e.g. calcium hydroxide is $Ca(OH)_2$. The little number outside the bracket applies to <u>everything</u> inside the brackets. So in $Ca(OH)_2$ there is <u>1 calcium atom</u>, <u>2 oxygen atoms</u> and <u>2 hydrogen atoms</u>.

Atoms *aren't lost or made* in chemical reactions

1) During chemical reactions, things <u>don't</u> appear out of nowhere and things <u>don't</u> just disappear.

2) You still have the <u>same atoms</u> at the <u>end</u> of a chemical reaction as you had at the <u>start</u>. They're just <u>arranged</u> in different ways.

3) <u>Balanced symbol equations</u> show the atoms at the <u>start</u> (the <u>reactant</u> atoms) and the atoms at the <u>end</u> (the <u>product atoms</u>) and how they're arranged. For example:

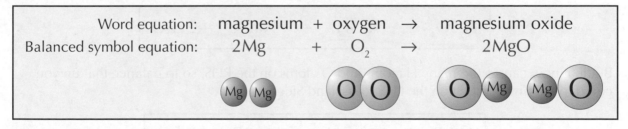

| Word equation: | magnesium + oxygen → magnesium oxide |
| Balanced symbol equation: | $2Mg$ + O_2 → $2MgO$ |

4) Because atoms aren't gained or lost, the mass of the reactants <u>equals</u> the mass of the products. So, if you completely react <u>6 g of magnesium</u> with <u>4 g of oxygen</u>, you'd end up with <u>10 g of magnesium oxide</u>.

Not learning this stuff will only compound your problems...

Formulas are pretty useful. The formula of a compound tells you <u>what atoms</u> it's made up of. You can use formulas to write out <u>balanced symbol equations</u> for reactions. And remember — you'll always have the <u>same number of atoms</u> at the end of a reaction as at the start.

Balancing Equations

Equations need a lot of practice if you're going to get them right — don't just skate over this stuff.

Balancing the equation — match them up one by one

1) There must always be the <u>same</u> number of atoms of each element on <u>both sides</u> — they can't just <u>disappear</u>.

2) You <u>balance</u> the equation by putting numbers <u>in front</u> of the formulas where needed. Take this equation for reacting sulfuric acid (H_2SO_4) with sodium hydroxide (NaOH) to get sodium sulfate (Na_2SO_4) and water (H_2O):

$$H_2SO_4 \ + \ NaOH \ \rightarrow \ Na_2SO_4 + H_2O$$

The <u>formulas</u> are all correct but the numbers of some atoms <u>don't match up</u> on both sides. E.g. there are 3 Hs on the left, but only 2 on the right. You <u>can't change formulas</u> like H_2O to H_3O. You can only put numbers <u>in front of them</u>:

Method: balance just one type of atom at a time

The more you practise, the quicker you get, but all you do is this:

1) Find an element that <u>doesn't balance</u> and <u>pencil in a number</u> to try and sort it out.
2) <u>See where it gets you</u>. It may create <u>another imbalance</u> — if so, just pencil in <u>another number</u> and see where that gets you.
3) Carry on chasing <u>unbalanced</u> elements and it'll <u>sort itself out</u> pretty quickly.

<u>I'll show you</u>. In the equation above you soon notice we're short of H atoms on the RHS (Right-Hand Side).

1) The only thing you can do about that is make it $2H_2O$ instead of just H_2O:

$$H_2SO_4 \ + \ NaOH \ \rightarrow \ Na_2SO_4 + 2H_2O$$

2) But that now causes too many H atoms and O atoms on the RHS, so to balance that up you could try putting 2NaOH on the LHS (Left-Hand Side):

$$H_2SO_4 \ + \ 2NaOH \ \rightarrow \ Na_2SO_4 + 2H_2O$$

3) And suddenly there it is! <u>Everything balances</u>. And you'll notice the Na just sorted itself out.

Balancing equations — weigh it up in your mind...

REMEMBER WHAT THOSE NUMBERS MEAN: A number in <u>front</u> of a formula applies to the <u>entire formula</u>. So, <u>3</u>Na_2SO_4 means three lots of Na_2SO_4. The little numbers in the <u>middle</u> or at the <u>end</u> of a formula <u>only</u> apply to the atom or brackets <u>immediately before</u>. So the 4 in Na_2SO_4 just means 4 Os, not 4 Ss.

Using Limestone

Limestone's often formed from sea shells, so you might not expect it to be useful as a building material.

Limestone is mainly calcium carbonate

Limestone's quarried out of the ground — it's great for making into blocks for building with. Fine old buildings like cathedrals are often made purely from limestone blocks. It's pretty sturdy stuff, but don't go thinking it doesn't react with anything.

St Paul's Cathedral is made from limestone.

1) Limestone is mainly calcium carbonate — $CaCO_3$.
2) When it's heated it thermally decomposes to make calcium oxide and carbon dioxide.

> **calcium carbonate → calcium oxide + carbon dioxide**
>
> $$CaCO_{3(s)} \rightarrow CaO_{(s)} + CO_{2(g)}$$

Thermal decomposition is when one substance chemically changes into at least two new substances when it's heated.

- When magnesium, copper, zinc and sodium carbonates are heated, they decompose in the same way.
  E.g. magnesium carbonate → magnesium oxide + carbon dioxide (i.e. $MgCO_3 \rightarrow MgO + CO_2$)
- However, you might have difficulty doing some of these reactions in class — a Bunsen burner can't reach a high enough temperature to thermally decompose some carbonates of Group I metals.

3) Calcium carbonate also reacts with acid to make a calcium salt, carbon dioxide and water. E.g.:

> **calcium carbonate + sulfuric acid → calcium sulfate + carbon dioxide + water**
>
> $$CaCO_3 + H_2SO_4 \rightarrow CaSO_4 + CO_2 + H_2O$$

- The type of salt produced depends on the type of acid. For example, a reaction with hydrochloric acid would make a chloride (e.g. $CaCl_2$).
- Other carbonates that react with acids are magnesium, copper, zinc and sodium.

This reaction means that limestone is damaged by acid rain (see p. 48).

Calcium oxide reacts with water to produce calcium hydroxide

1) When you add water to calcium oxide you get calcium hydroxide.

> **calcium oxide + water ⟶ calcium hydroxide**
>
> or $CaO + H_2O \longrightarrow Ca(OH)_2$

2) Calcium hydroxide is an alkali which can be used to neutralise acidic soil in fields. Powdered limestone can be used for this too, but the advantage of calcium hydroxide is that it works much faster.
3) Calcium hydroxide can also be used in a test for carbon dioxide. If you make a solution of calcium hydroxide in water (called limewater) and bubble gas through it, the solution will turn cloudy if there's carbon dioxide in the gas. The cloudiness is caused by the formation of calcium carbonate.

> **calcium hydroxide + carbon dioxide → calcium carbonate + water**
>
> $$Ca(OH)_2 + CO_2 \rightarrow CaCO_3 + H_2O$$

Using Limestone

Limestone is really very handy. However, digging huge amounts of limestone out of the ground can have a quite a significant negative effect on the environment.

*Limestone is used to make **other useful things** too*

1) Powdered limestone is <u>heated</u> in a kiln with <u>powdered clay</u> to make <u>cement</u>.

2) Cement can be mixed with <u>sand</u> and <u>water</u> to make <u>mortar</u>. <u>Mortar</u> is the stuff you stick <u>bricks</u> together with. You can also add <u>calcium hydroxide</u> to mortar.

3) Or you can mix cement with <u>sand</u> and <u>aggregate</u> (water and gravel) to make <u>concrete</u>.

*Quarrying limestone makes a **right mess** of the **landscape***

Digging limestone out of the ground can cause environmental problems.

1) For a start, it makes <u>huge ugly holes</u> which permanently change the landscape.

2) <u>Quarrying</u> processes, like blasting rocks apart with explosives, make lots of <u>noise</u> and <u>dust</u> in quiet, scenic areas.

3) Quarrying <u>destroys the habitats</u> of animals and birds.

4) The limestone needs to be <u>transported away</u> from the quarry — usually in lorries. This causes more noise and pollution.

5) Waste materials produce unsightly <u>tips</u>.

Limestone's amazingly useful

Wow. It sounds like you can achieve <u>pretty much anything</u> with limestone, possibly apart from a bouncy castle. I wonder what we'd be using instead if all those sea creatures hadn't died and conveniently become rock? But don't forget that quarrying is a messy business.

Using Limestone

So using limestone ain't all hunky-dory — making stuff from it causes quite a few <u>problems</u>.

Making stuff from limestone causes pollution too

1) <u>Cement factories</u> make a lot of <u>dust</u>, which can cause <u>breathing problems</u> for some people.

2) <u>Energy</u> is needed to produce cement and quicklime. The energy is likely to come from burning <u>fossil fuels</u>, which causes pollution.

See page 48 for more on pollution caused by burning fossil fuels.

But on the plus side...

1) Limestone provides things that people want — like <u>houses</u> and <u>roads</u>. Chemicals used in making <u>dyes</u>, <u>paints</u> and <u>medicines</u> also come from limestone.

2) Limestone products are used to <u>neutralise acidic soil</u>. Acidity in lakes and rivers caused by <u>acid rain</u> is also <u>neutralised</u> by limestone products.

3) Limestone is also used in power station chimneys to <u>neutralise sulfur dioxide</u>, which is a cause of acid rain.

4) The quarry and associated businesses provide <u>jobs</u> for people and bring more money into the <u>local economy</u>. This can lead to <u>local improvements</u> in transport, roads, recreation facilities and health.

5) Once quarrying is complete, <u>landscaping</u> and <u>restoration</u> of the area is normally required as part of the planning permission.

Limestone products have advantages and disadvantages

1) Limestone and concrete (made from cement) are used as <u>building materials</u>. In some cases they're <u>perfect</u> for the job, but in other cases they're a bit of a compromise.

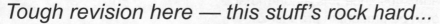

2) Limestone is <u>widely available</u> and is <u>cheaper</u> than granite or marble. It's also a fairly easy rock to <u>cut</u>.

3) Some limestone is more <u>hard-wearing</u> than marble, but it still looks <u>attractive</u>.

4) Concrete can be poured into <u>moulds</u> to make blocks or panels that can be joined together. It's a <u>very quick and cheap</u> way of constructing buildings — <u>and it shows</u>... — concrete has got to be the most <u>hideously unattractive</u> building material ever known.

5) Limestone, concrete and cement <u>don't rot</u> when they get wet like wood does. They can't be gnawed away by <u>insects</u> or <u>rodents</u> either. And to top it off, they're <u>fire-resistant</u> too.

6) Concrete <u>doesn't corrode</u> like lots of metals do. It does have a fairly <u>low tensile strength</u> though, and can crack. If it's <u>reinforced</u> with steel bars it'll be much stronger.

Tough revision here — this stuff's rock hard...

There's a <u>downside</u> to everything, including using limestone — ripping open huge quarries definitely <u>spoils the countryside</u>. But you have to find a <u>balance</u> between the environmental and ecological factors and the economic and social factors — is it worth keeping the countryside pristine if it means loads of people have nowhere to live because there's no stuff available to build houses with?

Warm-Up and Exam Questions

It's easy to think you've learnt everything in the section until you try the warm-up questions. Don't panic if there are bits you've forgotten. Just go back over those bits until they're firmly fixed in your brain.

Warm-Up Questions

1) What is the definition of an element? Roughly how many different elements are there?
2) How many electrons can be held in:
   a) the first shell, and
   b) the second shell?
3) What does a compound formed from a metal and a non-metal consist of?
4) What type of bonds do compounds formed from non-metals contain?
5) Balance this equation for the reaction of glucose ($C_6H_{12}O_6$) and oxygen:
   $$C_6H_{12}O_6 + O_2 \rightarrow CO_2 + H_2O$$
6) Describe the difference between cement and mortar.
7) Give an example of environmental damage caused by quarrying.

Exam Questions

1   Nitrogen has 7 protons and 7 neutrons.

   (a) How many electrons does nitrogen have?

(1 mark)

   (b) What is the chemical symbol for nitrogen?

(1 mark)

   (c) Look at the position of nitrogen on a periodic table. Is it a metal or non-metal?

(1 mark)

   (d) Give another element that will have similar chemical properties to nitrogen. Explain why you chose this element.

(3 marks)

2   The equation for a reaction is shown below.

$$X + Y \rightarrow Z$$

Substance **Y** reacts with 4 g of substance **X**. 17 g of **Z** is produced.

   (a) Describe what happens to the number of atoms during a chemical reaction.

(1 mark)

   (b) Work out the mass of substance **Y** involved in the reaction.

(2 marks)

   (c) Substance **Y** is sodium and substance **X** is a non-metal. What type of bonding would be present in product **Z**?

(1 mark)

Exam Questions

3　The electron arrangement of sodium is shown in the diagram:

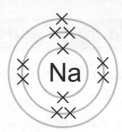

(a)　How many protons does sodium have?

(1 mark)

(b)　Sodium is in Group 1. Give another element that would have the same number of outer shell electrons.

(1 mark)

(c)　How many electrons does sodium need to lose so that it has a full outer shell?

(1 mark)

4　Sulfuric acid, H_2SO_4, reacts with ammonia, NH_3, to form ammonium sulfate, $(NH_4)_2SO_4$.

(a)　Write the word equation for this reaction.

(1 mark)

(b)　Write a balanced symbol equation for this reaction.

(2 marks)

(c)　In the balanced equation, how many atoms are there in the reactants?

(1 mark)

5　Limestone is mainly calcium carbonate, $CaCO_3$.
Calcium carbonate can be thermally decomposed.

(a)　Write a balanced symbol equation for this reaction.

(2 marks)

(b)　Explain why you cannot carry out this reaction with all carbonates of Group 1 metals in the lab.

(1 mark)

(c)　Explain why limestone is affected by acid rain.

(2 marks)

6　Limestone is often used to make building materials.

(a)　How is cement made from limestone?

(2 marks)

(b)　How is concrete made from limestone?

(2 marks)

Getting Metals From Rocks

A few <u>unreactive metals</u> like <u>gold</u> are found in the Earth as the <u>metal itself</u>, rather than as a compound. The rest of the metals we get by extracting them from rocks — and I bet you're just itching to find out how...

Ores contain *enough metal* to make *extraction* worthwhile

1) A <u>metal ore</u> is a <u>rock</u> which contains <u>enough metal</u> to make it <u>worthwhile</u> extracting the metal from it.

2) In many cases the ore is an <u>oxide</u> of the metal. For example, the main <u>aluminium ore</u> is called <u>bauxite</u> — it's aluminium oxide (Al_2O_3).

3) <u>Most metals</u> need to be extracted from their ores using a <u>chemical reaction</u>.

4) The <u>economics</u> (profitability) of metal extraction can <u>change</u> over <u>time</u>. For example:

> • If the market <u>price</u> of a metal <u>drops</u> a lot, it <u>might not</u> be worth extracting it. If the <u>price increases</u> a lot then it <u>might be worth</u> extracting <u>more</u> of it.
>
> • As <u>technology improves</u>, it becomes possible to <u>extract more</u> metal from a sample of rock than was originally possible. So it might now be <u>worth</u> extracting metal that <u>wasn't</u> worth extracting <u>in the past</u>.

Metals are *extracted* from their ores *chemically*

1) A metal can be extracted from its ore <u>chemically</u> — by <u>reduction</u> (see next page) or by <u>electrolysis</u> (splitting with electricity, see page 33).

2) Some ores may have to be <u>concentrated</u> before the metal is extracted — this just involves getting rid of the <u>unwanted rocky material</u>.

3) <u>Electrolysis</u> can also be used to <u>purify</u> the extracted metal (see page 32).

Occasionally, some metals are extracted from their ores using displacement reactions (see page 34).

You've got to keep your mind on the money

Extracting metals is all about <u>money</u>. If extracting a metal from a rock isn't going to make any cash then quite frankly not many people are interested. That's just the way it is.

The Reactivity Series

How easy it is to get a metal out of its ore all comes down to the metal's position in the reactivity series.

Some metals can be extracted by reduction with carbon

1) A metal can be extracted from its ore chemically by reduction using carbon.

2) When an ore is reduced, oxygen is removed from it, e.g.

$$2Fe_2O_3 \quad + \quad 3C \quad \rightarrow \quad 4Fe \quad + \quad 3CO_2$$

$$\text{iron(III) oxide} \quad + \quad \text{carbon} \quad \rightarrow \quad \text{iron} \quad + \quad \text{carbon dioxide}$$

3) The position of the metal in the reactivity series determines whether it can be extracted by reduction with carbon.

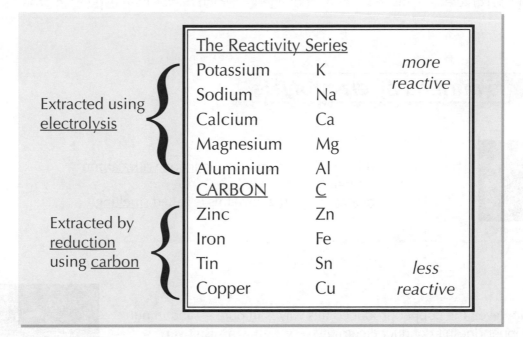

Extracted using electrolysis {

Extracted by reduction using carbon {

The Reactivity Series

Potassium	K	*more reactive*
Sodium	Na	
Calcium	Ca	
Magnesium	Mg	
Aluminium	Al	
CARBON	C	
Zinc	Zn	
Iron	Fe	
Tin	Sn	*less reactive*
Copper	Cu	

- Metals higher than carbon in the reactivity series have to be extracted using electrolysis, which is expensive.

- Metals below carbon in the reactivity series can be extracted by reduction using carbon. For example, iron oxide is reduced in a blast furnace to make iron.
  This is because carbon can only take the oxygen away from metals which are less reactive than carbon itself is.

Extraction of metals is difficult

Extracting metals isn't cheap. You have to pay for special equipment, energy and labour. Then there's the cost of getting the ore to the extraction plant. If there's a choice of extraction methods, a company always picks the cheapest, unless there's a good reason not to — they're not extracting it for fun.

Extraction of Metals

You may think you know all you could ever want to know about how to get metals from rocks, but no — there's <u>more</u> of it. Think of each of the facts on this page as a little <u>gold nugget</u>. Or, er, a copper one.

Some metals *have to be* **extracted** *by* **electrolysis**

1) Metals that are <u>more reactive</u> than carbon (see previous page) have to be extracted using electrolysis of <u>molten compounds</u>.

2) An example of a metal that has to be extracted this way is <u>aluminium</u>.

3) However, the process is <u>much more expensive</u> than reduction with carbon (see previous page) because it <u>uses a lot of energy</u>.

> <u>FOR EXAMPLE</u>: a <u>high temperature</u> is needed to <u>melt</u> aluminium oxide so that <u>aluminium</u> can be extracted — this requires a lot of <u>energy</u>, which makes it an <u>expensive</u> process.

Copper *is* **purified** *by* **electrolysis**

A copper ore

1) Copper can be easily extracted by <u>reduction with carbon</u> (see previous page).
The ore is <u>heated</u> in a <u>furnace</u> — this is called <u>smelting</u>.

2) However, the copper produced this way is <u>impure</u> — and impure copper <u>doesn't</u> conduct electricity very well. This <u>isn't</u> very <u>useful</u> because a lot of copper is used to make <u>electrical wiring</u>.

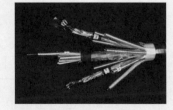

3) So <u>electrolysis</u> is also used to <u>purify</u> it, even though it's quite <u>expensive</u>.

4) This produces <u>very pure</u> copper, which is a <u>much better conductor</u>.

Electrolysis is expensive...

...but it's also pretty <u>useful</u> when it comes to getting hold of metals. It's used to <u>extract</u> some metals and to <u>purify</u> others — now that's what I call multitasking. Just think where we'd be without quality <u>copper wire</u> to conduct <u>electricity</u> — in the dark, for a start.

Extraction of Metals

You need to know the ins and outs of how <u>electrolysis</u> is used to extract and purify metals.

Electrolysis means "splitting up with electricity"

You could <u>extract</u> copper straight from its ore by electrolysis if you wanted to, but it's more expensive than using reduction with carbon.

1) <u>Electrolysis</u> is the <u>breaking down</u> of a substance using <u>electricity</u>.

2) It requires a <u>liquid</u> to <u>conduct</u> the <u>electricity</u>, called the <u>electrolyte</u>.

3) Electrolytes are often <u>metal salt solutions</u> made from the ore (e.g. copper sulfate) or <u>molten metal oxides</u>.

4) The electrolyte has <u>free ions</u> — these <u>conduct</u> the electricity and allow the whole thing to work.

5) Electrons are <u>taken away</u> by the <u>positive electrode</u> and <u>given away</u> by the <u>negative electrode</u>. As ions gain or lose electrons they become atoms or molecules and are released.

Here's how electrolysis is used to get <u>copper</u>:

1) <u>Electrons</u> are <u>pulled off</u> copper atoms at the <u>positive electrode</u>, causing them to go into solution as Cu^{2+} ions.

2) Cu^{2+} ions near the <u>negative electrode</u> gain electrons and turn back into <u>copper atoms</u>.

3) The <u>impurities</u> are dropped at the <u>positive electrode</u> as a <u>sludge</u>, whilst <u>pure copper atoms</u> bond to the <u>negative electrode</u>.

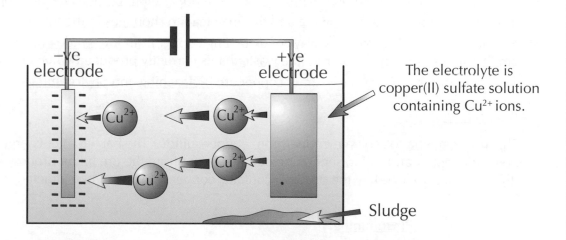

−ve electrode

+ve electrode

The electrolyte is copper(II) sulfate solution containing Cu^{2+} ions.

Sludge

The <u>negative electrode</u> starts as a <u>thin</u> piece of <u>pure copper</u> and more pure copper <u>adds</u> to it.

The <u>positive electrode</u> is just a big lump of <u>impure copper</u>, which will <u>dissolve</u>.

Copper is a really useful metal

The skin of the <u>Statue of Liberty</u> is made of copper — about 80 tonnes of it in fact. Its surface reacts with gases in the air to form <u>copper carbonate</u> — which is why it's that pretty shade of <u>green</u>. It was a present from France to the United States — I wonder if they found any wrapping paper big enough?

Extraction of Metals

Just to top it off, you need to know even more about <u>copper extraction</u>... sigh, it's a hard life.

A *displacement reaction* can be used to **extract copper**

1) <u>More reactive</u> metals react <u>more vigorously</u> than <u>less reactive</u> metals.

2) If you put a <u>reactive metal</u> into a solution of a <u>dissolved metal compound</u>, the reactive metal will <u>replace</u> the <u>less reactive metal</u> in the compound.

3) This is because the more reactive metal bonds <u>more strongly</u> to the non-metal bit of the compound and <u>pushes out</u> the less reactive metal.

4) For example, <u>scrap iron</u> can be used to displace copper from solution — this is really useful because iron is cheap but copper is expensive. If some iron is put in a solution of <u>copper sulfate</u>, the more reactive iron will "<u>kick out</u>" the less reactive copper from the solution. You end up with <u>iron sulfate solution</u> and <u>copper metal</u>.

> copper sulfate + iron → iron sulfate + copper

5) If a piece of <u>silver metal</u> is put into a solution of copper sulfate, <u>nothing happens</u>. The more reactive metal (copper) is <u>already</u> in the solution.

Copper-rich ores are in short supply

1) The supply of copper-rich ores is <u>limited</u>, so it's important to <u>recycle</u> as much copper as possible.

2) The demand for copper is <u>growing</u> and this may lead to <u>shortages</u> in the future.

3) Scientists are looking into new ways of extracting copper from <u>low-grade ores</u> (ores that only contain small amounts of copper) or from the <u>waste</u> that is currently produced when copper is extracted.

4) Examples of new methods to extract copper are <u>bioleaching</u> and <u>phytomining</u>:

Bioleaching

This uses <u>bacteria</u> to separate copper from copper sulfide. The bacteria get energy from the bond between copper and sulfur, separating out the <u>copper</u> from the ore in the process. The <u>leachate</u> (the solution produced by the process) contains copper, which can be extracted, e.g. by filtering.

Phytomining

This involves growing <u>plants</u> in <u>soil</u> that <u>contains copper</u>. The plants <u>can't use</u> or <u>get rid</u> of the copper so it gradually <u>builds up</u> in the <u>leaves</u>. The plants can be <u>harvested</u>, <u>dried</u> and <u>burned</u> in a furnace. The <u>copper</u> can be <u>collected</u> from the <u>ash</u> left in the furnace.

5) Traditional methods of copper mining are pretty <u>damaging</u> to the <u>environment</u> (see next page). These new methods of extraction have a much <u>smaller impact</u>, but the disadvantage is that they're <u>slow</u>.

Personally, I'd rather be pound rich than copper rich...

The fact that copper-rich ore supplies are dwindling means that scientists have to come up with <u>ever-more-cunning</u> methods to extract it. It also means that you have to learn all about it.

Impacts of Extracting Metals

Metals are very useful. Just imagine if all knives and forks were made of plastic instead — there'd be prongs snapping all over the place at dinner time. However, metal extraction uses a lot of <u>energy</u> and is <u>bad</u> for the <u>environment</u>. And that's where recycling comes in handy.

Metal extraction can be *bad* for the *environment*

1) People have to balance the <u>social</u>, <u>economic</u> and <u>environmental</u> effects of mining the ores.
2) Most of the issues are exactly the same as those to do with quarrying limestone on page 26.

So mining metal ores is <u>good</u> because it means that <u>useful products</u> can be made. It also provides local people with <u>jobs</u> and brings <u>money</u> into the area. This means services such as <u>transport</u> and <u>health</u> can be improved.

But mining ores is <u>bad for the environment</u> as it causes noise, scarring of the landscape and loss of habitats. Deep mine shafts can also be <u>dangerous</u> for a long time after the mine has been abandoned.

Recycling metals is *important*

1) Mining and extracting metals takes lots of <u>energy</u>, most of which comes from burning <u>fossil fuels</u>.

2) Fossil fuels are <u>running out</u> so it's important to <u>conserve</u> them. Not only this, but burning them contributes to <u>acid rain</u>, <u>global dimming</u> and <u>climate change</u> (see pages 48 and 49).

3) Recycling metals only uses a <u>small fraction</u> of the energy needed to mine and extract new metal. E.g. recycling copper only takes 15% of the energy that's needed to mine and extract new copper.

4) Energy doesn't come cheap, so recycling <u>saves money</u> too.

5) Also, there's a <u>finite amount</u> of each <u>metal</u> in the Earth. Recycling conserves these resources.

6) Recycling metal cuts down on the amount of rubbish that gets sent to <u>landfill</u>. Landfill takes up space and <u>pollutes</u> the surroundings. If all the aluminium cans in the UK were recycled, there'd be 14 million fewer dustbins to empty each year.

Get back on your bike again — recycle...

Recycling metals saves <u>natural resources</u> and <u>money</u> and reduces <u>environmental problems</u>. It's great. There's no limit to the number of times metals like aluminium, copper and steel can be recycled. So your humble little drink can may one day form part of a powerful robot who takes over the galaxy.

Warm-Up and Exam Questions

You've arrived at the next set of warm-up and exam questions. It's really important to find out what you know (as well as what you think you know but actually don't). So give them a go.

Warm-Up Questions

1) What is an ore?
2) Name a metal which can be extracted from its ore by reduction with carbon.
3) Why is electrolysis expensive?
4) Name a process used to purify copper.
5) Explain how phytomining can be used to extract copper.

Exam Questions

1   Copper is not usually extracted form its ore by electrolysis.
   (a)   Suggest why this is.

(2 marks)

   (b)   Copper sulfate solution can be electrolysed to obtain pure copper.
       Explain what happens to the Cu^{2+} ions in the solution during this process.

(1 mark)

2   Copper needs to be extracted from its ore before it can be used.
   (a)   Why are scientists trying to find new ways to extract copper
       from low-grade ores?

(1 mark)

   (b)   It is possible to extract copper from copper sulfide using bacteria.

      (i)   What is the name of this method?

(1 mark)

      (ii)   Describe the process involved in this method.

(1 mark)

      (iii)   Give **one** advantage of using this method rather than other methods.

(1 mark)

      (iv)   Give **one** disadvantage of using this method rather than other methods.

(1 mark)

3   *In this question you will be assessed on the quality of your English,
the organisation of your ideas and your use of appropriate specialist vocabulary.*

Mining ores has social, economic and environmental effects.
Discuss the positive and negative effects of mining metal ores.

(6 marks)

Exam Questions

4　The diagram shows part of the reactivity series of metals, together with carbon.

Potassium	K	more reactive
Sodium	Na	
Calcium	Ca	
Magnesium	Mg	
Aluminium	Al	
<u>CARBON</u>	<u>C</u>	
Zinc	Zn	
Iron	Fe	
Tin	Sn	less reactive
Copper	Cu	

(a)　Name one metal which is extracted from its ore using electrolysis.

(1 mark)

(b)　Some metals can be extracted from their ores by reduction with carbon, producing the metal and carbon dioxide.

(i)　Explain the meaning of reduction.

(1 mark)

(ii)　Write a word equation for the reduction of zinc oxide by carbon.

(1 mark)

(c)　Iron can be extracted by the reduction of iron(III) oxide (Fe_2O_3) with carbon (C), to produce iron and carbon dioxide.

Write a balanced symbol equation for this reaction.

(2 marks)

(d)　(i)　In which of these test tubes will a reaction occur?

(1 mark)

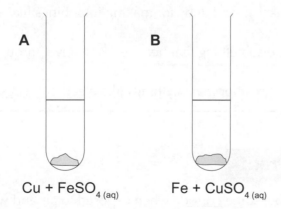

A $Cu + FeSO_{4\ (aq)}$　　　**B** $Fe + CuSO_{4\ (aq)}$

(ii)　Explain your answer.

(2 marks)

(e)　Explain why recycling metals is important.

(6 marks)

Properties of Metals

Metals are all the <u>same</u> but slightly <u>different</u>. They have some <u>basic properties</u> in common, but each has its own <u>specific combination</u> of properties, which mean you use different ones for different purposes.

Metals are strong and bendy and they're great conductors

1) <u>Most of the elements</u> are <u>metals</u> — so they cover most of the periodic table. In fact, <u>only</u> the elements on the <u>far right</u> are <u>non-metals</u>.

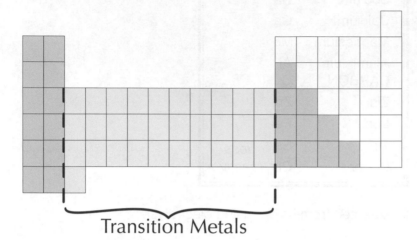

Only the unshaded elements are non-metals.

Transition Metals

2) All metals have some fairly similar <u>basic properties</u>:

> - Metals are <u>strong</u> (hard to break), but they can be <u>bent or hammered</u> into different shapes.
> - They're great at <u>conducting heat</u>.
> - They <u>conduct electricity well</u>.

3) Metals (and especially <u>transition metals</u>, which are found in the <u>centre block</u> of the periodic table) have loads of <u>everyday</u> uses because of these properties...

> - Their strength and 'bendability' makes them handy for making into things like <u>bridges</u> and <u>car bodies</u>.
> - Metals are ideal if you want to make something that heat needs to travel through, like a <u>saucepan base</u>.
> - And their conductivity makes them great for making things like <u>electrical wires</u>.

Metals are good — but not perfect

1) Metals are very useful <u>structural materials</u>, but some <u>corrode</u> when exposed to air and water, so they need to be <u>protected</u>, e.g. by painting. If metals corrode, they lose their strength and hardness.

2) Metals can get 'tired' when stresses and strains are repeatedly put on them over time. This is known as <u>metal fatigue</u> and leads to metals breaking, which can be very <u>dangerous</u>, e.g. in planes.

Metals have lots of properties in common

So, all metals <u>conduct electricity and heat</u> and can be <u>bent into shape</u>. This makes them pretty useful. Don't go thinking metals are perfect though — they're not immune to corrosion and fatigue.

Properties of Metals

Some metals like titanium, aluminium and copper have special properties.

A metal's **exact properties** decide how it's best **used**

1) The properties on the previous page are <u>typical properties</u> of metals.
   Not all metals are the same though — you need to learn the <u>specific</u> properties of these <u>three metals</u>:

> <u>Copper</u> is a <u>good conductor</u> of <u>electricity</u>, so it's ideal for drawing out into electrical wires.
> It's <u>hard</u> and <u>strong</u> but can be <u>bent</u>. It also <u>doesn't react with water</u>.

> <u>Aluminium</u> is <u>corrosion-resistant</u> and has a <u>low density</u>.
> Pure aluminium <u>isn't</u> particularly strong, but it forms
> hard, strong alloys (see page 41).

> <u>Titanium</u> is another <u>low density metal</u>.
> Unlike aluminium it's <u>very strong</u>.
> It is also <u>corrosion-resistant</u>.

2) <u>Different metals</u> are chosen for <u>different uses</u> because of their specific properties.
   For example:

> • If you were doing some <u>plumbing</u>, you'd pick a
>   metal that could be <u>bent</u> to make pipes and tanks,
>   and is below hydrogen in the reactivity series so it
>   <u>doesn't react with water</u>. <u>Copper</u> is great for this.

> • If you wanted to make an <u>aeroplane</u>, you'd probably use
>   metal as it's <u>strong</u> and can be <u>bent into shape</u>. But you'd also
>   need it to be <u>light</u>, so <u>aluminium</u> would be a good choice.

> • And if you were making <u>replacement hips</u>, you'd pick a
>   metal that <u>won't corrode</u> when it comes in contact with
>   water. It'd also have to be <u>light</u> too, and not too bendy.
>   <u>Titanium</u> has all of these properties so it's used for this.

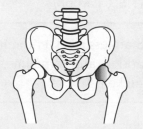

Aluminium isn't just used for drinks cans

Once you've got the general idea that a metal's <u>properties</u> affect how it's used, you just need to focus
on the properties of the three metals covered on this page — <u>copper</u>, <u>aluminium</u> and <u>titanium</u>.

Alloys

Pure metals often aren't quite right for certain jobs. So scientists mix two metals together (or mix a metal with a non-metal) — creating an alloy with the properties they want.

Pure iron tends to be a bit too bendy

1) 'Iron' straight from the blast furnace is only 96% iron.
   The other 4% is impurities such as carbon.

2) This impure iron is used as cast iron. It's handy for making ornamental railings, but it doesn't have many other uses because it's brittle.

3) So all the impurities are removed from most of the blast furnace iron.
   This pure iron has a regular arrangement of identical atoms.
   The layers of atoms can slide over each other, which makes the iron soft and easily shaped. This iron is far too bendy for most uses.

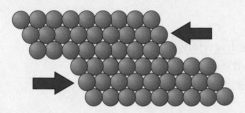

Most iron is converted into steel — an alloy

Most of the pure iron is changed into alloys called steels. Steels are formed by adding small amounts of carbon and sometimes other metals to the iron.

TYPE OF STEEL	PROPERTIES	USES
Low carbon steel (0.1% carbon)	easily shaped	car bodies
High carbon steel (1.5% carbon)	very hard, inflexible	blades for cutting tools, bridges
Stainless steel (chromium added, and sometimes nickel)	corrosion-resistant	cutlery, containers for corrosive substances

Most iron is changed into steel, otherwise it's too bendy or too brittle

The Eiffel Tower is made of iron — but the problem with iron is, it goes rusty if air and water get to it. So the Eiffel Tower has to be painted every seven years to make sure that it doesn't rust. This is quite a job and takes an entire year for a team of 25 painters. Too bad they didn't use stainless steel.

Alloys

Alloys are really useful. Lots of the metals we use are alloys...

Alloys are **harder** than **pure metals**

1) Different elements have different sized atoms. So when an element such as carbon is added to pure iron, the smaller carbon atom will upset the layers of pure iron atoms, making it more difficult for them to slide over each other. So alloys are harder.

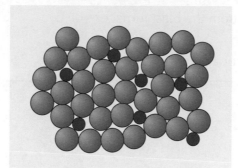

2) Many metals in use today are actually alloys. E.g.:

BRONZE = COPPER + TIN

Bronze is harder than copper.
It's good for making medals and statues from.

CUPRONICKEL = COPPER + NICKEL

This is hard and corrosion resistant.
It's used to make "silver" coins.

GOLD ALLOYS ARE USED TO MAKE JEWELLERY

Pure gold is too soft. Metals such as zinc, copper, silver, palladium and nickel are used to harden the "gold".

ALUMINIUM ALLOYS ARE USED TO MAKE AIRCRAFT

Aluminium has a low density, but it's alloyed with small amounts of other metals to make it stronger.

3) In the past, the development of alloys was by trial and error. But nowadays we understand much more about the properties of metals, so alloys can be designed for specific uses.

Alloys are really important in industry

If the properties of a metal aren't quite suited to a job, an alloy is often used instead. To make an alloy you mix one metal with another metal or non-metal. The finished alloy can be a lot harder, or less brittle — the properties can be varied and they can be made to suit a particular job really well.

Warm-Up and Exam Questions

The warm-up questions run quickly over the basic facts you'll need in the exam. Unless you've learnt the facts first you'll find the exam questions pretty difficult.

Warm-Up Questions

1) Give three useful physical properties of most metals.
2) Where are the transition metals found in the periodic table?
3) What is the problem with iron from the blast furnace?
4) What is an alloy?
5) Which are harder, pure metals or alloys?

Exam Questions

1 Aluminium is used to make aircraft.

   (a) Give two properties of aluminium that make it suitable for this use.

   (2 marks)

   (b) Aircraft need to be strong but aluminium is not a strong metal.
   Explain how aluminium can be made stronger.

   (1 mark)

2 Titanium is a transition metal that is used in hip replacements.

   (a) Give two properties of titanium that make it suitable for this use.

   (2 marks)

   (b) Give one other property of titanium.

   (1 mark)

3 Low carbon steel and high carbon steel are two different alloys of iron.

   (a) Give one difference in the properties of these two alloys.

   (2 marks)

   (b) Give one use for each of these alloys.

   (2 marks)

   (c) Steel **X** is an alloy of iron that is resistant to corrosion.
      (i) Name this alloy.

   (1 mark)

      (ii) Give one use of steel **X**.

   (1 mark)

   (d) Suggest why scientists are now able to design alloys for specific uses.

   (1 mark)

Fractional Distillation of Crude Oil

Crude oil is formed from the buried remains of plants and animals — it's a fossil fuel. Over millions of years, the remains turn to crude oil, which can be extracted by drilling and pumping.

Crude oil is a **mixture** of **hydrocarbons**

1) A mixture consists of two (or more) elements or compounds that aren't chemically bonded to each other.

2) Crude oil is a mixture of many different compounds. Most of the compounds are hydrocarbon molecules.

3) Hydrocarbons are basically fuels such as petrol and diesel. They're made of just carbon and hydrogen.

4) There are no chemical bonds between the different parts of a mixture, so the different hydrocarbon molecules in crude oil aren't chemically bonded to one another.

5) This means that they all keep their original properties, such as their condensing points. The properties of a mixture are just a mixture of the properties of the separate parts.

6) The parts of a mixture can be separated out by physical methods, e.g. crude oil can be split up into its separate fractions by fractional distillation. Each fraction contains molecules with a similar number of carbon atoms to each other (see next page).

Crude oil is **split** into **separate groups of hydrocarbons**

The fractionating column works continuously, with heated crude oil piped in at the bottom. The vaporised oil rises up the column and the various fractions are constantly tapped off at the different levels where they condense.

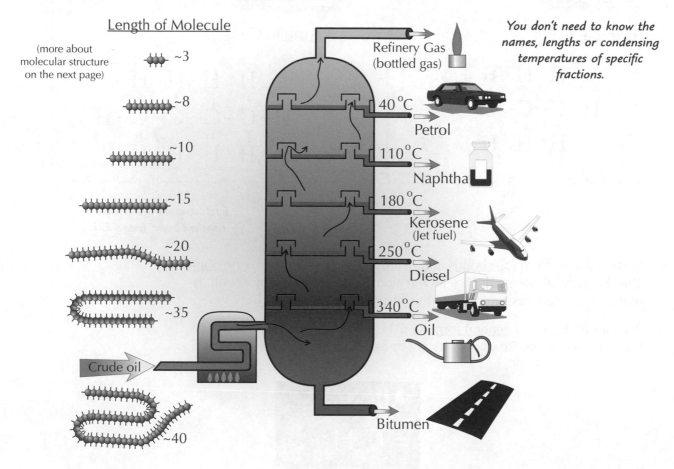

Length of Molecule

(more about molecular structure on the next page)

~3

~8

~10

~15

~20

~35

Crude oil

~40

Refinery Gas (bottled gas)

40 °C — Petrol

110 °C — Naphtha

180 °C — Kerosene (Jet fuel)

250 °C — Diesel

340 °C — Oil

Bitumen

You don't need to know the names, lengths or condensing temperatures of specific fractions.

Properties and Uses of Crude Oil

The <u>different fractions</u> of crude oil have <u>different properties</u>, and it's all down to their <u>structure</u>. You need to know the <u>basic structure</u> and a few <u>trends</u>, so you can apply what you've learnt to <u>exam questions</u>.

Crude oil is mostly alkanes

1) All the fractions of crude oil are hydrocarbons called <u>alkanes</u>.

2) Alkanes are made up of <u>chains of carbon atoms</u> surrounded by <u>hydrogen atoms</u>.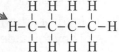

3) Different alkanes have chains of different <u>lengths</u>.

4) The first four alkanes are <u>methane</u> (natural gas), <u>ethane</u>, <u>propane</u> and <u>butane</u>.

1) Methane

Formula: CH_4

(natural gas)

2) Ethane

Formula: C_2H_6

3) Propane

Formula: C_3H_8

4) Butane

Formula: C_4H_{10}

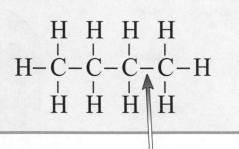

Each straight line shows a covalent bond (page 22).

5) Carbon atoms form <u>four bonds</u> and hydrogen atoms only form <u>one bond</u>. The diagrams above show that all the atoms have formed bonds with as many other atoms as they can — this means they're <u>saturated</u>.

6) Alkanes all have the <u>general formula</u> C_nH_{2n+2}. So if an alkane has 5 carbons, it's got to have $(2 \times 5) + 2 = 12$ hydrogens.

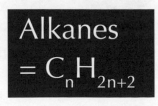

Alkanes = C_nH_{2n+2}

Properties and Uses of Crude Oil

The different fractions of crude oil have different properties, and it's all down to their alkane structure. You need to know a few trends about how the structure of alkanes affects the fraction's properties.

Learn the basic trends:

1) The shorter the molecules, the more runny the hydrocarbon is — that is, the less viscous (gloopy) it is.

2) The shorter the molecules, the more volatile they are. "More volatile" means they turn into a gas at a lower temperature. So, the shorter the molecules, the lower the temperature at which that fraction vaporises or condenses — and the lower its boiling point.

3) Also, the shorter the molecules, the more flammable (easier to ignite) the hydrocarbon is.

The uses of hydrocarbons depend on their properties

1) The volatility helps decide what the fraction is used for. The refinery gas fraction has the shortest molecules, so it has the lowest boiling point — in fact it's a gas at room temperature. This makes it ideal for using as bottled gas. It's stored under pressure as liquid in 'bottles'. When the tap on the bottle is opened, the fuel vaporises and flows to the burner where it's ignited.

2) The petrol fraction has longer molecules, so it has a higher boiling point. Petrol is a liquid which is ideal for storing in the fuel tank of a car. It can flow to the engine where it's easily vaporised to mix with the air before it is ignited.

3) The viscosity also helps decide how the hydrocarbons are used. The really gloopy, viscous hydrocarbons are used for lubricating engine parts and for covering roads.

Alkane ya if you don't learn this...

So short-chain hydrocarbons are less viscous, more volatile and easier to ignite than longer-chain hydrocarbons. If you learn the properties of short-chain hydrocarbons, you should be able to work out the properties of longer-chain ones in the exam. These properties decide how they're used. In the real world there's more demand for stuff like petrol than there is for long gloopy hydrocarbons like bitumen — I guess there's only so many roads that need covering.

Using Crude Oil as a Fuel

Nothing as amazingly useful as crude oil would be without its problems.
No, that'd be too good to be true.

Crude oil provides an important fuel for modern life

1) Crude oil fractions burn cleanly so they make good <u>fuels</u>.
Most modern transport is fuelled by a crude oil fraction, e.g. cars, boats, trains and planes. Parts of crude oil are also burned in <u>central heating systems</u> in homes and in <u>power stations</u> to <u>generate electricity</u>.

2) There's a <u>massive industry</u> with scientists working to find oil reserves, take it out of the ground, and turn it into useful products. As well as fuels, crude oil also provides the raw materials for making various <u>chemicals</u>, including <u>plastics</u>.

3) Often, <u>alternatives</u> to using crude oil fractions as fuel are possible. E.g. electricity can be generated by <u>nuclear</u> power or <u>wind</u> power, there are <u>ethanol</u>-powered cars, and <u>solar</u> energy can be used to heat water.

4) But things tend to be <u>set up</u> for using oil fractions. For example, cars are designed for <u>petrol or diesel</u> and it's <u>readily available</u>. There are filling stations all over the country, with storage facilities and pumps specifically designed for these crude oil fractions. So crude oil fractions are often the <u>easiest and cheapest</u> thing to use.

5) Crude oil fractions are often <u>more reliable</u> too — e.g. solar and wind power won't work without the right weather conditions. Nuclear energy is reliable, but there are lots of concerns about its <u>safety</u> and the storage of radioactive waste.

Using Crude Oil as a Fuel

Crude oil is a really useful fuel that we use every day — there is a possibility that it might run out.

Crude oil might **run out** one day... *eeek*

1) Most scientists think that oil will <u>run out</u> — it's a <u>non-renewable fuel</u>.

2) No one knows exactly when it'll run out but there have been heaps of <u>different predictions</u> — e.g. about 40 years ago, scientists predicted that it'd all be gone by the year 2000.

3) <u>New oil reserves</u> are discovered from time to time and <u>technology</u> is constantly improving, so it's now possible to extract oil that was once too <u>difficult</u> or <u>expensive</u> to extract.

4) In the <u>worst-case scenario</u>, oil may be pretty much gone in about 25 years — and that's not far off.

5) Some people think we should <u>immediately stop</u> using oil for things like transport, for which there are alternatives, and keep it for things that it's absolutely <u>essential</u> for, like some chemicals and medicines.

6) It will take time to <u>develop</u> alternative fuels that will satisfy all our energy needs (see page 50 for more info). It'll also take time to <u>adapt things</u> so that the fuels can be used on a wide scale. E.g. we might need different kinds of car engines, or special storage tanks built.

7) One alternative is to generate energy from <u>renewable</u> sources — these are sources that <u>won't run out</u>. Examples of renewable energy sources are <u>wind power</u>, <u>solar power</u> and <u>tidal power</u>.

8) So however long oil does last for, it's a good idea to start <u>conserving</u> it and finding <u>alternatives</u> now.

Crude oil is **not** the **environment's** best friend

1) <u>Oil spills</u> can happen as the oil is being transported by tanker — this spells <u>disaster</u> for the local environment. <u>Birds</u> get covered in the stuff and are <u>poisoned</u> as they try to clean themselves. Other creatures, like <u>sea otters</u> and <u>whales</u>, are poisoned too.

2) You have to <u>burn oil</u> to release the energy from it. But burning oil is thought to be a major cause of <u>global warming</u>, <u>acid rain</u> and <u>global dimming</u> — see pages 48 and 49.

If oil alternatives aren't developed, we might get caught short...

Crude oil is <u>really important</u> to our lives. Take <u>petrol</u> for instance — at the first whisper of a shortage, there's mayhem. Loads of people dash to the petrol station and start filling up their tanks. This causes a queue, which starts everyone else panicking. I don't know what they'll do when it runs out totally.

Environmental Problems

90% of crude oil is used as fuel. It's burnt to release the energy stored inside it.

Burning fossil fuels releases *gases* and *particles*

1) <u>Power stations</u> burn huge amounts of fossil fuels to make <u>electricity</u>. <u>Cars</u> are also a major culprit in burning fossil fuels.

   Pure hydrogen can also be used as a fuel (see page 50). It only produces water vapour when burnt.

2) Most fuels, such as crude oil and coal, contain <u>carbon</u> and <u>hydrogen</u>. During combustion, the carbon and hydrogen are oxidised so that <u>carbon dioxide</u> and <u>water vapour</u> are released into the atmosphere. <u>Energy</u> (heat) is also produced. E.g.:

   > **hydrocarbon + oxygen → carbon dioxide + water vapour**

3) If the fuel contains <u>sulfur</u> impurities, the sulfur will be released as <u>sulfur dioxide</u> when the fuel is burnt.

4) Oxides of <u>nitrogen</u> will also form if the fuel burns at a <u>high temperature</u>.

5) When there's <u>plenty of oxygen</u>, <u>all</u> the fuel burns — this is called <u>complete combustion</u>.

6) If there's <u>not enough oxygen</u>, some of the fuel <u>doesn't burn</u> — this is called <u>partial combustion</u>. Under these conditions, <u>solid particles</u> (called particulates) of <u>soot</u> (carbon) and <u>unburnt fuel</u> are released. <u>Carbon monoxide</u> (a poisonous gas) is also released.

Sulfur dioxide causes *acid rain*

1) <u>Sulfur dioxide</u> is one of the gases that causes acid rain.

2) When the <u>sulfur dioxide</u> mixes with <u>clouds</u> it forms dilute <u>sulfuric acid</u>. This then falls as <u>acid rain</u>.

3) In the same way, <u>oxides of nitrogen</u> cause acid rain by forming <u>dilute nitric acid</u> in clouds.

4) <u>Acid rain</u> causes <u>lakes</u> to become <u>acidic</u> and many plants and animals <u>die</u> as a result.

5) Acid rain kills <u>trees</u> and damages <u>limestone buildings</u> and ruins <u>stone statues</u>. It's shocking.

6) Links between acid rain and human health problems have been suggested.

7) The <u>benefits</u> of electricity and travel have to be <u>balanced</u> against the <u>environmental impacts</u>. Governments have recognised the importance of this and <u>international agreements</u> have been put in place to <u>reduce emissions</u> of air pollutants such as sulfur dioxide.

You can reduce acid rain by reducing sulfur emissions

1) Most of the sulfur can be <u>removed</u> from fuels <u>before</u> they're burnt, but it <u>costs more</u> to do it.

2) Also, removing sulfur from fuels takes <u>more energy</u>. This usually comes from burning more fuel, which releases more of the greenhouse gas <u>carbon dioxide</u>.

3) However, petrol and diesel are starting to be replaced by <u>low-sulfur</u> versions.

4) <u>Power stations</u> now have <u>Acid Gas Scrubbers</u> to take the harmful gases <u>out</u> before they release their fumes into the atmosphere.

5) The other way of reducing acid rain is simply to <u>reduce</u> our usage of <u>fossil fuels</u>.

Environmental Problems

More doom and gloom on this page I'm afraid... You've got to know it all though.

Increasing Carbon Dioxide Causes Climate Change

1) The level of <u>carbon dioxide</u> in the atmosphere is <u>increasing</u> — because of the large amounts of <u>fossil fuels</u> humans burn.

2) There's a <u>scientific consensus</u> that this extra carbon dioxide has caused the average <u>temperature</u> of the Earth to <u>increase</u> — <u>global warming</u>.

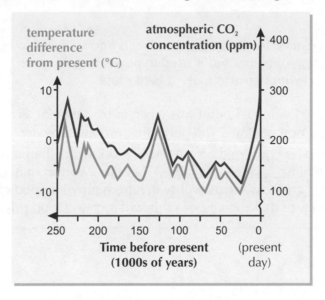

3) Global warming is a type of <u>climate change</u> and causes other types of climate change, e.g. changing rainfall patterns. It could also cause severe <u>flooding</u> due to the polar ice caps melting.

Particles Cause Global Dimming

1) In the last few years, some scientists have been measuring how much <u>sunlight</u> is reaching the surface of the Earth and comparing it to records from the last 50 years.

2) They have been amazed to find that in some areas nearly <u>25% less sunlight</u> has been reaching the surface compared to 50 years ago. They have called this <u>global dimming</u>.

3) They think that it is caused by <u>particles</u> of soot and ash that are produced when <u>fossil fuels</u> are burnt. These particles <u>reflect</u> sunlight back into space, or they can help to produce more <u>clouds</u> that reflect the sunlight back into space.

London by day — if global dimming gets really bad.

4) There are many scientists who <u>don't believe</u> the change is real and blame it on <u>inaccurate</u> recording equipment.

Global dimming — romantic lighting all day...

On a cold winter's day, I often think that a bit of global warming would be nice — but it seems that it does <u>mess things up</u>. There have been lots of other times in the past when the climate has <u>changed</u> — volcanic eruptions, changes in the Earth's orbit and the movements of tectonic plates (see page 67) have all had effects. But this is the <u>first time</u> we've had the technology and knowledge to investigate it.

Environmental Problems

As the demand on resources increases it's important to develop new, alternative fuels.

Alternative fuels are being developed

Some alternative fuels have already been developed, and there are others in the pipeline (so to speak). Many of them are renewable fuels so, unlike fossil fuels, they won't run out. However, none of them are perfect — they all have pros and cons. For example:

Ethanol

ETHANOL can be produced from plant material so is known as a biofuel. It's made by fermentation of plants and is used to power cars in some places. It's often mixed with petrol to make a better fuel.

PROS: The CO_2 released when it's burnt was taken in by the plant as it grew, so it's 'carbon neutral'. The only other product is water.

CONS: Engines need to be converted before they'll work with ethanol fuels. And ethanol fuel isn't widely available. There are worries that as demand for it increases farmers will switch from growing food crops to growing crops to make ethanol — this will increase food prices.

Biodiesel

BIODIESEL is another type of biofuel. It can be produced from vegetable oils such as rapeseed oil and soybean oil. Biodiesel can be mixed with ordinary diesel fuel and used to run a diesel engine.

PROS: Biodiesel is 'carbon neutral'. Engines don't need to be converted. It produces much less sulfur dioxide and 'particulates' than ordinary diesel or petrol.

CONS: We can't make enough to completely replace diesel. It's expensive to make. It could increase food prices like using more ethanol could (see above).

Hydrogen gas

HYDROGEN GAS can also be used to power vehicles. You get the hydrogen from the electrolysis of water — there's plenty of water about but it takes electrical energy to split it up. This energy can come from a renewable source, e.g. solar.

PROS: Hydrogen combines with oxygen in the air to form just water — so it's very clean.

CONS: You need a special, expensive engine and hydrogen isn't widely available. You still need to use energy from another source to make it. Also, hydrogen's hard to store because it's explosive.

We should probably be using alternative fuels already...

You may have heard about these fuels in the news. Some of the big car manufacturers are spending loads of money trying to make hydrogen-powered cars a reality. These are the fuels of the future...

Warm-Up and Exam Questions

Give these questions your best shot. If they highlight areas where your knowledge falls short, it's time to re-revise those sections so you can boost you confidence for the exam.

Warm-Up Questions

1) What does a mixture consist of?
2) What are hydrocarbons made from?
3) Name the first three alkanes.
4) List three modern-day activities that depend on crude oil and its fractions.

Exam Questions

1   Alkanes are made up of chains of carbon atoms surrounded by hydrogen atoms.

   (a)   Butane contains four carbon atoms. Give its formula.

(1 mark)

   (b)   Draw the structural formula of butane showing all of the bonds.

(1 mark)

2   Crude oil can be separated into a number of different compounds as shown in the diagram:

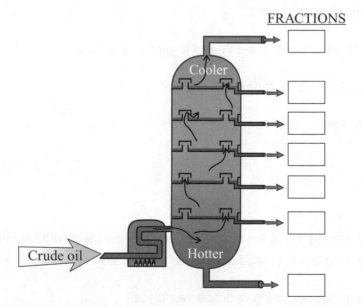

FRACTIONS

   (a)   (i)   Put an **M** in the box of the fraction with the longest hydrocarbon molecules.

(1 mark)

         (ii)   Put a **B** in the box of the fraction with the lowest boiling point.

(1 mark)

   (b)   Briefly explain how the separation process works.

(3 marks)

Exam Questions

3   When fossil fuels like petrol are burnt, they produce carbon dioxide, sulfur dioxide and particulate matter.

    (a)   Name the atmospheric environmental problem caused by increased levels of carbon dioxide.

(1 mark)

    (b)   (i)   Describe how acid rain is formed.

(3 marks)

          (ii)   Give **one** effect of acid rain.

(1 mark)

    (c)   (i)   What is global dimming?

(1 mark)

          (ii)   What causes global dimming?

(1 mark)

    (d)   One advantage of burning ethanol is that it produces no sulfur. Give **two** disadvantages of using ethanol as a fuel compared to petrol.

(2 marks)

4   Currently, fossil fuels provide about 60-70% of the world's electricity.

Since fossils fuels will eventually run out, it is important to find alternative energy sources for the future. An example of an alternative fuel is biodiesel. It can be used in diesel engines.

    (a)   What is biodiesel made from?

(1 mark)

    (b)   (i)   Explain why biodiesel doesn't add to global warming.

(3 marks)

          (ii)   Give two other advantages of biodiesel.

(2 marks)

    (c)   Give two disadvantages of biodiesel.

(2 marks)

5   Scientists are developing 'fuels for the future'. One example could be hydrogen.

    (a)   Describe how hydrogen is produced on a large scale.

(1 mark)

    (b)   Give **one** advantage of using hydrogen as a fuel.

(1 mark)

    (c)   Why is hydrogen difficult to store?

(1 mark)

    (d)   Give **one** other disadvantage of using hydrogen as a fuel in a car compared with using petrol or diesel.

(1 mark)

Revision Summary for Chemistry 1a

There wasn't anything too ghastly in this section, and a few bits were even quite interesting I reckon. But you've got to make sure the facts are all firmly embedded in your brain and that you really understand the issues. These questions will let you see what you know and what you don't. If you get stuck on any, you need to look at that stuff again. Keep going till you can do them all without coming up for air.

1) Sketch an atom. Label the nucleus and the electrons.
2) What are the symbols for: a) calcium, b) carbon, c) sodium?
3)* Which element's properties are more similar to magnesium's: calcium or iron?
4) Describe how you would work out the electronic structure of an atom given its atomic number.
5) Describe the process of ionic bonding.
6) What is covalent bonding?
7)* Say which of the diagrams on the right show:
    a) an element   and   b) a compound
    Suggest what elements or compounds could be in each.
8)* Balance these equations:
    a) $CaCO_3 + HCl \rightarrow CaCl_2 + H_2O + CO_2$ b) $Ca + H_2O \rightarrow Ca(OH)_2 + H_2$

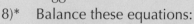

9) Write down the symbol equation showing the thermal decomposition of limestone.
10) What products are produced when limestone reacts with an acid?
11) What is calcium hydroxide used for?
12) Name three building materials made from limestone.
13) Plans to develop a limestone quarry and a cement factory on some hills next to your town are announced. Describe the views that the following might have:
    a) dog owners   b) a mother of young children
    c) the owner of a cafe   d) a beetle
14) What is the name given to a rock that contains enough metal to make it worthwhile extracting it?
15) Explain why zinc can be extracted by reduction with carbon but magnesium can't.
16) Give a reason why aluminium is an expensive metal.
17) What is electrolysis?
18) Describe the process of purifying copper by electrolysis.
19) Describe how scrap iron is used to displace copper from solution.
20) What is the name of the method where plants are used to extract metals from soil?
21) Give three properties of metals.
22) Briefly describe two problems with metals.
23) What is the problem with using very pure iron?
24) Give two examples of alloys and say what's in them.
25) What does crude oil consist of? What does fractional distillation do to crude oil?
26) What's the general formula for an alkane?
27) Is a short-chain hydrocarbon more viscous than a long-chain hydrocarbon? Is it more volatile?
28)* You're going on holiday to a very cold place. The temperature will be about −10 °C. Which of the fuels shown on the right do you think will work best in your camping stove? Explain your answer.

Fuel	Boiling point (°C)
Propane	−42
Butane	−0.4
Pentane	36.2

29) Name three pollutants released into the atmosphere when fuels are burned. What environmental problems are associated with each?
30) List three ways of reducing acid rain.
31) Has the theory of global dimming been proven?
32) List three alternative ways of powering cars. What are the pros and cons of each?

* Answers on page 216.

Cracking Crude Oil

After the distillation of crude oil (see page 43), you've still got both short and long hydrocarbons, just not all mixed together. But there's <u>more demand</u> for some products, like <u>petrol</u>, than for others.

Cracking means splitting up long–chain hydrocarbons...

1) <u>Long-chain hydrocarbons</u> form <u>thick gloopy liquids</u> like <u>tar</u> which aren't all that useful, so...

2) ... a lot of the longer molecules produced from <u>fractional distillation</u> are <u>turned into smaller ones</u> by a process called <u>cracking</u>.

3) Some of the products of cracking are useful as fuels, e.g. petrol for cars and paraffin for jet fuel.

4) Cracking also produces substances like <u>ethene</u>, which are needed for <u>making plastics</u> (see p. 57).

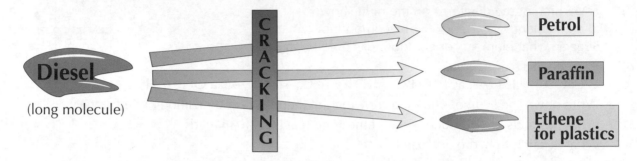

...by passing vapour over a hot catalyst

1) <u>Cracking</u> is a <u>thermal decomposition</u> reaction — <u>breaking molecules down</u> by <u>heating</u> them.

2) The first step is to <u>heat</u> the long-chain hydrocarbon to <u>vaporise</u> it (turn it into a gas).

3) Then the <u>vapour</u> is passed over a <u>powdered catalyst</u> at a temperature of about <u>400 °C – 700 °C</u>.

4) <u>Aluminium oxide</u> is the catalyst used.

5) The <u>long-chain</u> molecules <u>split apart</u> or "crack" on the <u>surface</u> of the specks of catalyst.

6) Most of the <u>products</u> of cracking are <u>alkanes</u> (see page 44) and unsaturated hydrocarbons called <u>alkenes</u> (see page 55)...

An alternative way of cracking long-chain hydrocarbons is to mix the vapour with steam at a very high temperature.

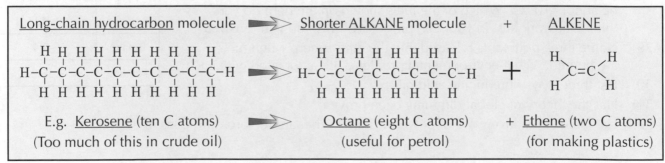

Alkenes

Alkenes are very useful. Here are the basics for you to learn.

Alkenes have a C=C double bond

1) Alkenes are hydrocarbons which have a <u>double bond</u> between two of the <u>carbon</u> atoms in their chain.

2) They are known as <u>unsaturated</u> because they <u>can make more bonds</u> — the double bond can open up, allowing the two carbon atoms to bond with other atoms.

3) The first two alkenes are <u>ethene</u> (with two carbon atoms) and <u>propene</u> (three Cs).

4) <u>All alkenes</u> have the general formula: C_nH_{2n} — they have twice as many hydrogens as carbons.

1) Ethene

Formula: C_2H_4

$$H\diagdown C=C\diagup H$$
$$H\diagup \qquad \diagdown H$$

Carbon atoms always make four bonds, but hydrogen atoms only make one.

This is a double bond — so each carbon atom is still making four bonds.

2) Propene

Formula: C_3H_6

$$H-\overset{\displaystyle H}{\underset{\displaystyle H}{C}}-\overset{\displaystyle H}{C}=C\diagup^H_{\diagdown H}$$

Alkenes turn bromine water colourless

1) You can test for an alkene by adding the substance to <u>bromine water</u>.

2) An alkene will <u>decolourise</u> the bromine water, turning it from <u>orange</u> to <u>colourless</u>.

3) This is because the <u>double bond</u> has <u>opened</u> up and formed bonds with the bromine.

bromine water + alkene — decolourised

That double bond makes all the difference...

Don't get alkenes confused with alkanes. Alkenes have a C=C bond, alkanes don't. The first part of their names is the same though. "<u>Meth-</u>" means "<u>one</u> carbon atom", "<u>eth-</u>" means "<u>two</u> C atoms", "<u>prop-</u>" means "<u>three</u> C atoms", "<u>but-</u>" means "<u>four</u> C atoms", etc.

Ethanol

Ethene can be used to make ethanol. Ethanol is the alcohol in beer and wine.

Ethene *can be reacted with* **steam** *to produce* **ethanol**

1) Ethene (C_2H_4) can be hydrated with steam (H_2O) in the presence of a catalyst to make ethanol.

2) At the moment this is a cheap process, because ethene's fairly cheap and not much of it is wasted.

3) The trouble is that ethene's produced from crude oil, which is a non-renewable resource that could start running out fairly soon.

4) This means using ethene to make ethanol will become very expensive.

Ethanol *can also be produced from* **renewable resources**

1) The alcohol in beer and wine, etc. isn't made from ethene — it's made by fermentation.

2) The raw material for fermentation is sugar.

3) Sugar is converted into ethanol using yeast. The word equation for this is:

sugar → carbon dioxide + ethanol

4) This process needs a lower temperature and simpler equipment than when using ethene.

5) Another advantage is that the raw material is a renewable resource. Sugar is grown as a major crop in several parts of the world, including many poorer countries.

6) The ethanol produced this way can also be used as quite a cheap fuel in countries which don't have oil reserves for making petrol.

7) There are disadvantages though. The ethanol you get from this process isn't very concentrated, so if you want to increase its strength you have to distil it (as in whisky distilleries). It also needs to be purified.

Make ethanol — not war...

Fermentation is great for making ethanol — sugar is a renewable resource and sugar plants can be grown pretty much anywhere. But it's also expensive to concentrate and purify the ethanol. Hydrating ethene from crude oil to make ethanol is much cheaper, but the oil's going to run out one day (p. 47).

Using Alkenes to Make Polymers

Before we knew how to make <u>polymers</u>, there were no <u>polythene bags</u>. Everyone used string bags for their shopping. Now we have plastic bags that hurt your hands and split halfway home.

Alkenes can be used to make polymers

1) Probably the most useful thing you can do with alkenes is <u>polymerisation</u>.

2) This means joining together lots of <u>small alkene molecules</u> (<u>monomers</u>) to form <u>very large molecules</u> — these long-chain molecules are called <u>polymers</u>.

Polymers are often written without the brackets — e.g. polyethene.

3) For instance, many <u>ethene</u> molecules can be joined up to produce <u>poly(ethene)</u> or "polythene".

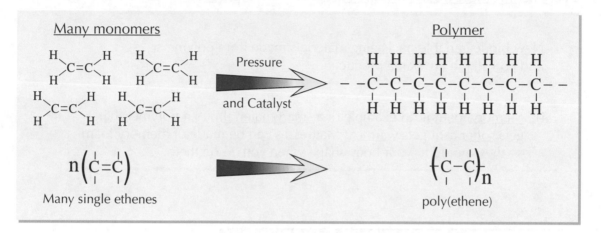

Many monomers   Polymer

Pressure and Catalyst

Many single ethenes   poly(ethene)

4) In the same way, if you join lots of <u>propene</u> molecules together, you've got <u>poly(propene)</u>.

Different polymers have different physical properties

1) The physical properties of a polymer depend on <u>what it's made from</u>. Polyamides are usually stronger than poly(ethene), for example.

2) A polymer's <u>physical properties</u> are also affected by the <u>temperature and pressure</u> of polymerisation.

3) For example, poly(ethene) made at <u>200 °C</u> and <u>2000 atmospheres pressure</u> is <u>flexible</u>, and has <u>low density</u>. But poly(ethene) made at <u>60 °C</u> and a <u>few atmospheres pressure</u> with a <u>catalyst</u> is <u>rigid</u> and <u>dense</u>.

Polymers are really important...

...so it's really important that you know the basics. Monomers are often alkenes that contain double bonds. When they are put under <u>pressure</u> in the presence of a <u>catalyst</u>, they join together to form really big, long-chain molecules called polymers. So remember <u>monomers</u> form <u>polymers</u>...

Using Alkenes to Make Polymers

Polymers are suitable for various different **uses**

1) <u>Light, stretchable</u> polymers such as low density poly(ethene) are used to make plastic bags. <u>Elastic</u> polymer fibres are used to make super-stretchy <u>LYCRA® fibre</u> for tights.

2) <u>New uses</u> are developed all the time. <u>Waterproof</u> coatings for fabrics are made of polymers. <u>Dental polymers</u> are used in resin <u>tooth fillings</u>. Polymer <u>hydrogel wound dressings</u> keep wounds moist.

3) <u>New biodegradable packaging</u> materials made from polymers and <u>cornstarch</u> are being produced.

4) <u>Memory foam</u> is an example of a <u>smart material</u>. It's a polymer that gets <u>softer</u> as it gets <u>warmer</u>. Mattresses can be made of memory foam — they mould to your body shape when you lie on them.

Polymers are cheap, but most **don't rot**
— they're hard to get rid of

1) Most polymers aren't "<u>biodegradable</u>" — they're not broken down by microorganisms, so they <u>don't rot</u>.

2) It's difficult to get rid of them — if you bury them in a landfill site, they'll <u>still</u> be there <u>years later</u>. The best thing is to <u>re-use</u> them as many times as possible and then <u>recycle</u> them if you can.

3) Things made from polymers are usually <u>cheaper</u> than things made from metal. However, as <u>crude oil resources</u> get <u>used up</u>, the <u>price</u> of crude oil will rise. Crude oil products like polymers will get dearer.

4) It may be that one day there won't be <u>enough</u> oil for fuel AND plastics AND all the other uses. Choosing how to use the oil that's left means weighing up advantages and disadvantages on all sides.

Revision's like a polymer — you join lots of little facts up...

Polymers are all over the place — and I don't just mean all those plastic bags stuck in trees. There are naturally occurring polymers, like <u>rubber</u> and <u>silk</u>. That's quite a few clothing options, even without synthetic polymers like <u>polyester</u> and <u>PVC</u>. You also have polymers on the inside — <u>DNA's</u> a polymer.

Warm-Up and Exam Questions

These warm-up questions should ease you in gently before you move onto the exam questions. Unless you've learnt the facts you'll find the exam questions tougher than leather sandwiches.

Warm-Up Questions

1) What sort of hydrocarbon molecules are cracked, and why are they cracked?
2) Describe the conditions used for cracking hydrocarbons.
3) Why are alkenes described as unsaturated hydrocarbons?
4) How is ethanol produced from ethene?
5) How is poly(ethene) made?

Exam Questions

1 (a) Complete this equation for the formation of polypropene.

$$n \left(\begin{array}{c} H \\ C=C \\ H \end{array} \begin{array}{c} H \\ CH_3 \end{array} \right) \longrightarrow$$

(1 mark)

(b) The structural formula of polystyrene is shown below.
Draw the structural formula of its monomer.

(1 mark)

2 The symbol equation shows the reaction of ethene with steam.

$$C_2H_4 + H_2O \rightarrow C_2H_5OH$$

(a) Name the product with the formula C_2H_5OH.

(1 mark)

(b) (i) Describe another method of making this product.

(2 marks)

(ii) Give one advantage of using this method rather than reacting ethene with steam.

(1 mark)

Plant Oils

Plant oils come from <u>plants</u>. I know it's tricky, but just do your best to remember.

*We can **extract oils** from **plants***

olive mush

weight

olive oil

1) Some <u>fruits</u> and <u>seeds</u> contain a lot of <u>oil</u>. For example, avocados and olives are oily fruits. Brazil nuts, peanuts and sesame seeds are oily seeds (a nut is just a big seed really).

2) These oils can be extracted and used for <u>food</u> or for <u>fuel</u>.

3) To get the oil out, the plant material is <u>crushed</u>. The next step is to <u>press</u> the crushed plant material between metal plates and squash the oil out. This is the traditional method of producing <u>olive oil</u>.

4) Oil can be separated from crushed plant material by a <u>centrifuge</u> — rather like using a spin-dryer to get water out of wet clothes.

5) Or <u>solvents</u> can be used to get oil from plant material.

6) <u>Distillation</u> refines oil, and <u>removes water</u>, <u>solvents</u> and <u>impurities</u>.

*Vegetable oils **are used in food***

1) Vegetable oils provide a lot of <u>energy</u> — they have a very high energy content.

2) There are other nutrients in vegetable oils. For example, oils from seeds contain <u>vitamin E</u>.

3) Vegetable oils contain <u>essential fatty acids</u>, which the body needs for many metabolic processes.

*Vegetable oils **have benefits for cooking***

1) Vegetable oils have <u>higher boiling points</u> than water. This means they can be used to cook foods at higher temperatures and at <u>faster</u> speeds.

2) Cooking with vegetable oil gives food a <u>different flavour</u>. This is because of the oil's <u>own</u> flavour, but it's also down to the fact that many flavours come from chemicals that are <u>soluble</u> in oil. This means the oil '<u>carries</u>' the flavour, making it seem more <u>intense</u>.

3) Using oil to cook food <u>increases</u> the <u>energy</u> we get from eating it.

*Vegetable oils **can be used to produce fuels***

1) Vegetable oils such as rapeseed oil and soybean oil can be <u>processed</u> and turned into <u>fuels</u>.

2) Because vegetable oils provide a lot of <u>energy</u> they're really suitable for use as fuels.

3) A particularly useful fuel made from vegetable oils is called <u>biodiesel</u>. Biodiesel has similar properties to ordinary diesel fuel — it burns in the same way, so you can use it to fuel a diesel engine. *See page 50 for more about biodiesel.*

Plant Oils

Oils are usually quite runny at room temperature. That's fine for salad dressing, say, but not so good for spreading in your sandwiches. For that, you could <u>hydrogenate</u> the oil to make <u>margarine</u>...

Unsaturated oils contain C=C double bonds

1) Oils and fats contain <u>long-chain molecules</u> with lots of <u>carbon</u> atoms.

2) Oils and fats are either <u>saturated</u> or <u>unsaturated</u>.

3) Unsaturated oils contain <u>double bonds</u> between some of the carbon atoms in their carbon chains.

bromine water
+ unsaturated oil
— decolourised

4) So, an unsaturated oil will <u>decolourise</u> bromine water (as the bromine opens up the double bond and joins on).

5) <u>Monounsaturated</u> fats contain <u>one</u> C=C double bond somewhere in their carbon chains. <u>Polyunsaturated</u> fats contain <u>more than one</u> C=C double bond.

Unsaturated oils can be hydrogenated

1) <u>Unsaturated</u> vegetable oils are <u>liquid</u> at room temperature.

2) They can be hardened by reacting them with <u>hydrogen</u> in the presence of a <u>nickel catalyst</u> at about <u>60 °C</u>. This is called <u>hydrogenation</u>. The hydrogen reacts with the double-bonded carbons and opens out the double bonds.

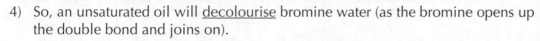

3) Hydrogenated oils have <u>higher melting points</u> than unsaturated oils, so they're <u>more solid</u> at room temperature. This makes them useful as <u>spreads</u> and for baking cakes and pastries.

4) Margarine is usually made from <u>partially</u> hydrogenated vegetable oil — turning <u>all</u> the double bonds in vegetable oil to single bonds would make margarine <u>too hard</u> and difficult to spread. Hydrogenating <u>most</u> of them gives margarine a nice, buttery, spreadable consistency.

5) Partially hydrogenated vegetable oils are often used instead of butter in processed foods, e.g. biscuits. These oils are a lot <u>cheaper</u> than butter and they <u>keep longer</u>. This makes biscuits cheaper and gives them a long shelf life.

6) But partially hydrogenating vegetable oils means you end up with a lot of so-called <u>trans fats</u>. And there's evidence to suggest that trans fats are <u>very bad</u> for you.

Vegetable oils in foods can affect health

1) Vegetable oils tend to be <u>unsaturated</u>, while animal fats tend to be <u>saturated</u>.

2) In general, <u>saturated fats</u> are less healthy than <u>unsaturated fats</u> (as <u>saturated</u> fats <u>increase</u> the amount of <u>cholesterol</u> in the blood, which can block up the arteries and increase the risk of <u>heart disease</u>).

3) Natural <u>unsaturated</u> fats such as olive oil and sunflower oil <u>reduce</u> the amount of blood cholesterol. But because of the trans fats, <u>partially hydrogenated vegetable oil</u> increases the amount of <u>cholesterol</u> in the blood. So eating a lot of foods made with partially hydrogenated vegetable oils can actually increase the risk of heart disease.

4) <u>Cooking</u> food in oil, whether saturated, unsaturated or partially hydrogenated, makes it more <u>fattening</u>.

Emulsions

Emulsions are all over the place in <u>foods</u>, <u>cosmetics</u> and <u>paint</u>. And in exams...

Emulsions can be made from oil and water

1) Oils <u>don't dissolve in water</u>. So far so good...

2) However, you <u>can</u> mix an oil with water to make an <u>emulsion</u>. Emulsions are made up of lots of <u>droplets</u> of one liquid <u>suspended</u> in another liquid. You can have an oil-in-water emulsion (oil droplets suspended in water) or a water-in-oil emulsion (water droplets suspended in oil).

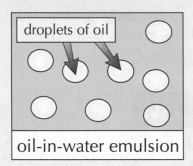

droplets of oil

oil-in-water emulsion

droplets of water

water-in-oil emulsion

3) Emulsions are <u>thicker</u> than either oil or water. E.g. mayonnaise is an emulsion of sunflower oil (or olive oil) and vinegar — it's thicker than either.

4) The physical properties of emulsions make them suited to <u>lots of uses</u> in food — e.g. as salad dressings and in sauces. For instance, a salad dressing made by shaking olive oil and vinegar together forms an <u>emulsion</u> that <u>coats</u> salad better than plain oil or plain vinegar.

5) Generally, the <u>more oil</u> you've got in an oil-in-water emulsion, the <u>thicker</u> it is. Milk is an oil-in-water emulsion with not much oil and a lot of water — there's about 3% oil in full-fat milk. Single cream has a bit more oil — about 18%. Double cream has lots of oil — nearly 50%.

6) <u>Whipped cream</u> and ice cream are oil-in-water emulsions with an extra ingredient — <u>air</u>. Air is whipped into cream to give it a <u>fluffy</u>, frothy consistency for use as a topping. Whipping air into ice cream gives it a <u>softer texture</u>, which makes it easier to scoop out of the tub.

7) Emulsions also have <u>non-food uses</u>. Most <u>moisturising lotions</u> are oil-in-water emulsions. The smooth texture of an emulsion makes it easy to rub into the skin.

Emulsions

Some foods contain **emulsifiers** to help **oil** and **water mix**

Oil and water mixtures naturally <u>separate out</u>. But here's where emulsifiers come in...

1) Emulsifiers are molecules with one part that's <u>attracted to water</u> and another part that's <u>attracted to oil</u> or fat. The bit that's attracted to water is called <u>hydrophilic</u>, and the bit that's attracted to oil is called <u>hydrophobic</u>.

2) The <u>hydrophilic</u> end of each emulsifier molecule latches onto <u>water molecules</u>.

3) The <u>hydrophobic</u> end of each emulsifier molecule cosies up to <u>oil molecules</u>.

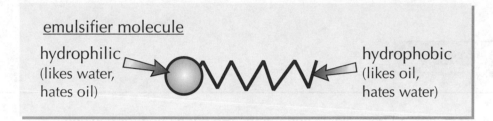

emulsifier molecule

hydrophilic
(likes water,
hates oil)

hydrophobic
(likes oil,
hates water)

4) When you shake oil and water together with a bit of emulsifier, the oil forms droplets, surrounded by a coating of emulsifier... <u>with the hydrophilic bit facing outwards</u>. Other oil droplets are <u>repelled</u> by the hydrophilic bit of the emulsifier, while water molecules latch on. So the emulsion won't separate out. Clever.

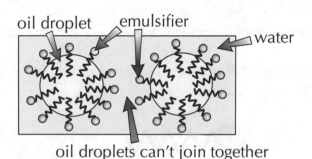

oil droplet   emulsifier   water

oil droplets can't join together

Using **emulsifiers** has **pros** and **cons**

1) Emulsifiers <u>stop</u> emulsions from <u>separating</u> out and this gives them a longer <u>shelf-life</u>.

2) Emulsifiers allow food companies to produce food that's <u>lower in fat</u> but that still has a <u>good texture</u>.

3) The <u>down side</u> is that some people are <u>allergic</u> to certain emulsifiers. For example, <u>egg yolk</u> is often used as an emulsifier — so people who are allergic to eggs need to <u>check</u> the <u>ingredients</u> very carefully.

Emulsion paint — spread mayonnaise all over the walls...

Before fancy stuff from abroad like olive oil, we fried our bacon and eggs in <u>lard</u>. Lard wouldn't be so good for making salad cream though. Emulsions like salad cream have to be made from shaking up two liquids — tiny droplets of one liquid are 'suspended' (NOT dissolved) in the other liquid.

Warm-Up and Exam Questions

1) Why are vegetable oils suitable for use as fuels?
2) What conditions are used for the hydrogenation of unsaturated vegetable oils?
3) Why are natural unsaturated fats typically healthier than saturated fats?
4) What is an emulsion?

Exam Questions

1   Oils that are extracted from plants and refined are often used for cooking.
    (a)   Describe the process used to extract and refine oils from plants.

(4 marks)

    (b)   Give three benefits of using vegetable oils for cooking.

(3 marks)

2   Mayonnaise contains emulsifiers — molecules that have a hydrophilic end and
    a hydrophobic end.
    (a)   On this diagram of an emulsifier molecule, label the hydrophilic and
        hydrophobic ends.

(1 mark)

    (b)   Explain the meanings of hydrophilic and hydrophobic.

(2 marks)

    (c)   The diagram below shows an oil molecule in water.
        Show on the diagram how emulsifier molecules arrange themselves.

(1 mark)

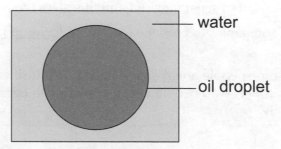

    (d)   What effect do emulsifiers have on the mayonnaise?

(1 mark)

Plate Tectonics

The Earth's surface is very <u>crinkly</u> — lots of mountains and valleys. Scientists used to think that these 'wrinkles' were caused by the shrinkage of the surface as it cooled down after the Earth was formed. Wegener's theory of continental drift replaced this theory, but most people took a lot of persuading...

Wegener's theory describes continental drift

1) <u>Alfred Wegener</u> came across some work listing the fossils of <u>very similar</u> plants and animals which had been found on <u>opposite sides</u> of the Atlantic Ocean.

2) He investigated further, and found other cases of very similar fossils on opposite sides of oceans.

3) Other people had probably noticed this too. The accepted explanation was that there had once been <u>land bridges</u> linking the continents — so animals had been able to cross. The bridges had 'sunk' or been covered over since then.

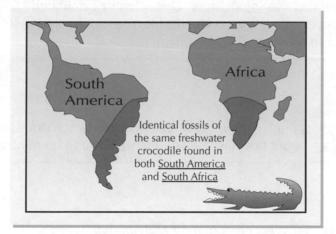

Identical fossils of the same freshwater crocodile found in both <u>South America</u> and <u>South Africa</u>

4) But Wegener had also noticed that the coastlines of Africa and South America seemed to 'match' like the pieces of a <u>jigsaw</u>. He wondered if these two continents had previously been one continent which then split. He started to look for more evidence, and found it...

5) There were <u>matching layers</u> in the rocks in different continents.

6) Fossils had been found in the 'wrong' places — e.g. fossils of tropical plants had been discovered on Arctic islands, where the present climate would clearly have killed them off.

7) In 1915, Wegener felt he had enough evidence. He published his theory of "<u>continental drift</u>".

8) Wegener said that about 300 million years ago, there had been just one '<u>supercontinent</u>'. This landmass, Pangaea, broke into smaller chunks which moved apart. He claimed that these chunks — our modern-day <u>continents</u> — were still slowly 'drifting' apart.

Plate Tectonics

Wegener's theory **wasn't accepted** for **many years**

The reaction from other scientists was mostly very <u>hostile</u>. The main problem was that Wegener's explanation of <u>how</u> the '<u>drifting</u>' happened wasn't very convincing.

1) Wegener thought that the continents were 'ploughing through' the sea bed, and that their movement was caused by tidal forces and the earth's rotation.

2) Other geologists said this was <u>impossible</u>. One scientist calculated that the forces needed to move the continents like this would also have stopped the Earth rotating. (Which it hadn't.)

3) Wegener had used <u>inaccurate data</u> in his calculations, so he'd made some rather <u>wild predictions</u> about how fast the continents ought to be moving apart.

4) A few scientists supported Wegener, but most of them didn't see any reason to believe such a strange theory. It probably didn't help that he wasn't a 'proper' geologist — he'd studied astronomy.

5) Then in the 1950s, scientists were able to investigate the <u>ocean floor</u> and found <u>new evidence</u> to support Wegener's theory. He wasn't right about everything, but his <u>main idea</u> was <u>correct</u>.

6) By the 1960s, geologists were <u>convinced</u>. We now think the Earth's crust is made of several chunks called <u>tectonic plates</u> which move about, and that colliding chunks push the land up to create mountains.

I told you so — but no one ever believes me...

Sadly, Wegener died before his theory was accepted (when hundreds of geologists had to rewrite their textbooks). His story is a classic example of how science progresses — someone puts forward an idea, everyone else points out why it's nonsense, and eventually the really <u>good</u> ideas are accepted.

The Earth's Structure

No one accepted the theory of <u>plate tectonics</u> for ages. Almost everyone does now. How times change.

The **Earth** has a **crust**, **mantle**, **outer** and **inner core**

The Earth is <u>almost spherical</u> and it has a <u>layered</u> structure, a bit like a scotch egg. Or a peach.

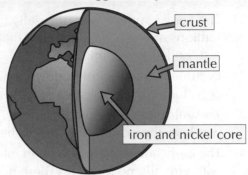

1) The bit we live on, the <u>crust</u>, is very <u>thin</u> (it varies between 5 km and 50 km) and is surrounded by the <u>atmosphere</u>.

2) Below that is the <u>mantle</u>. The <u>mantle</u> has all the properties of a <u>solid</u>, except that it can flow very <u>slowly</u>.

3) Within the mantle, <u>radioactive decay</u> takes place. This produces a lot of <u>heat</u>, which causes the mantle to <u>flow</u> in <u>convection currents</u>.

4) At the centre of the Earth is the <u>core</u>, which we think is made of <u>iron and nickel</u>.

The **Earth's surface** is made up of **tectonic plates**

1) The crust and the upper part of the mantle are cracked into a number of large pieces called <u>tectonic plates</u>. These plates are a bit like <u>big rafts</u> that 'float' on the mantle.

2) The plates don't stay in one place though. That's because the <u>convection currents</u> in the mantle cause the plates to <u>drift</u>.

You don't need to know the names and locations of the plates.

3) The map shows the <u>edges</u> of the plates as they are now, and the <u>directions</u> they're moving in (red arrows).

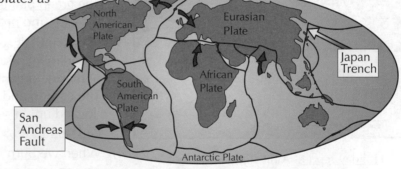

4) Most of the plates are moving at speeds of <u>a few cm per year</u> relative to each other.

5) Occasionally, the plates move very <u>suddenly</u>, causing an <u>earthquake</u>.

6) <u>Volcanoes</u> and <u>earthquakes</u> often occur at the boundaries between two tectonic plates.

Scientists can't **predict** earthquakes and volcanic eruptions

1) Tectonic plates can stay more or less put for a while and then <u>suddenly</u> lurch forwards. It's <u>impossible to predict</u> exactly when they'll move.

2) Scientists are trying to find out if there are any <u>clues</u> that an earthquake might happen soon — things like strain in underground rocks. Even with these clues they'll only be able to say an earthquake's <u>likely</u> to happen, not <u>exactly when</u> it'll happen.

3) There are some <u>clues</u> that say a volcanic eruption might happen soon. Before an eruption, molten rock rises up into chambers near the surface, causing the ground surface to bulge slightly. This causes <u>mini-earthquakes</u> near the volcano.

4) But sometimes molten rock cools down instead of erupting, so mini-earthquakes can be a <u>false alarm</u>.

The Evolution of the Atmosphere

For 200 million years or so, the atmosphere has been about how it is now: <u>78% nitrogen</u>, <u>21% oxygen</u>, and small amounts of other gases, mainly <u>carbon dioxide</u>, <u>noble gases</u> and <u>water vapour</u>. But it wasn't always like this. Here's how the past 4.5 billion years may have gone:

Phase 1 — *Volcanoes* gave out *gases*

1) The Earth's surface was originally <u>molten</u> for many millions of years. It was so hot that any atmosphere just '<u>boiled away</u>' into space.

2) Eventually things cooled down a bit and a <u>thin crust</u> formed, but <u>volcanoes</u> kept erupting.

3) The volcanoes gave out lots of gas. We think this was how the oceans and atmosphere were formed.

4) The early atmosphere was probably <u>mostly CO_2</u>, with virtually <u>no oxygen</u>. There may also have been <u>water vapour</u>, and small amounts of <u>methane</u> and <u>ammonia</u>. This is quite like the atmospheres of Mars and Venus today.

5) The <u>oceans</u> formed when the water vapour <u>condensed</u>.

<u>Holiday report</u>: Not a nice place to be. Take strong walking boots and a good coat.

Phase 2 — *Green plants* evolved and produced *oxygen*

<u>Holiday report</u>: A bit slimy underfoot. Take wellies and a lot of suncream.

1) <u>Green plants</u> and <u>algae</u> evolved over most of the Earth. They were quite happy in the <u>CO_2 atmosphere</u>.

2) A lot of the early CO_2 <u>dissolved</u> into the oceans. The <u>green plants</u> and <u>algae</u> also absorbed some of the <u>CO_2</u> and <u>produced O_2</u> by <u>photosynthesis</u>.

3) Plants and algae died and were buried under layers of sediment, along with the skeletons and shells of marine organisms that had slowly evolved. The <u>carbon</u> and <u>hydrocarbons</u> inside them became 'locked up' in <u>sedimentary rocks</u> as <u>insoluble carbonates</u> (e.g. limestone) and <u>fossil fuels</u>.

4) When we <u>burn</u> fossil fuels today, this 'locked-up' carbon is released and the concentration of CO_2 in the atmosphere rises.

Phase 3 — *Ozone layer* allows evolution of *complex animals*

1) The build-up of <u>oxygen</u> in the atmosphere <u>killed off</u> some early organisms that couldn't tolerate it, but allowed other, more complex organisms to evolve and flourish.

2) The oxygen also created the <u>ozone layer</u> (O_3) which <u>blocked</u> harmful rays from the Sun and <u>enabled</u> even <u>more complex</u> organisms to evolve — us, eventually.

3) There is virtually <u>no CO_2</u> left now.

<u>Holiday report</u>: A nice place to be. Visit before the crowds ruin it.

Life, Resources and Atmospheric Change

Life on Earth began <u>billions of years</u> ago, but there's no way of knowing for definite how it all started.

Primordial soup is just one theory of how life was formed

1) The primordial soup theory states that billions of years ago, the Earth's <u>atmosphere</u> was rich in <u>nitrogen</u>, <u>hydrogen</u>, <u>ammonia</u> and <u>methane</u>.

2) <u>Lightning</u> struck, causing a chemical reaction between the gases, resulting in the formation of <u>amino acids</u>.

3) The amino acids collected in a '<u>primordial soup</u>' — a body of water out of which life gradually crawled.

4) The amino acids gradually combined to produce <u>organic matter</u> which eventually evolved into simple <u>living organisms</u>.

5) In the 1950s, <u>Miller and Urey</u> carried out an experiment to prove this theory. They sealed the gases in their apparatus, heated them and applied an electrical charge for a week.

6) They found that <u>amino acids were made</u>, but not as many as there are on Earth. This suggests the theory could be along the <u>right lines</u>, but isn't quite right.

The Earth has all the resources humans need

The Earth's crust, oceans and atmosphere are the <u>ultimate source</u> of minerals and resources — we can get everything we need from them. For example, we can <u>fractionally distil air</u> to get a variety of products (e.g. nitrogen and oxygen) for use in <u>industry</u>:

1) Air is <u>filtered</u> to remove dust.

2) It's then <u>cooled</u> to around <u>-200 °C</u> and becomes a liquid.

3) During cooling <u>water vapour</u> condenses and is removed.

4) <u>Carbon dioxide</u> freezes and is removed.

5) The liquified air then enters the fractionating column and is <u>heated</u> slowly.

6) The remaining gases are separated by <u>fractional distillation</u>. Oxygen and argon come out together so <u>another</u> column is used to separate them.

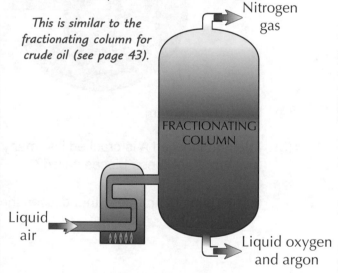

This is similar to the fractionating column for crude oil (see page 43).

Nitrogen gas

FRACTIONATING COLUMN

Liquid air

Liquid oxygen and argon

Carbon dioxide level affects the climate and the oceans

<u>Burning fossil fuels</u> releases CO_2 — and as the world's become more industrialised, more fossil fuels have been burnt in power stations and in car engines. This CO_2 is thought to be altering our planet...

1) An increase in carbon dioxide is causing <u>global warming</u> — a type of <u>climate change</u> (see p. 49).

2) The oceans are a <u>natural store</u> of CO_2 — they absorb it from the atmosphere. However the extra CO_2 we're releasing is making them too <u>acidic</u>. This is bad news for <u>coral</u> and <u>shellfish</u>, and also means that in the future they won't be able to absorb any more carbon dioxide.

Warm-Up and Exam Questions

If you still think the Earth is flat, you may want to re-read the last few pages. If you think you know otherwise, and also know more interesting facts about the Earth's structure, test yourself with these...

Warm-Up Questions

1) Explain why Wegener's continental drift theory wasn't accepted for a long time.
2) State one geological feature often seen at the boundary of two tectonic plates.
3) Where did the gases that made up the early atmosphere come from?
4) What is the name of the process used to separate the gases in air?

Exam Questions

1   The following diagram shows the internal structure of the Earth.

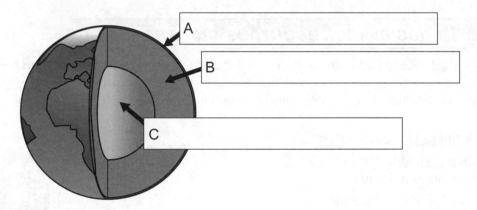

A

B

C

(a)   Label the diagram.

(3 marks)

(b)   The part labelled A is cracked into many pieces.
    (i)   What are these pieces called?

(1 mark)

    (ii) Explain the process that causes these pieces to move.

(3 marks)

2   The following graph shows how atmospheric CO_2 concentration and global temperature have varied over the last 250 000 years.

(a)   Describe what the graph shows about temperature and CO_2 levels.

(2 marks)

(b)   Mark with an X on the graph the time when the temperature was most different from its present value.

(1 mark)

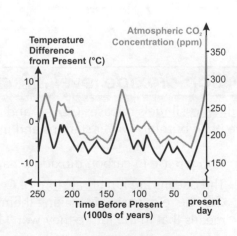

Revision Summary for Chemistry 1b

Cracking alkanes, making mayonnaise, food additives and earthquakes — can they really belong in the same section, I almost hear you ask. Whether you find the topics easy or hard, interesting or dull, you need to learn it all before the exam. Try these questions and see how much you really know:

1) What is "cracking"?

2) Give an example of a substance that is cracked, and the products that you get from cracking it.

3) What kind of carbon-carbon bond do alkenes have?

4) What is the general formula for alkenes?

5) Draw the chemical structure of ethene.

6) What are polymers? What kinds of substances can form polymers?

7) Give two factors which affect the physical properties of a polymer.

8) List four uses of polymers.

9) Why might polymers become more expensive in the future?

10) Why are oils distilled after they have been extracted?

11) List two advantages of using vegetable oils in food.

12) Apart from in food, give one use of vegetable oils.

13) What kind of carbon-carbon bond do unsaturated oils contain?

14) What happens when you react unsaturated oils with hydrogen?

15) Why do some foods contain partially hydrogenated vegetable oil instead of butter?

16) Give an example of an emulsion.

17) How do emulsifiers keep emulsions stable?

18) Suggest one problem of adding emulsifiers to food.

19) What evidence did Wegener use to support his continental drift theory?

20) What can be found beneath the Earth's crust?

21) A geologist places a very heavy marker on the seabed in the middle of the Atlantic ocean. She records the marker's position over a period of four years. The geologist finds that the marker moves in a straight-line away from its original position. Her measurements are shown in the graph on the right.

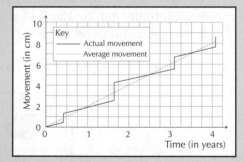

a) Every few years the marker moves suddenly. What happens when the plates lurch suddenly like this?

b)* What is the marker's average movement each year?

c)* On average, how many years will it take for the marker to move 7 cm?

22) Name the two main gases that make up the Earth's atmosphere today.

23) Explain why today's atmosphere is different from the Earth's early atmosphere.

24) What is meant by 'primordial soup'?

25) Why do we fractionally distil air?

26) The burning of fossils fuels is causing a rise in the level of carbon dioxide in the atmosphere. How is this affecting the oceans and the climate?

* Answers on page 217.

Atoms and Compounds

Just to refresh your memory, atoms contain <u>three</u> types of particle — <u>protons</u>, <u>neutrons</u> and <u>electrons</u>.

Atomic number and *mass number* describe an atom

These two numbers tell you how many of each kind of particle an atom has.

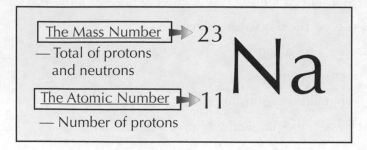

1) The <u>atomic number</u> tells you how many <u>protons</u> there are.

2) Atoms of the <u>same</u> element all have the <u>same</u> number of <u>protons</u> —
   so atoms of <u>different</u> elements will have <u>different</u> numbers of <u>protons</u>.

3) To get the number of <u>neutrons</u>, just <u>subtract</u> the <u>atomic number</u> from the <u>mass number</u>.
   Electrons aren't counted in the mass number because their <u>relative mass</u> is very small.

PARTICLE	MASS
Proton	1
Neutron	1
Electron	very small

*Compounds are **chemically bonded***

1) Compounds are formed when <u>atoms</u> of <u>two or more</u> elements are <u>chemically combined</u> together.
   For example, carbon dioxide is a <u>compound</u> formed from a <u>chemical reaction</u>
   between carbon and oxygen.

2) It's difficult to <u>separate</u> the two original elements out again.

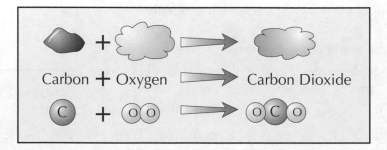

Atomic number = number of protons

If you look at a periodic table you can find the <u>atomic number</u> and <u>mass number</u> of any element.
You can then use these to find out the number of <u>protons</u>, <u>neutrons</u> or <u>electrons</u> in that element.

Isotopes

This page is all to do with the stuff inside the nucleus...

Isotopes are the same except for an extra neutron or two

A favourite exam question: "Explain what is meant by the term isotope".
LEARN the definition:

> Isotopes are: different atomic forms of the same element, which have the SAME number of PROTONS but a DIFFERENT number of NEUTRONS.

1) The upshot is: isotopes must have the same atomic number but different mass numbers.

2) If they had different atomic numbers, they'd be different elements altogether.

3) Carbon-12 and carbon-14 are a very popular pair of isotopes.

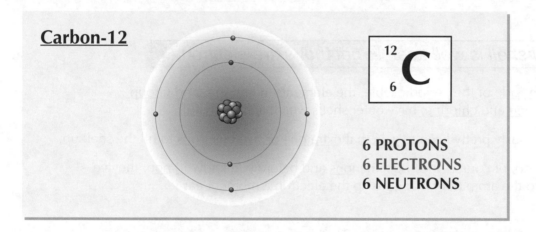

Carbon-12

$^{12}_{6}\text{C}$

6 PROTONS
6 ELECTRONS
6 NEUTRONS

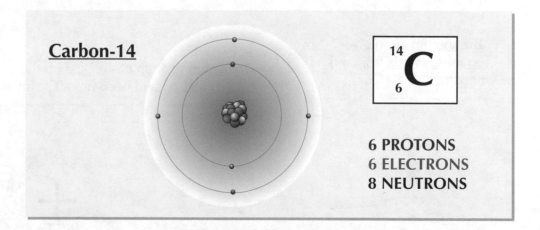

Carbon-14

$^{14}_{6}\text{C}$

6 PROTONS
6 ELECTRONS
8 NEUTRONS

Will this be in your exam — isotope so...

Carbon-14 is unstable. It makes up about one ten-millionth of the carbon in living things. When things die, the C-14 is trapped inside the dead material, and it gradually decays into nitrogen. So by measuring the proportion of C-14 found in some old wood you can calculate how long ago it was living wood.

Ionic Bonding

Ionic bonding is one of the ways atoms can form compounds.

Ionic bonding — *transferring* electrons

In ionic bonding, atoms lose or gain electrons to form charged particles (called ions) which are then strongly attracted to one another (because of the attraction of opposite charges, + and –).

A shell with just one electron is well keen to get rid...

1) All the atoms over at the left-hand side of the periodic table, e.g. sodium, potassium, calcium etc. have just one or two electrons in their outer shell (highest energy level).

2) And they're pretty keen to get shot of them, because then they'll only have full shells left, which is how they like it. (They try to have the same electronic structure as a noble gas.)

3) So given half a chance they do get rid, and that leaves the atom as an ion instead.

4) Now ions aren't the kind of things that sit around quietly watching the world go by. They tend to leap at the first passing ion with an opposite charge and stick to it like glue.

A nearly full shell is well keen to get that extra electron...

1) On the other side of the periodic table, the elements in Group 6 and Group 7, such as oxygen and chlorine, have outer shells which are nearly full.

2) They're obviously pretty keen to gain that extra one or two electrons to fill the shell up.

3) When they do, of course, they become ions and before you know it, pop, they've latched onto the atom (ion) that gave up the electron a moment earlier.

The reaction of sodium and chlorine is a classic case:

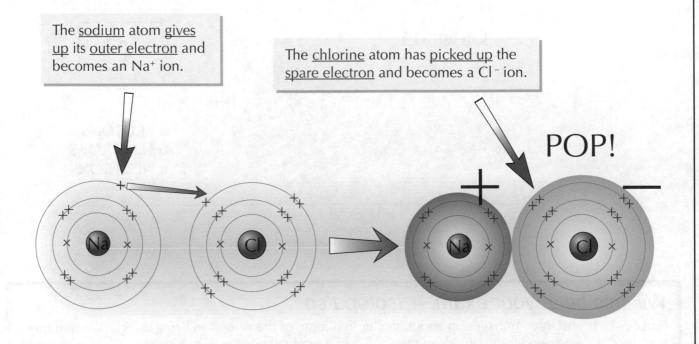

The sodium atom gives up its outer electron and becomes an Na⁺ ion.

The chlorine atom has picked up the spare electron and becomes a Cl⁻ ion.

POP!

Ionic Bonding

Ionic bonds produce <u>giant ionic structures</u>.

Ionic compounds *have a* **regular lattice** *structure*

1) <u>Ionic compounds</u> always have <u>giant ionic lattices</u>.

2) The ions form a closely packed <u>regular lattice</u> arrangement.

3) There are very strong <u>electrostatic forces of attraction</u>
   between <u>oppositely charged</u> ions, in <u>all directions</u>.

4) A single crystal of <u>sodium chloride</u> (salt) is <u>one giant ionic lattice</u>, which is why salt crystals
   tend to be cuboid in shape. The <u>Na$^+$</u> and <u>Cl$^-$ ions</u> are held together in a regular lattice.

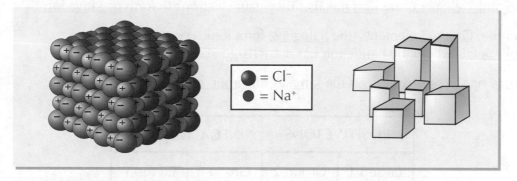

$\bullet$ = Cl$^-$
$\bullet$ = Na$^+$

Ionic compounds *all have* **similar properties**

1) They all have <u>high melting points</u> and <u>high boiling points</u> due to the <u>strong attraction</u>
   between the ions. It takes a large amount of <u>energy</u> to overcome this attraction.
   When ionic compounds <u>melt</u>, the ions are <u>free to move</u> and they'll <u>carry electric current</u>.

2) They do <u>dissolve easily</u> in water though. The ions <u>separate</u> and are
   all <u>free to move</u> in the solution, so they'll <u>carry electric current</u>.

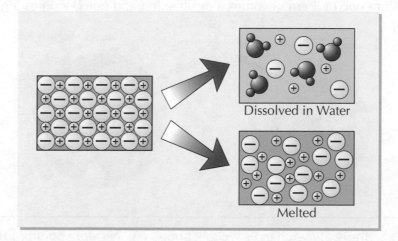

Dissolved in Water

Melted

Ionic compounds are always giant ionic lattices

You can get ionic compounds to <u>conduct electricity</u> by <u>melting</u> them or by <u>dissolving</u> them in water.
Dissolving them is easier though as it takes a lot of energy to melt an ionic compound.
Either way, it's the free ions that carry the electric current.

Ions

Make sure you've really got your head around the idea of ionic bonding before you start on this page.

Groups *1* & *2* and *6* & *7* are the most likely to form *ions*

1) Remember, atoms that have <u>lost</u> or <u>gained</u> an electron (or electrons) are <u>ions</u>.

2) Ions have the <u>electronic structure</u> of a <u>noble gas</u>.

3) The elements that most readily form ions are those in <u>Groups 1</u>, <u>2</u>, <u>6 and 7</u>.

4) <u>Group 1 and 2 elements</u> are <u>metals</u> and they <u>lose</u> electrons to form <u>positive ions</u>.

5) For example, <u>Group 1</u> elements (the <u>alkali metals</u>) form ionic compounds with <u>non-metals</u> where the metal ion has a 1^+ charge. E.g. K^+Cl^-.

6) <u>Group 6 and 7 elements</u> are <u>non-metals</u>. They <u>gain</u> electrons to form <u>negative ions</u>.

7) For example, <u>Group 7</u> elements (the <u>halogens</u>) form ionic compounds with the <u>alkali metals</u> where the halide ion has a 1^- charge. E.g. Na^+Cl^-.

8) The <u>charge</u> on the <u>positive ions</u> is the <u>same</u> as the <u>group number</u> of the element:

POSITIVE IONS		NEGATIVE IONS	
Group 1	Group 2	Group 6	Group 7
Li^+	Be^{2+}	O^{2-}	F^-
Na^+	Mg^{2+}		Cl^-
K^+	Ca^{2+}		

9) Any of the positive ions above can <u>combine</u> with any of the negative ions to form an <u>ionic compound</u>.

10) Only elements at <u>opposite sides</u> of the periodic table will form ionic compounds, e.g. Na and Cl, where one of them becomes a <u>positive ion</u> and one becomes a <u>negative ion</u>.

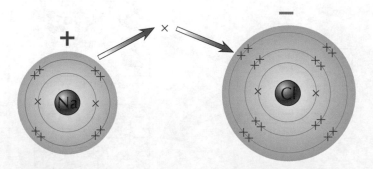

> Remember, the + and – charges we talk about, e.g. Na^+ for sodium, just tell you <u>what type of ion the atom WILL FORM</u> in a chemical reaction. In sodium <u>metal</u> there are <u>only neutral sodium atoms, Na</u>. The Na^+ ions <u>will only appear</u> if the sodium metal <u>reacts</u> with something like water or chlorine.

Formulas of Ionic Compounds

You need to be able to write down the right chemical formulas for ionic compounds.

Look at **charges** to work out the **formula** of an **ionic compound**

1) Ionic compounds are made up of a positively charged part and a negatively charged part.

2) The overall charge of any compound is zero.

3) So all the negative charges in the compound must balance all the positive charges.

4) You can use the charges on the individual ions present to work out the formula for the ionic compound:

Sodium chloride

Sodium chloride contains Na^+ (+1) and Cl^- (–1) ions.
$(+1) + (–1) = 0$. The charges are balanced with one of each ion, so the formula for sodium chloride = NaCl.

NaCl

Magnesium chloride

Magnesium chloride contains Mg^{2+} (+2) and Cl^- (–1) ions.

Because a chloride ion only has a 1^- charge we will need two of them to balance out the 2^+ charge of a magnesium ion. This gives us the formula $MgCl_2$.

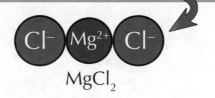

$MgCl_2$

The formula for exam success = revision...

The main thing to remember is that in compounds the total charge must always add up to zero. But, you won't be able to work out a formula if you don't know the charges of the ions involved. So, if you haven't already, learn the charges in the table on the previous page.

Electronic Structure of Ions

This page has some lovely drawings of the <u>electronic structures</u> of ions.
It's your job to make sure you can do drawings just like them in the exam.

Show the electronic structure of **simple** ions with **diagrams**

A useful way of representing ions is by <u>drawing</u> out their electronic structure. Just use a big <u>square bracket</u> and a + or − to show the charge. A few <u>ions</u> and the <u>ionic compounds</u> they form are shown below. You need to know how to draw them:

Sodium Chloride

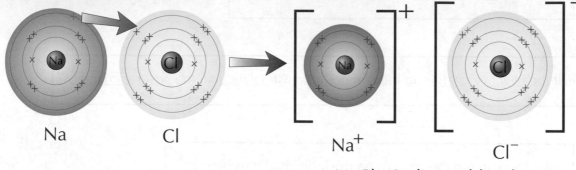

$$Na \qquad Cl \qquad Na^+ \qquad Cl^-$$

NaCl (Sodium Chloride)

Magnesium Oxide

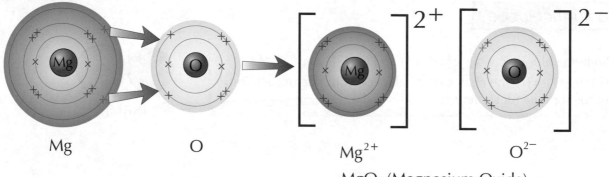

$$Mg \qquad O \qquad Mg^{2+} \qquad O^{2-}$$

MgO (Magnesium Oxide)

Calcium Chloride

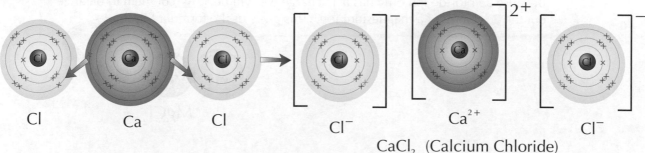

$$Cl \qquad Ca \qquad Cl \qquad Cl^- \qquad Ca^{2+} \qquad Cl^-$$

$CaCl_2$ (Calcium Chloride)

Show the electronic structure of ions with square brackets

Whether or not you're able to reproduce the drawings on this page all comes down to how well you've understood <u>ionic bonding</u>. (So if you're struggling, try reading the last few pages again.)

Warm-Up and Exam Questions

These questions will help you find out if you've learnt all the basics about atoms, compounds, isotopes and ionic bonding. Have a look back through the last few pages if you're unsure about any of these questions. It's really important to get these basics right.

Warm-Up Questions

1) Explain the difference between mass number and atomic number.
2) What is the name given to atoms of the same element with different mass numbers?
3) Sodium chloride has a giant ionic structure. Does it have a high or a low boiling point?
4) Why do ionic compounds conduct electricity when dissolved?
5) Do elements from Group 1 form positive ions or negative ions?
6) Do elements from Group 7 form positive ions or negative ions?
7) What is the formula of the compound containing Al^{3+} and OH^- ions only?

Exam Questions

1   Carbon has several isotopes, for example carbon-12 and carbon-13.
    Details about the carbon-13 isotope are shown below.

$$^{13}_{6}C$$

(a)   Explain what an isotope is.

(3 marks)

(b)   Draw a diagram to represent the carbon-13 atom. Label the number of protons and neutrons in the nucleus and show the electron arrangement.

(3 marks)

(c)   Details of element **X** are shown below.

$$^{13}_{7}X$$

Explain how you can tell that element X is not an isotope of carbon.

(1 mark)

2   (a)   A proton has a relative mass of 1. What is the relative mass of a neutron?

(1 mark)

(b)   Electrons aren't counted in the mass number of elements.
      Give a reason for this.

(1 mark)

Exam Questions

3   When lithium reacts with oxygen it forms an ionic compound, Li_2O.
   (a) Name the compound formed.

   (1 mark)

   (b) (i)   Complete the diagram below using arrows to show how the electrons
            are transferred when Li_2O is formed.

   (1 mark)

       (ii) Show the electron arrangements and the charges on the ions formed.

   (2 marks)

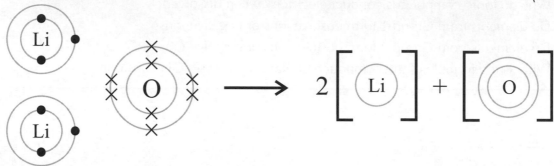

4   Magnesium (atomic number 12) and fluorine (atomic number 9) combine vigorously to form
    magnesium fluoride, an ionic compound.
   (a) Draw dot and cross diagrams to show the electron arrangement of each atom.

   (2 marks)

   (b) Give the symbol (including the charge) for each of the ions formed.

   (2 marks)

   (c) Using your answer to (b), work out the formula of magnesium fluoride.

   (1 mark)

   (d) Once formed, explain why the ions remain together in a compound.

   (1 mark)

   (e) Magnesium fluoride has a giant ionic structure. Explain why:
       (i)   it doesn't melt easily.

   (2 marks)

       (ii) it conducts electricity when molten.

   (1 mark)

5   Potassium and chlorine react to form potassium chloride.
   (a) Complete the following table.

   (3 marks)

	Potassium atom, K	Potassium ion, K^+	Chlorine atom, Cl	Chloride ion, Cl^-
Number of electrons	19			
Electron arrangement	2, 8, 8, 1			

   (b) Draw a dot and cross diagram to show the formation of potassium chloride.

   (2 marks)

Covalent Bonding

Some elements bond ionically (see page 74) but others form strong <u>covalent bonds</u>. This is where atoms <u>share electrons</u> with each other so that they've got <u>full outer shells</u>.

Covalent bonds — sharing electrons

1) Sometimes atoms prefer to make <u>covalent bonds</u> by <u>sharing</u> electrons with other atoms.

2) They only share electrons in their <u>outer shells</u> (highest energy levels).

3) This way <u>both</u> atoms feel that they have a <u>full outer shell</u>, and that makes them happy. Having a full outer shell gives them the electronic structure of a <u>noble gas</u>.

4) Each <u>covalent bond</u> provides one <u>extra</u> shared electron for each atom.

5) So, a covalent bond is a <u>shared pair</u> of electrons.

6) Each atom involved has to make <u>enough</u> covalent bonds to <u>fill up</u> its outer shell.

7) <u>Learn</u> these <u>seven important examples</u>:

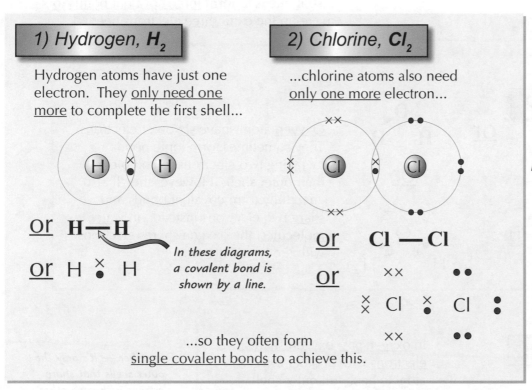

1) Hydrogen, H₂

Hydrogen atoms have just one electron. They <u>only need one more</u> to complete the first shell...

In these diagrams, a covalent bond is shown by a line.

...so they often form <u>single covalent bonds</u> to achieve this.

2) Chlorine, Cl₂

...chlorine atoms also need <u>only one more</u> electron...

In a dot and cross diagram, you only have to draw the outer shell of electrons.

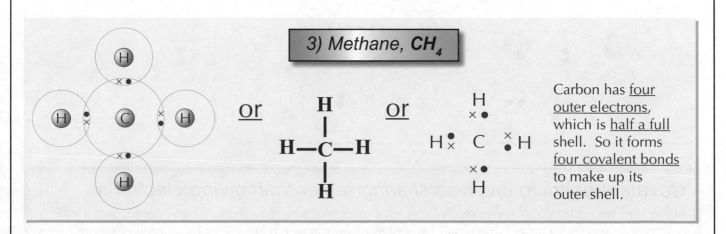

3) Methane, CH₄

Carbon has <u>four outer electrons</u>, which is <u>half a full</u> shell. So it forms <u>four covalent bonds</u> to make up its outer shell.

More Covalent Bonding

There are four more examples of covalent bonding on this page — just a few diagrams and a smattering of words. What a pleasant page.

4) Hydrogen Chloride, **HCl**

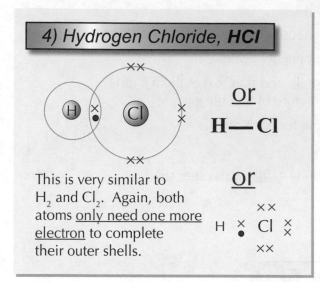

or

H—Cl

or

H ×•Cl ××

This is very similar to H_2 and Cl_2. Again, both atoms <u>only need one more electron</u> to complete their outer shells.

5) Ammonia, **NH₃**

Nitrogen has <u>five</u> outer electrons...

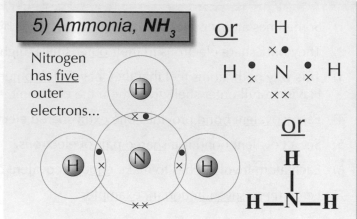

or

H ×•
H ×• N •× H
××

or

H
|
H—N—H

...so it needs to form <u>three covalent bonds</u> to make up the extra <u>three</u> electrons needed.

6) Water, **H₂O**

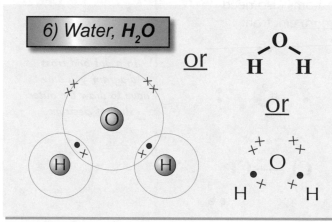

or

O
H   H

or

+× O ×+
+ +
H   H

<u>Oxygen</u> atoms have <u>six</u> outer electrons. They sometimes form <u>ionic</u> bonds by <u>taking</u> two electrons to complete their outer shell. However they'll also cheerfully form <u>covalent bonds</u> and <u>share</u> two electrons instead. In <u>water molecules</u>, the oxygen <u>shares</u> electrons with the two H atoms.

7) Oxygen, **O₂**

In <u>oxygen gas</u>, oxygen <u>shares two electrons</u> with another oxygen atom to get a full outer shell. A <u>double</u> covalent bond is formed.

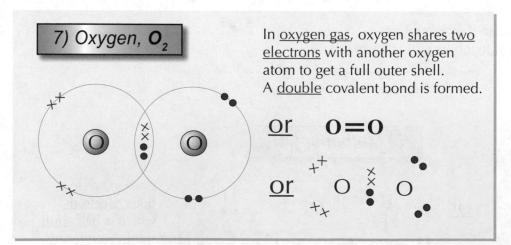

or

O═O

or

O ×× O

Remember — it's only the outer shells that share electrons with each other.

Covalent bonding involves sharing rather than giving electrons

Make sure you learn these seven really basic examples and <u>why they work</u>. Every atom wants a full outer shell, and they can get that either by becoming an <u>ion</u> (see page 74) or by <u>sharing electrons</u>. Once you understand that, you should be able to apply it to any example they give you in the exam.

Covalent Substances: Simple Molecular

Substances with <u>covalent bonds</u> (electron sharing) can form <u>simple molecules</u>.

Simple *molecular* substances

1) The atoms form <u>very strong</u> covalent bonds to form <u>small</u> molecules of several atoms.

2) By contrast, the forces of attraction <u>between</u> these molecules are <u>very weak</u>.

3) The result of these feeble <u>intermolecular forces</u> is that the <u>melting</u> and <u>boiling points</u> are <u>very low</u>, because the molecules are <u>easily parted</u> from each other. It's the <u>intermolecular forces</u> that get <u>broken</u> when simple molecular substances melt or boil — <u>not</u> the much <u>stronger covalent bonds</u>.

4) Most molecular substances are <u>gases or liquids</u> at room temperature, but they can be <u>solids</u>.

5) Molecular substances <u>don't conduct electricity</u> — there are <u>no ions</u> so there's <u>no electrical charge</u>.

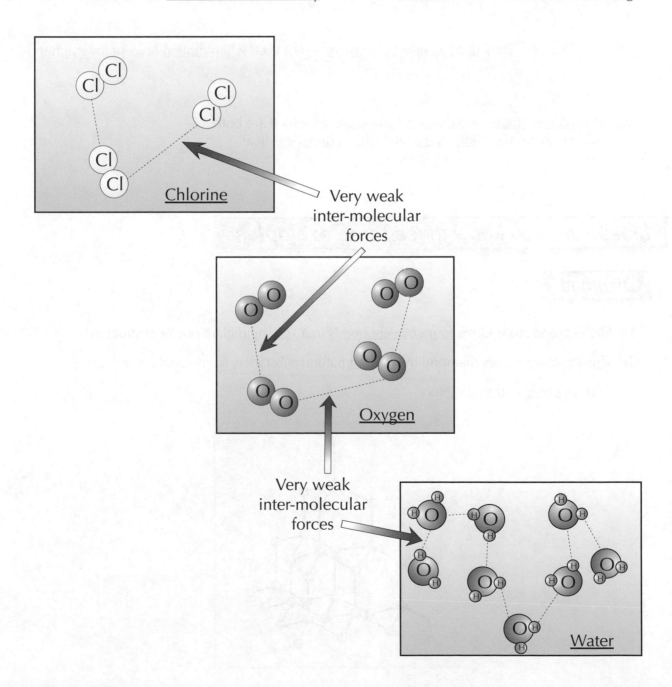

Very weak inter-molecular forces

Very weak inter-molecular forces

<u>Chlorine</u>

<u>Oxygen</u>

<u>Water</u>

Covalent Substances: Giant Covalent

Substances formed from <u>covalent bonds</u> aren't always <u>simple molecules</u> (see p. 83). They can also be <u>giant covalent structures</u>. There are three examples to learn.

Giant covalent structures are macromolecules

1) These are similar to giant ionic structures (lattices) <u>except</u> that there are <u>no charged ions</u>.

2) <u>All</u> the atoms are <u>bonded</u> to <u>each other</u> by <u>strong</u> covalent bonds.

3) This means that they have <u>very high</u> melting and boiling points.

4) They <u>don't conduct electricity</u> — not even when <u>molten</u> (except for graphite).

5) The <u>main examples</u> are <u>diamond</u> and <u>graphite</u>, which are both made only from <u>carbon atoms</u>, and <u>silicon dioxide</u> (silica).

Make sure you know these three examples

Diamond

1) Each carbon atom forms <u>four covalent bonds</u> in a <u>very rigid</u> giant covalent structure.

2) This structure makes diamond the <u>hardest</u> natural substance, so it's used for drill tips.

3) And it's <u>pretty</u> and <u>sparkly</u> too.

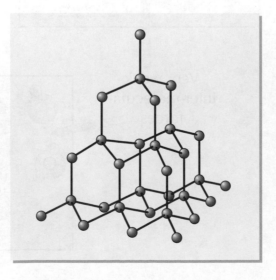

Covalent Substances: Giant Covalent

Here are the other two examples of <u>giant covalent structures</u> that you need to learn.

Graphite

1) Each carbon atom only forms <u>three covalent bonds</u>. This creates <u>layers</u> which are free to <u>slide over each other</u>, like a pack of cards — so graphite is <u>soft</u> and <u>slippery</u>.

2) The layers are held together so loosely that they can be <u>rubbed off</u> onto paper — that's how a <u>pencil</u> works. This is because there are <u>weak intermolecular forces</u> between the layers.

3) Graphite is the only <u>non-metal</u> which is a <u>good conductor of heat and electricity</u>. Each carbon atom has one <u>delocalised</u> (free) electron and it's these free electrons that <u>conduct</u> heat and electricity.

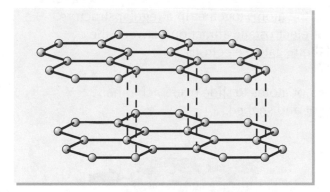

Silicon Dioxide (Silica)

1) Sometimes called <u>silica</u>, this is what <u>sand</u> is made of.

2) Each grain of sand is <u>one giant structure</u> of silicon and oxygen.

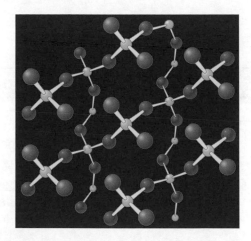

Graphite and diamond contain exactly the same atoms

Graphite and diamond are both made purely from <u>carbon</u> — there's no difference at all in their <u>atoms</u>. The difference in properties (and price) of the two substances is all down to the way the atoms are <u>held together</u>. Don't get confused though — they're both still giant covalent substances. Giant covalent substances and simple molecular substances are very different — make sure you know about them both. You should be able to recognise a <u>giant structure</u> from diagrams of its <u>bonding</u>.

Metallic Structures

Ever wondered what makes <u>metals</u> tick? Well, either way, this is the page for you.

Metal properties are all due to the sea of free electrons

1) <u>Metals</u> also consist of a <u>giant structure</u>.

2) <u>Metallic bonds</u> involve the all-important
   '<u>free electrons</u>' which produce <u>all</u> the
   properties of metals. These delocalised
   (free) electrons come from the <u>outer shell</u>
   of <u>every</u> metal atom in the structure.

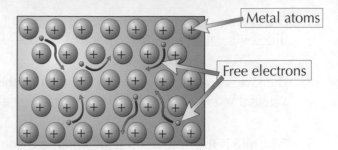

3) These electrons are <u>free to move</u> through the whole structure and
   so metals are good conductors of <u>heat and electricity</u>.

4) These electrons also <u>hold</u> the <u>atoms</u> together in a <u>regular</u> structure.
   There are strong forces of <u>electrostatic attraction</u> between the
   <u>positive metal ions</u> and the <u>negative electrons</u>.

5) They also allow the layers of atoms to <u>slide</u> over each other,
   allowing metals to be <u>bent</u> and <u>shaped</u>.

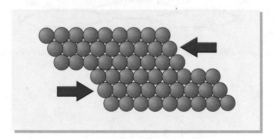

Alloys are harder than pure metals

1) <u>Pure metals</u> often aren't quite right for certain jobs. So scientists <u>mix two or more metals together</u>
   — creating an <u>alloy</u> with the properties they want.

2) Different elements have <u>different sized atoms</u>. So when another metal is mixed
   with a pure metal, the new metal atoms will <u>distort</u> the layers of metal atoms,
   making it more difficult for them to slide over each other. So alloys are <u>harder</u>.

Identifying Structures

If you've learnt the <u>properties</u> of the four types of substance then this page shouldn't be a problem. If you haven't then you should go and learn them first.

Identifying the structure of a substance by its properties

You should be able to easily <u>identify</u> most substances just by the way they <u>behave</u> as either:

- <u>giant ionic</u>,
- <u>simple molecular</u>,
- <u>giant covalent</u>,
- or <u>giant metallic</u>.

The way they might test you in the Exam is by describing the <u>physical properties</u> of a substance and asking you to decide <u>which type of structure</u> it has.

Try this one:

> <u>Example</u>:
>
> Four substances were tested for various properties with the following results.
>
> Identify the structure of each substance. (Answers on page 217.)

Substance	Melting point (°C)	Boiling point (°C)	Good electrical conductor?
A	−219.62	−188.12	No
B	1535	2750	Yes
C	1410	2355	No
D	770	1420	When molten

Look at the properties to identify the structure

You have to be able to identify the structure of <u>any</u> substance based on its properties and justify your answer too. It's not as hard as it sounds because a substance will always be one of four things — giant ionic, simple molecular, giant covalent or giant metallic. So, if you know how to identify those four substances, then you know how to identify anything. Phew.

Warm-Up and Exam Questions

Don't charge past this page, it's a lot more important than it looks.

Warm-Up Questions

1) How is covalent bonding different from ionic bonding?
2) Describe the differences in the physical properties of diamond and graphite.
3) Give another example of a substance that has a giant covalent structure.
4) Why does chlorine have a very low boiling point?

Exam Questions

1   Methane is a covalently bonded molecule with the formula CH_4.
    Draw a dot and cross diagram for the methane molecule,
    showing only the outer electrons.

    (2 marks)

2   The table compares some physical properties of silicon dioxide, bromine and graphite.

Property	silicon dioxide	bromine	graphite
Melting point (°C)	1610	−7	3657
Electrical conductivity	poor	poor	good
Solubility in water	insoluble	slightly soluble	insoluble

(a) What is the structure in:
    (i)   silicon dioxide?

    (1 mark)

    (ii) graphite?

    (1 mark)

    (iii) bromine?

    (1 mark)

(b) Explain why bromine has poor electrical conductivity.

    (1 mark)

(c) Explain why graphite has good electrical conductivity.

    (1 mark)

(d) Bromine is a liquid at room temperature (20 °C).
    Explain why bromine has such a low melting point compared with
    silicon dioxide and graphite.

    (2 marks)

Exam Questions

3   The diagram below shows the arrangement of atoms in pure iron.

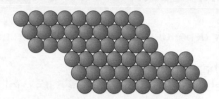

Steel is an alloy of iron and carbon.
(a)   Draw a similar diagram to show the arrangement of atoms in steel.

(2 marks)

(b)   Steel is harder than iron. Explain why.

(3 marks)

4   The table gives data for some physical properties of a selection of substances.

Substance	Melting point	Boiling point	Electrical conductivity
A	-219	-183	poor
B	3550	4827	poor
C	1495	2870	good
D	801	1413	good when molten

(a)   What state would expect substance D to be at room temperature?

(1 mark)

(b)   What is the structure of:
(i)   substance B?

(1 mark)

(ii)   substance D?

(1 mark)

(c)   Substance A is oxygen.
(i)   Draw a dot and cross diagram to show the outer electrons in
an oxygen molecule.

(2 marks)

(ii)   Explain why oxygen has such a low melting point.

(2 marks)

(d)   Substance C is a metal. According to the table, it is a good conductor of electricity.
(i)   Explain why this is.

(2 marks)

(ii)   Would substance C be a good conductor of heat?

(1 mark)

CHEMISTRY 2A — BONDING AND CALCULATIONS

New Materials

New materials are continually being developed, with new properties. The two groups of materials you really need to know about are <u>smart materials</u> and <u>nanoparticles</u>.

Smart materials have some really weird properties

1) <u>Smart</u> materials <u>behave differently</u> depending on the <u>conditions</u>, e.g. temperature.

2) A good example is <u>nitinol</u> — a "<u>shape memory alloy</u>".
It's a metal <u>alloy</u> (about half nickel, half titanium) but when it's cool you can <u>bend it</u> and <u>twist it</u> like rubber. Bend it too far, though, and it stays bent. But here's the really clever bit — if you heat it above a certain temperature, it goes back to a "<u>remembered</u>" shape.

3) It's really handy for <u>glasses frames</u>. If you accidentally bend them, you can just pop them into a bowl of hot water and they'll <u>jump</u> back <u>into shape</u>.

4) Nitinol is also used for <u>dental braces</u>. In the mouth it <u>warms</u> and tries to return to a '<u>remembered</u>' shape, and so it gently <u>pulls the teeth</u> with it.

Nanoparticles are really really really really tiny   ...smaller than that.

1) Really tiny particles, <u>1–100 nanometres</u> across, are called 'nanoparticles' (1 nm = 0.000 000 001 m).

2) Nanoparticles contain roughly <u>a few hundred atoms</u>.

3) Nanoparticles include <u>fullerenes</u>. These are molecules of <u>carbon</u>, shaped like <u>hollow balls</u> or <u>closed tubes</u>. The carbon atoms are arranged in <u>hexagonal rings</u>. Different fullerenes contain <u>different numbers</u> of carbon atoms.

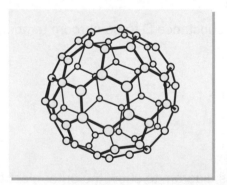

4) A nanoparticle has very <u>different properties</u> from the 'bulk' chemical that it's made from — e.g. <u>fullerenes</u> have different properties from big <u>lumps of carbon</u>.

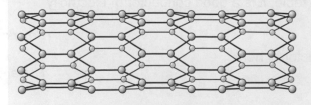

1) Fullerenes can be joined together to form <u>nanotubes</u> — teeny tiny hollow carbon tubes, a few nanometres across.

2) All those covalent bonds make carbon nanotubes <u>very strong</u>. They can be used to reinforce graphite in <u>tennis rackets</u>.

New Materials

Nanomaterials *are becoming more and more* **widely used**

Using nanoparticles is known as <u>nanoscience</u>. Many <u>new uses</u> of nanoparticles are being developed.

1) They have a <u>huge surface area to volume ratio</u>, so they could help make new industrial <u>catalysts</u> (see page 116).

2) You can use nanoparticles to make <u>sensors</u> to detect one type of molecule and nothing else. These <u>highly specific</u> sensors are already being used to test water purity.

3) Nanotubes can be used to make <u>stronger</u>, <u>lighter</u> building materials.

4) New cosmetics, e.g. <u>sun tan cream</u> and <u>deodorant</u>, have been made using nanoparticles. The small particles do their job but don't leave <u>white marks</u> on the skin.

5) <u>Nanomedicine</u> is a hot topic. The idea is that tiny fullerenes are <u>absorbed</u> more easily by the body than most particles. This means they could <u>deliver drugs</u> right into the cells where they're needed.

6) New <u>lubricant coatings</u> are being developed using fullerenes. These coatings reduce friction a bit like <u>ball bearings</u> and could be used in all sorts of places from <u>artificial joints</u> to <u>gears</u>.

7) Nanotubes <u>conduct</u> electricity, so they can be used in tiny <u>electric circuits</u> for computer chips.

Bendy specs, tennis rackets and computer chips — cool...

Some nanoparticles have really <u>unexpected properties</u>. Silver's normally very unreactive, but silver nanoparticles can kill bacteria. Gold nanoparticles aren't gold-coloured — they're either red or purple. On the flipside, we also need to watch out for any unexpected harmful properties.

Polymers

Plastics are made up of <u>lots</u> of molecules <u>joined together</u> in long chains.

Forces between molecules determine the **properties** of plastics

Strong <u>covalent</u> bonds hold the <u>atoms</u> together in <u>long chains</u>. But it's the bonds <u>between</u> the different molecule chains that determine the <u>properties</u> of the plastic.

Weak Forces:

<u>Individual tangled chains</u> of polymers, held together by <u>weak intermolecular forces</u>, are free to <u>slide</u> over each other.

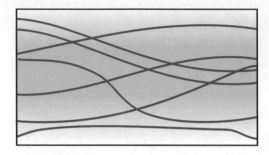

1) <u>THERMOSOFTENING POLYMERS</u> don't have cross-linking between chains.

2) The forces between the chains are really easy to overcome, so it's easy to <u>melt</u> the plastic.

3) When it <u>cools</u>, the polymer hardens into a new shape.

4) You can melt these plastics and <u>remould</u> them as many times as you like.

Strong Forces:

Some plastics have <u>stronger intermolecular forces</u> between the polymer chains, called <u>crosslinks</u>, that hold the chains firmly together.

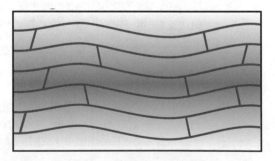

1) <u>THERMOSETTING POLYMERS</u> have <u>crosslinks</u>.

2) These hold the chains together in a <u>solid structure</u>.

3) The polymer doesn't soften when it's heated.

4) Thermosetting polymers are <u>strong</u>, <u>hard</u> and <u>rigid</u>.

Polymers

There's plastic and there's... well, plastic. You wouldn't want to make a chair with the same plastic that gets used for flimsy old carrier bags. But whatever the plastic, it's always a polymer.

How you **make** a **polymer** affects its **properties**

1) The starting materials and reaction conditions will both affect the properties of a polymer.

2) Two types of polythene can be made using different conditions:

> - Low density (LD) polythene is made by heating ethene to about 200 °C under high pressure. It's flexible and is used for bags and bottles.
>
> - High density (HD) polythene is made at a lower temperature and pressure (with a catalyst). It's more rigid and is used for water tanks and drainpipes.

The **use** of a plastic depends on its **properties**

You might need to answer a question like this one in the exam.

Choose from the table the plastic that would be best suited for making:

a) a disposable cup for hot drinks,

b) clothing,

c) a measuring cylinder.

Give reasons for each choice.

Plastic	Cost	Resistance to chemicals	Melting point	Transparency	Rigidity	Can be made into fibres
W	High	High	High	Low	High	No
X	Low	Low	Low	Low	Low	Yes
Y	High	High	High	High	High	No
Z	Low	Low	High	High	High	No

Answers

a) Z — low cost (disposable) and high melting point (for hot drinks),

b) X — flexible (essential for clothing) and able to be made into fibres (clothing is usually woven),

c) Y — transparent and resistant to chemicals (you need to be able to see the liquid inside and the liquid and measuring cylinder mustn't react with each other).

Polymers have different uses

You need to understand that different reaction conditions result in polymers with different properties (like low density and high density polythene). You also might be given information about the properties of a certain polymer and have to explain why it's suited to its use.

Warm-Up and Exam Questions

Warm-Up Questions

1) What is nitinol?
2) What does a plastic's melting point tell you about the forces between its polymer chains?
3) What are intermolecular forces between polymer chains called?
4) Give two things that can affect the properties of a polymer.

Exam Questions

1   Scientists have developed new materials using nanoparticles, which show different properties from the same materials in bulk.

(a)   Use words from the box to help you complete the sentences below.

volume   mm   catalysts   surface area   nm   circuits

(i)   Nanoparticles are up to 100 .... in size.

(1 mark)

(ii)   Nanoparticles have a large .... to

.... ratio.

(2 marks)

(b)   Floyd Landis used a bike in the Tour de France with a frame weighing about 1 kg. Carbon nanotubes (CNT) were used in the manufacture of the frame of the bike.

(i)   Suggest two properties of a material made using CNTs that make it suitable for use in a bike frame.

(2 marks)

(ii)   Give the name of a type of molecule that can be joined together to make carbon nanotubes.

(1 mark)

(c)   Give one other application of nanoparticles.

(1 mark)

2   The table below shows the properties of three polymers, **A**, **B** and **C**.

Give the polymer that would be best suited for each of the following uses:

Polymer	Properties
A	heat resistant and strong
B	very flexible and biodegradable
C	very rigid

(a)   sandwich bag

(1 mark)

(b)   drainpipe

(1 mark)

(c)   disposable cup

(1 mark)

Relative Formula Mass

The biggest trouble with <u>relative atomic mass</u> and <u>relative formula mass</u> is that they <u>sound</u> so blood-curdling. Take a few deep breaths, and just enjoy, as the mists slowly clear...

Relative atomic mass, A_r, is easy

1) This is just a way of saying how <u>heavy</u> different atoms are <u>compared</u> with the mass of an atom of carbon-12. So carbon-12 has A_r of <u>exactly 12</u>.

2) It turns out that the <u>relative atomic mass</u> A_r is usually just the same as the <u>mass number</u> of the element.

3) In the periodic table, the elements all have <u>two</u> numbers. The smaller one is the atomic number (how many protons it has). But the <u>bigger one</u> is the <u>mass number</u> or <u>relative atomic mass</u>.

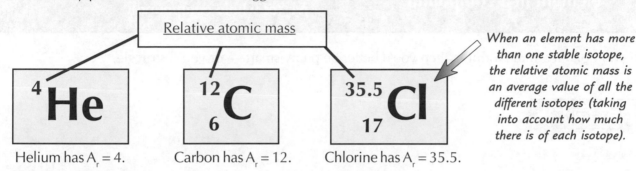

Relative atomic mass

^{4}He

$^{12}_{6}$C

$^{35.5}_{17}$Cl

When an element has more than one stable isotope, the relative atomic mass is an average value of all the different isotopes (taking into account how much there is of each isotope).

Helium has $A_r = 4$.   Carbon has $A_r = 12$.   Chlorine has $A_r = 35.5$.

Relative formula mass, M_r, is also easy

If you have a compound like $MgCl_2$ then it has a <u>relative formula mass</u>, M_r, which is just all the relative atomic masses <u>added together</u>.

For $MgCl_2$ it would be:

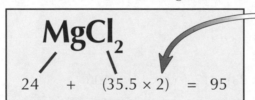

$MgCl_2$

$24 \quad + \quad (35.5 \times 2) \quad = \quad 95$

The relative atomic mass of chlorine is multiplied by 2 because there are two chlorine atoms.

So M_r for $MgCl_2$ is simply <u>95</u>.

You can easily get A_r for any element from the periodic table, but in a lot of questions they give you them anyway. And that's all it is. A big fancy name like <u>relative formula mass</u> and all it means is "<u>add up all the relative atomic masses</u>".

"ONE MOLE" of a substance is equal to its M_r in grams

> The <u>relative formula mass</u> (A_r or M_r) of a substance <u>in grams</u> is known as <u>one mole</u> of that substance.

<u>Examples:</u>

Iron has an A_r of 56.   So one mole of iron weighs exactly 56 g

Nitrogen gas, N_2, has an M_r of 28 (2×14).   So one mole of N_2 weighs exactly 28 g

You can convert between moles and grams using this formula:

> <u>NUMBER OF MOLES</u> = Mass in g (of element or compound) / M_r (of element or compound)

<u>Example:</u> How many moles are there in 42 g of carbon?

<u>Answer:</u> No. of moles = Mass (g) / M_r = 42/12 = <u>3.5 moles</u>   Easy Peasy

Formula Mass Calculations

Although relative atomic mass and relative formula mass are <u>easy enough</u>, it can get just a tad <u>trickier</u> when you start getting into other calculations which use them. It depends on how good your maths is basically, because it's all to do with ratios and percentages.

Calculating % mass of an element in a compound

This is actually dead easy — so long as you've learnt this formula:

$$\text{Percentage mass of an element in a compound} = \frac{A_r \times \text{no. of atoms (of that element)}}{M_r \text{ (of whole compound)}} \times 100$$

If you don't learn the formula then you'd better be pretty smart — or you'll struggle.

Example:

Find the percentage mass of sodium in sodium carbonate, Na_2CO_3.

<u>ANSWER:</u>

- A_r of sodium = 23
- A_r of carbon = 12
- A_r of oxygen = 16

M_r of Na_2CO_3 = $(2 \times 23) + 12 + (3 \times 16) = 106$

Now use the formula:

$$\text{Percentage Mass} = \frac{A_r \times \text{No. of atoms}}{M_r} \times 100 = \frac{23 \times 2}{106} \times 100 = 43.4\%$$

And there you have it.
Sodium makes up <u>43.4%</u> of the mass of sodium carbonate.

You can't just read these pages — work through the examples too

As usual with these calculations, <u>practice makes perfect</u>. Try these:

Find the percentage mass of oxygen in each of these:

Don't skip this bit, you'll be glad you're perfect when it comes to exam day.

a) Fe_2O_3
b) H_2O
c) $CaCO_3$
d) H_2SO_4

Answers on page 218.

Formula Mass Calculations

Finding the **empirical formula** (from masses or percentages)

This also sounds a lot worse than it really is. Try this for a nice simple <u>stepwise method</u>:

1) <u>List all the elements</u> in the compound (there's usually only two or three).

2) <u>Underneath them</u>, write their <u>experimental masses or percentages</u>.

3) <u>Divide</u> each mass or percentage <u>by the A$_r$</u> for that particular element.

4) Turn the numbers you get into <u>a nice simple ratio</u>
   by multiplying and/or dividing them by well-chosen numbers.

5) Get the ratio in its <u>simplest form</u>, and that tells you the <u>empirical formula</u> of the compound.

Example:

Find the empirical formula of the iron oxide produced when
44.8 g of iron react with 19.2 g of oxygen.
(A$_r$ for iron = 56, A$_r$ for oxygen = 16)

METHOD:

1) <u>List the two elements:</u>   **Fe**   **O**

2) Write in the <u>experimental masses</u>:   44.8   19.2

3) <u>Divide by the A$_r$</u> for each element: $\frac{44.8}{56} = 0.8$ $\frac{19.2}{16} = 1.2$

4) Multiply by 10...   8   12

   ...then divide by 4:   2   3

5) So the <u>simplest formula</u> is 2 atoms of Fe to 3 atoms of O, i.e. Fe_2O_3.

You need to realise (for the exam) that this <u>empirical method</u> (i.e. based on <u>experiment</u>) is the <u>only way</u> of finding out the formula of a compound. Rust is iron oxide, sure, but is it FeO, or Fe_2O_3? Only an experiment to determine the empirical formula will tell you for certain.

Don't learn that list of instructions — practise using it (it's much quicker)

These sort of questions are the backbone of chemistry. They're really common exam questions as well. If you find them a bit scary, just keep practising using the stepwise method until you've mastered it.
Try this:
Find the empirical formula of the compound formed from 2.4 g of carbon and 0.8 g of hydrogen.

Calculating Masses in Reactions

You can also work out masses of reactants (starting materials) and products in reactions.

The three important steps — *not to be missed...*

1) Write out the balanced equation.

2) Work out M_r — just for the two bits you want.

3) Apply the rule: Divide to get one, then multiply to get all.
(But you have to apply this first to the substance they give you information about, and then the other one!)

Don't worry — these steps should all make sense when you look at the example below.

Example:

> What mass of magnesium oxide is produced when 60 g of magnesium is burned in air?

Answer:

1) Write out the balanced equation: $2Mg + O_2 \rightarrow 2MgO$

2) Work out the relative formula masses: $2 \times 24 \rightarrow 2 \times (24 + 16)$
(don't do the oxygen — you don't need it) $48 \rightarrow 80$

3) Apply the rule: Divide to get one, then multiply to get all:

The two numbers, 48 and 80, tell us that 48 g of Mg react to give 80 g of MgO. Here's the tricky bit. You've now got to be able to write this down:

> 48 g of Mg ...... reacts to give ...... 80g of MgO
>
> 1 g of Mg ...... reacts to give ......
>
> 60 g of Mg ...... reacts to give ......

The big clue is that in the question they've said we want to burn "60 g of magnesium", i.e. they've told us how much magnesium to have, and that's how you know to write down the left-hand side of it first, because:

**We'll first need to ÷ by 48 to get 1 g of Mg
and then need to × by 60 to get 60 g of Mg.**

Then you can work out the numbers on the other side (shown in blue below) by realising that you must divide both sides by 48 and then multiply both sides by 60.

÷ 48   48 g of Mg .... 80 g of MgO   ÷ 48
              1 g of Mg .... 1.67 g of MgO
× 60   60 g of Mg .... 100 g of MgO   × 60

The mass of product is called the yield of a reaction. You should realise that in practice you never get 100% of the yield, so the amount of product will be slightly less than calculated (see page 101).

This finally tells us that 60 g of magnesium will produce 100 g of magnesium oxide.

If the question had said "Find how much magnesium gives 500 g of magnesium oxide", you'd fill in the MgO side first, because that's the one you'd have the information about.

Warm-Up and Exam Questions

Lots to remember on those four pages. Try these and see how good your understanding really is.

Warm-Up Questions

1) What name is given to the average mass of isotopes of an element?
2) What name is given to the sum of the relative atomic masses of the atoms in a molecule?
3) Write down the definition of a mole.
4) What is the mass of one mole of oxygen gas?

Exam Questions

1 (a) Boron has two main isotopes, $^{11}_{5}B$ and $^{10}_{5}B$. Its A_r value is 10.8.

   (i) What does A_r stand for?

   (1 mark)

   (ii) What is the difference in structure between the two boron isotopes?

   (1 mark)

   (iii) Which isotope is the most abundant? Explain your reasoning.

   (2 marks)

   (b) Use the A_r values B = 11, O = 16, F = 19 and H = 1 to calculate the relative formula masses of these boron compounds:

   (i) BF_3

   (1 mark)

   (ii) $B(OH)_3$.

   (1 mark)

2 Analysis of an oxide of sulfur shows that it contains 60% oxygen by mass.
  (A_r values: S = 32, O = 16.)

   (a) What is the percentage mass of sulfur in the oxide?

   (1 mark)

   (b) Work out the formula of the oxide.

   (2 marks)

3 Heating a test tube containing 2 g of calcium carbonate produced 1.08 g of calcium oxide when it was reweighed. The equation for the reaction is:

   $$CaCO_3(s) \rightarrow CaO(s) + CO_2(g)$$
   (M_r values: $CaCO_3$ = 100, CaO = 56.)

   (a) Calculate the amount of calcium oxide you would expect to be formed from 2 g of calcium carbonate.

   (1 mark)

   (b) Compare the value to the mass obtained in the experiment.
       Suggest a possible reason for the difference.

   (1 mark)

Percentage Yield

Percentage yield tells you about the <u>overall success</u> of an experiment. It compares what you calculate you should get (<u>predicted yield</u>) with what you get in practice (<u>actual yield</u>).

Percentage yield compares actual and predicted yield

The amount of product you get is known as the <u>yield</u>. The more reactants you start with, the higher the <u>actual yield</u> will be — that's pretty obvious. But the <u>percentage yield doesn't</u> depend on the amount of reactants you started with — it's a <u>percentage</u>.

> 1) The <u>predicted yield</u> of a reaction can be calculated from the <u>balanced reaction equation</u> (see page 24).

> 2) Percentage yield is given by the formula:

$$\text{percentage yield} = \frac{\text{actual yield (grams)}}{\text{predicted yield (grams)}} \times 100$$

The predicted yield is sometimes called the theoretical yield.

> 3) Percentage yield is <u>always</u> somewhere between 0 and 100%.

> 4) A 100% percentage yield means that you got <u>all</u> the product you expected to get.

> 5) A 0% yield means that <u>no</u> reactants were converted into product, i.e. no product at all was <u>made</u>.

Yields are always less than 100%

Even though <u>no atoms are gained or lost</u> in reactions, in real life, you <u>never</u> get a 100% percentage yield. Some product or reactant <u>always</u> gets lost along the way — and that goes for big <u>industrial processes</u> as well as school lab experiments.

Lots of things can go wrong, but you can find the three you need to know about conveniently located on the next page.

Even with the best equipment, you can't get the maximum product

A high percentage yield means there's <u>not much waste</u> — which is good for <u>preserving resources</u> and keeping production <u>costs down</u>. If a reaction's going to be worth doing commercially, it generally has to have a high percentage yield or recyclable reactants. Learn the <u>formula</u> for working out the all important percentage yield — if it comes up in the exam, it's easy calculation marks.

Percentage Yield and Sustainable Development

Learn these *three reasons* why yields *can't* be 100%

1) The reaction is *reversible*

A <u>reversible reaction</u> is one where the <u>products</u> of the
reaction can <u>themselves react</u> to produce the <u>original reactants</u>

$$A + B \rightleftharpoons C + D$$

<u>For example:</u>
ammonium chloride $\rightleftharpoons$ ammonia + hydrogen chloride

1) This means that the reactants will never be completely converted to
   products because the reaction goes both ways.
2) Some of the <u>products</u> are always <u>reacting together</u> to change back to the original reactants.
3) This will mean a <u>lower yield</u>.

2) *Filtration*

1) When you <u>filter a liquid</u> to remove <u>solid particles</u>, you nearly always
   <u>lose</u> a bit of liquid or a bit of solid.
2) So, some of the product may be lost when it's <u>separated</u> from the reaction mixture.

3) *Unexpected reactions*

1) Things don't always go exactly to plan. Sometimes there can be other
   <u>unexpected reactions</u> happening which <u>use up the reactants</u>.
2) This means there's not as much reactant to make the <u>product</u> you want.

Product yield is important for *sustainable development*

1) Thinking about product yield is important for <u>sustainable development</u>.

2) Sustainable development is about making sure that we don't use
   <u>resources</u> faster than they can be <u>replaced</u> — there needs to be
   enough for <u>future generations</u> too.

3) So, for example, using as <u>little energy</u> as possible to create the
   <u>highest product yield possible</u> means that resources are <u>saved</u>.
   A low yield means wasted chemicals — not very sustainable.

Chemical Analysis

Now time for some proper chemistry. You can sometimes tell what substances are present in a mixture using chromatography.

Artificial colours can be separated using paper chromatography

A food colouring might contain one dye or it might be a mixture of dyes.

Here's how you can tell:

1) Extract the colour from a food sample by placing it in a small cup with a few drops of solvent (can be water, ethanol, salt water, etc).

2) Put spots of the coloured solution on a pencil baseline on filter paper. (Don't use pen because it might dissolve in the solvent and confuse everything.)

3) Roll up the sheet and put it in a beaker with some solvent — but keep the baseline above the level of the solvent.

4) The solvent seeps up the paper, taking the dyes with it. Different dyes form spots in different places.

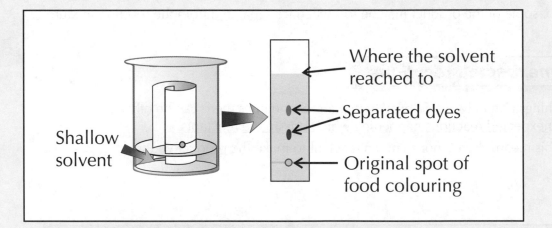

Shallow solvent

Where the solvent reached to

Separated dyes

Original spot of food colouring

5) Watch out though — a chromatogram with four spots means at least four dyes, not exactly four dyes. There could be five dyes, with two of them making a spot in the same place. It can't be three dyes though, because one dye can't split into two spots.

Make sure your solvent level is lower than the spots...

Chromatography is used all the time in industry — it can separate accurately even dead complex mixtures if you choose the right solvent, "filter paper" and conditions.

CHEMISTRY 2A — BONDING AND CALCULATIONS

Chemical Analysis and Instrumental Methods

Nowadays there are some pretty clever ways of <u>identifying</u> substances. We don't have to stick to filter paper — we can use <u>machines</u> as well.

Machines can also analyse unknown substances

You can identify elements and compounds using <u>instrumental methods</u> — this just means using machines.

> Advantages of Using Machines
> 1) <u>Very sensitive</u> — can detect even the <u>tiniest amounts</u> of substances.
> 2) <u>Very fast</u> and tests can be automated.
> 3) <u>Very accurate</u>

Gas chromatography can be used to identify substances

Gas chromatography can <u>separate out</u> a mixture of compounds and help you <u>identify</u> the substances present.

1) A <u>gas</u> is used to <u>carry</u> substances through a <u>column</u> packed with a <u>solid material</u>.

2) The substances travel through the tube at <u>different speeds</u>, so they're <u>separated</u>.

3) The time they take to reach the <u>detector</u> is called the <u>retention time</u>. It can be used to help <u>identify</u> the substances.

4) The recorder draws a <u>gas chromatograph</u>. The number of <u>peaks</u> shows the number of <u>different compounds</u> in the sample.

5) The <u>position of the peaks</u> shows the <u>retention time</u> of each substance.

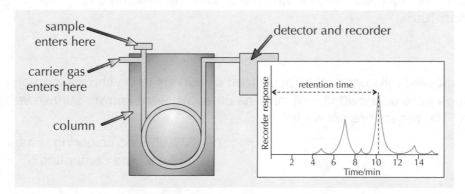

6) The gas chromatography column can also be linked to a <u>mass spectrometer</u>. This process is known as <u>GC-MS</u> and can identify the substances leaving the column very <u>accurately</u>.

7) You can work out the <u>relative molecular mass</u> of each of the substances from the graph it draws. You just <u>read off</u> from the <u>molecular ion peak</u>.

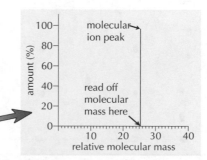

Unfortunately, machines can't do the exam for you...

Make sure you don't get the two types of chromatography muddled up... there's <u>paper</u> and then there's <u>gas</u>. Gas chromatography can tell you a lot more information about substances.

Warm-Up and Exam Questions

Try these questions to help make sure you won't get stuck in the exam. First a (fairly) gentle warm-up, and then some more exam-like questions to give you an idea of what you can expect.

Warm-Up Questions

1) Why might a reaction with a low percentage yield be bad for sustainable development?
2) Give three advantages of using instrumental methods to identify elements and compounds.
3) How can gas chromatography be used to work out the relative molecular mass of a substance?

Exam Questions

1   A sample of copper was made by reducing 4 g of copper oxide with methane gas. When the black copper oxide turned orange-red, the sample was scraped out into a beaker. Sulfuric acid was added to dissolve any copper oxide that remained. The sample was then washed, filtered and dried. 2.8 g of copper was obtained.
    (A_r values: Cu = 63.5, O = 16.)

The equation for this reaction is: $CH_4 + 4CuO \rightarrow 4Cu + 2H_2O + CO_2$

(a) Use the equation to calculate the maximum mass of copper which could be obtained from the reaction (the predicted yield).

(3 marks)

(b) Calculate the percentage yield of the reaction.

(2 marks)

(c) Suggest three different reasons why the yield of the reaction was less than 100%.

(3 marks)

2   Scientists analysed the composition of six food colourings using chromatography. Four of the colourings were unknown (**1 – 4**), and the other two were known, sunrise yellow and sunset red. The results are shown below.

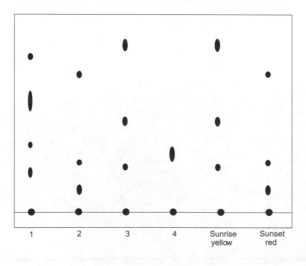

(a) Which food colouring is most likely to be a pure compound?

(1 mark)

(b) Which food colouring contains at least four different compounds?

(1 mark)

(c) Which food colouring contains the same compounds as sunrise yellow?

(1 mark)

(d) Which food colouring contains the same compounds as sunset red?

(1 mark)

Revision Summary for Chemistry 2a

Some people skip these pages. But what's the point in reading that great big section if you're not going to check if you really know it or not? Look, just read the first ten questions, and I guarantee there'll be an answer you'll have to look up. And when it comes up in the exam, you'll be so glad you did.

1) What do the mass number and atomic number represent?

2) Draw a table showing the relative masses of the three types of particle in an atom.

3) What is a compound?

4) Define the term isotope.

5) Describe the process of ionic bonding.

6) Describe the structure of a crystal of sodium chloride.

7) List the main properties of ionic compounds.

8) What type of ion do elements from the following groups form?
   a) Group 1   b) Group 7

9)* Use information from the periodic table to help you work out the formulas of these ionic compounds:
   a) potassium chloride   b) calcium chloride

10)* Draw a diagram to show the electronic structure of an Mg^{2+} ion (magnesium's atomic number is 12).

11) What is covalent bonding?

12) Sketch dot and cross diagrams showing the bonding in molecules of:
   a) hydrogen, b) hydrogen chloride, c) water, d) ammonia

13) What are the two types of covalent substance? Give three examples of each.

14) List three properties of metals and explain how metallic bonding causes these properties.

15) Explain why alloys are harder than pure metals.

16)* Identify the structure of each of the substances in the table:

Substance	Melting point (°C)	Electrical conductivity	Hardness [scale of 0 – 10 (10 being diamond)]
A	3410	Very high	7.5
B	2072	Zero	9
C	605	Zero in solid form High when molten	Low

17) Give an example of a "smart" material and describe how it behaves.

18) What are nanoparticles? Give two different applications of nanoparticles.

19) Explain the difference between thermosoftening and thermosetting polymers.

20) Define relative atomic mass and relative formula mass.

21)* Find A_r or M_r for these (use the periodic table at the front of the book):
   a) Ca   b) Ag   c) CO_2 d) $MgCO_3$ e) Na_2CO_3 f) ZnO   g) KOH   h) NH_3

22) What is the link between moles and relative formula mass?

23)* a) Calculate the percentage mass of carbon in: i) $CaCO_3$ ii) CO_2 iii) CH_4
    b) Calculate the percentage mass of metal in: i) Na_2O ii) Fe_2O_3 iii) Al_2O_3

24)* What is an empirical formula? Find the empirical formula of the compound formed when 21.9 g of magnesium, 29.2 g of sulfur and 58.4 g of oxygen react.

25)* What mass of sodium is needed to produce 108.2 g of sodium oxide (Na_2O)?

26) Describe three factors that can reduce the percentage yield of a reaction.

27) Explain how paper chromatography can be used to analyse the dyes used in a brown sweet.

28) Briefly describe how gas chromatography works.

* Answers on page 219.

Rate of Reaction

Reactions can be <u>fast</u> or <u>slow</u> — you've probably already realised that. But you need to know what affects the <u>rate of a reaction</u>, as well as what you can do to <u>measure it</u>.

Reactions can go at all sorts of **different rates**

1) One of the <u>slowest</u> is the <u>rusting</u> of iron.

2) A <u>moderate speed</u> reaction is a <u>metal</u> (like magnesium) reacting with <u>acid</u> to produce a gentle stream of <u>bubbles</u>.

3) A <u>really fast</u> reaction is an <u>explosion</u>, where it's all over in a <u>fraction</u> of a second.

The **rate of a reaction** depends on **four things**:

1) Temperature

2) Concentration — (or <u>pressure</u> for gases)

3) Catalyst

4) Surface area of solids — (or <u>size</u> of solid pieces)

Typical graphs for rate of reaction

The plot below shows how the rate of a particular reaction varies under <u>different conditions</u>. The <u>quickest reaction</u> is shown by the line with the <u>steepest slope</u>. Also, the faster a reaction goes, the sooner it finishes, which means that the line becomes <u>flat</u> earlier.

1) <u>Graph 1</u> represents the original <u>fairly slow</u> reaction. The graph is not too steep.

2) <u>Graphs 2 and 3</u> represent the reaction taking place <u>quicker</u> but with the <u>same initial amounts</u>. The slope of the graphs gets steeper.

3) The <u>increased rate</u> could be due to <u>any</u> of these:

> a) increase in <u>temperature</u>
> b) increase in <u>concentration</u> (or pressure)
> c) <u>catalyst</u> added
> d) solid reactant crushed up into <u>smaller bits</u>.

You could also show the amount of reactant used up over time instead — the graphs would have the same shape.

Amount of product evolved

④ faster, and more reactants

end of reaction

③ much faster reaction

② faster reaction

① original reaction

Time

4) <u>Graph 4</u> produces <u>more product</u> as well as going <u>faster</u>. This can <u>only</u> happen if <u>more reactant(s)</u> are added at the start. <u>Graphs 1, 2 and 3</u> all converge at the same level, showing that they all produce the same amount of product, although they take <u>different</u> times to get there.

It's really important that you understand the graph above

<u>Industrial</u> reactions generally use a <u>catalyst</u> and are done at <u>high temperature and pressure</u>. Time is money, so the faster an industrial reaction goes the better... but only <u>up to a point</u>. Chemical plants are quite expensive to rebuild if they get blown into lots and lots of teeny tiny pieces.

Measuring Rates of Reaction

If you want to know the rate of reaction then it's fairly easy to <u>measure</u> it.
There are <u>three</u> ways of measuring rate of reaction that you should know about.

Ways to **measure the rate** of a reaction

The <u>rate of a reaction</u> can be observed <u>either</u> by measuring how quickly the reactants are used up or how quickly the products are formed. It's usually a lot easier to measure <u>products forming</u>.

The rate of reaction can be calculated using the following formula:

$$\text{Rate of reaction} = \frac{\text{amount of reactant used or amount of product formed}}{\text{time}}$$

There are different ways that the rate of a reaction can be <u>measured</u>. Learn these three:

1) Precipitation

1) This is when the product of the reaction is a <u>precipitate</u> which <u>clouds</u> the solution.

2) Observe a <u>mark</u> through the solution and measure how long it takes for it to <u>disappear</u>.

3) The <u>quicker</u> the mark disappears, the <u>quicker</u> the reaction.

4) This only works for reactions where the initial solution is rather <u>see-through</u>.

5) The result is very <u>subjective</u> — <u>different people</u> might not agree over the <u>exact</u> point when the mark 'disappears'.

Measuring Rates of Reaction

2) *Change in mass* (usually gas given off)

1) Measuring the speed of a reaction that <u>produces a gas</u> can be carried out on a <u>mass balance</u>.

2) As the gas is released the mass <u>disappearing</u> is easily measured on the balance.

3) The <u>quicker</u> the reading on the balance <u>drops</u>, the <u>faster</u> the reaction.

4) <u>Rate of reaction graphs</u> are particularly easy to plot using the results from this method.

5) This is the <u>most accurate</u> of the three methods described because the mass balance is very accurate. But it has the <u>disadvantage</u> of releasing the gas straight into the room.

3) The **volume** of gas given off

1) This involves the use of a <u>gas syringe</u> to measure the <u>volume</u> of gas given off.

2) The <u>more</u> gas given off during a given <u>time interval</u>, the <u>faster</u> the reaction.

3) A graph of <u>gas volume</u> against <u>time elapsed</u> could be plotted to give a rate of reaction graph.

4) Gas syringes usually give volumes accurate to the <u>nearest millilitre</u>, so they're quite accurate. You have to be quite careful though — if the reaction is too <u>vigorous</u>, you can easily blow the plunger out of the end of the syringe.

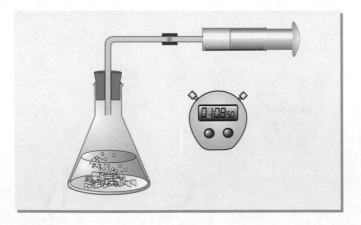

Each of these methods has pros and cons

The mass balance method is only accurate as long as the flask isn't too hot, otherwise you lose mass by <u>evaporation</u> as well as in the reaction. The first method <u>isn't</u> very accurate, but if you're not producing a gas you can't use either of the other two. Ah well.

Rate of Reaction Experiments

Remember: Any reaction can be used to investigate any of the four factors that affect the rate. The next four pages illustrate four important reactions, but only one factor is considered for each. But you can just as easily use, say, the marble chips/acid reaction to test the effect of temperature instead.

1) Reaction of *hydrochloric acid* and *marble chips*

This experiment is often used to demonstrate the effect of breaking the solid up into small bits.

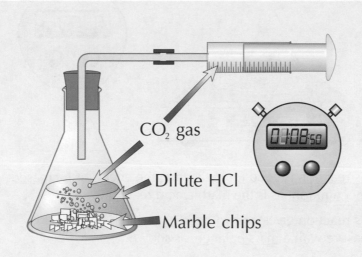

CO₂ gas

Dilute HCl

Marble chips

1) Measure the volume of gas evolved with a gas syringe and take readings at regular intervals.

2) Make a table of readings and plot them as a graph. You choose regular time intervals, and time goes on the x-axis and volume goes on the y-axis.

3) Repeat the experiment with exactly the same volume of acid, and exactly the same mass of marble chips, but with the marble more crunched up.

4) Then repeat with the same mass of powdered chalk instead of marble chips.

This graph shows the effect of using *finer particles of solid*

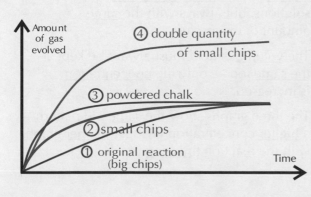

Amount of gas evolved
④ double quantity of small chips
③ powdered chalk
② small chips
① original reaction (big chips)
Time

1) Using finer particles means that the marble has a larger surface area.

2) A larger surface area causes more frequent collisions (see page 115) so the rate of reaction is faster.

3) Line 4 shows the reaction if a greater mass of small marble chips is added. The extra surface area gives a quicker reaction and there is also more gas evolved overall.

Rate of Reaction Experiments

The reaction of <u>magnesium metal</u> with <u>dilute HCl</u> is often used to determine the effect of <u>concentration</u>.

2) Reaction of *magnesium metal* with *dilute HCl*

1) <u>This reaction</u> is good for measuring the effects of <u>increased concentration</u> (as is the marble/acid reaction).

2) This reaction gives off <u>hydrogen gas</u>, which we can measure with a <u>mass balance</u>, as shown.

3) In this experiment, <u>time</u> also goes on the <u>x-axis</u> and <u>volume</u> goes on the <u>y-axis</u>.
(The other method is to use a gas syringe, see page 108.)

This graph shows the effect of using *more concentrated acid solutions*

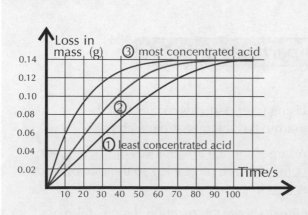

1) Take <u>readings</u> of mass at <u>regular</u> time intervals.

2) Put the results in a <u>table</u> and work out the <u>loss in mass</u> for each reading. <u>Plot a graph</u>.

3) <u>Repeat</u> with <u>more concentrated</u> acid solutions, but always with the <u>same</u> amount of magnesium.

4) The <u>volume</u> of acid must always be kept <u>the same</u> too — only the <u>concentration</u> is increased.

5) The three graphs show the <u>same</u> old pattern — a <u>higher</u> concentration giving a <u>steeper graph</u>, with the reaction <u>finishing</u> much quicker.

Rate of Reaction Experiments

The effect of <u>temperature</u> on the rate of a reaction can be measured using a <u>precipitation</u> reaction.

3) *Sodium thiosulfate* and *HCl* produce a *cloudy precipitate*

1) These two chemicals are both <u>clear solutions</u>.

2) They react together to form a <u>yellow precipitate</u> of <u>sulfur</u>.

3) The experiment involves watching a black mark <u>disappear</u> through the <u>cloudy sulfur</u> and <u>timing</u> how long it takes to go.

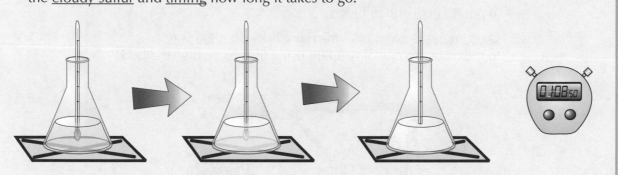

4) The reaction can be <u>repeated</u> for solutions at different <u>temperatures</u>. In practice, that's quite hard to do accurately and safely (it's not a good idea to heat an acid directly). The best way to do it is to use a <u>water bath</u> to heat both solutions to the right temperature <u>before you mix them</u>.

5) The <u>depth</u> of liquid must be kept the <u>same</u> each time, of course.

6) The results will of course show that the <u>higher</u> the temperature the <u>quicker</u> the reaction and therefore the <u>less time</u> it takes for the mark to <u>disappear</u>. These are typical results:

Temperature (ºC)	20	25	30	35	40
Time taken for mark to disappear (s)	193	151	112	87	52

This reaction can <u>also</u> be used to test the effects of <u>concentration</u>.

This reaction <u>doesn't</u> give a set of graphs. All you get is a set of <u>readings</u> of how long it took till the mark disappeared for each temperature.

Rate of Reaction Experiments

Good news — this is the last rate experiment. This one looks at how a <u>catalyst</u> affects rate of reaction.

4) The **decomposition** of **hydrogen peroxide**

This is a <u>good</u> reaction for showing the effect of different <u>catalysts</u>. The decomposition of hydrogen peroxide is:

$$2H_2O_{2\,(aq)} \rightleftharpoons 2H_2O_{(l)} + O_{2\,(g)}$$

1) This is normally quite <u>slow</u> but a sprinkle of <u>manganese(IV) oxide catalyst</u> speeds it up no end. Other catalysts which work are found in: a) <u>potato peel</u> and b) <u>blood</u>.

2) <u>Oxygen gas</u> is given off, which provides an <u>ideal way</u> to measure the rate of reaction using the <u>gas syringe</u> method.

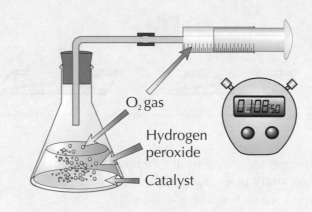

O₂ gas

Hydrogen peroxide

Catalyst

This graph shows the effect of using **different catalysts**

1) Same old graphs of course.

2) <u>Better</u> catalysts give a <u>quicker reaction</u>, which is shown by a <u>steeper graph</u> which levels off quickly.

3) This reaction can also be used to measure the effects of <u>temperature</u>, or of <u>concentration</u> of the H_2O_2 solution. The graphs will look just the same.

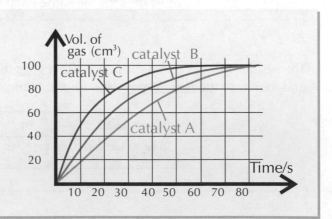

Blood is a catalyst? — eeurgh...

You don't need to know all the details of these specific reactions — but you do need to be able to look at <u>graphs</u> showing the amount of product formed (or reactant used up) over time and comment on the <u>reaction rate</u>. If you understand how all this works, you should be able to apply it to <u>any</u> reaction.

Warm-Up and Exam Questions

Time to test your knowledge again. This time on the rates of chemical reactions. If you struggle with these questions and you don't feel up to speed, it's time to have another look at the last few pages.

Warm-Up Questions

1) Give an example of a reaction that happens very slowly, and one that is very fast.
2) Give three ways of increasing the rate of a reaction between magnesium and sulfuric acid.
3) Describe one way of monitoring a reaction in which a gas is given off.
4) How would reducing the concentration of an acid affect the time taken for a piece of zinc to react with it?
5) Oxidation of lactose in milk makes it go 'sour'. How could this reaction be slowed down?

Exam Questions

1 Set volumes of sodium thiosulfate and hydrochloric acid were reacted at different temperatures. The time taken for a black cross to be obscured by the sulfur precipitated was measured at each temperature. The results are shown in the table.

Temperature (°C)	Time (s)
55	6
36	11
24	17
16	27
9	40
5	51

(a) Give two variables that should be kept constant in this experiment.

(2 marks)

(b) Plot the results on a graph (with time on the x-axis) and draw a best-fit curve.

(2 marks)

(c) Describe the relationship illustrated by your graph.

(1 mark)

(d) Describe how the results would change if the sodium thiosulfate concentration was reduced.

(2 marks)

(e) Suggest how the results of the experiment could be made more reliable.

(1 mark)

2 The table shows the results of reactions between excess marble and 50 cm³ of 1 mol/dm³ hydrochloric acid.

Time (min)	Mass of flask A (g)	Mass of flask B (g)
0	121.6	121.6
1	120.3	119.8
2	119.7	119.2
3	119.4	119.1
4	119.2	119
5	119.1	119
6	119	119
7	119	

(a) Explain why the mass of the contents of the flasks decreased during the reaction.

(1 mark)

(b) Explain why the mass of each flask and its contents fell by the same total amount.

(1 mark)

(c) Suggest what conditions may have been different inside flask B.

(1 mark)

(d) In both reactions, the rate is fastest at the beginning. Suggest why.

(1 mark)

Collision Theory

Reaction rates are explained by collision theory. It's really simple.

1) Collision theory just says that the rate of a reaction simply depends on how often and how hard the reacting particles collide with each other.

2) The basic idea is that particles have to collide in order to react, and they have to collide hard enough (with enough energy).

More collisions increases the rate of reaction

The effects of temperature, concentration and surface area on the rate of reaction can be explained in terms of how often the reacting particles collide successfully.

1) HIGHER TEMPERATURE increases collisions

When the temperature is increased the particles all move quicker. If they're moving quicker, they're going to collide more often.

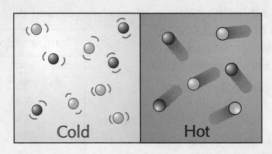

2) HIGHER CONCENTRATION (or PRESSURE) increases collisions

If a solution is made more concentrated it means there are more particles of reactant knocking about between the water molecules which makes collisions between the important particles more likely.

In a gas, increasing the pressure means the particles are more squashed up together so there will be more frequent collisions.

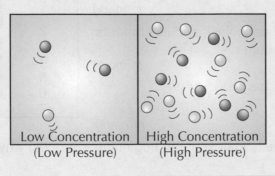

Collision Theory

3) LARGER SURFACE AREA increases collisions

If one of the reactants is a solid then breaking it up into smaller pieces will increase the total surface area. This means the particles around it in the solution will have more area to work on, so there'll be more frequent collisions.

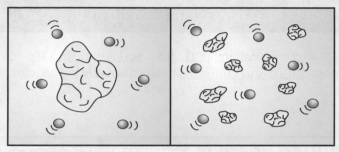

Small surface area   Big surface area

Faster collisions increase the rate of reaction

Higher temperature also increases the energy of the collisions, because it makes all the particles move faster.

Increasing the temperature causes faster collisions.

Reactions only happen if the particles collide with enough energy.

The minimum amount of energy needed by the particles to react is known as the activation energy.

At a higher temperature there will be more particles colliding with enough energy to make the reaction happen.

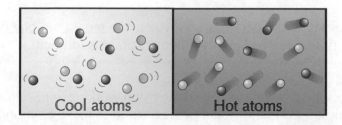

Cool atoms   Hot atoms

It's easier to learn stuff when you know the reasons for it

Once you've learnt everything off this page, the rates of reaction stuff should start making a lot more sense to you. The concept's fairly simple — the more often particles bump into each other, and the harder they hit when they do, the faster the reaction happens.

Catalysts

In industrial reactions, the main thing they're interested in is making a <u>nice profit</u>.
Catalysts are helpful for this — they can reduce costs and increase the amount of product.

Catalysts **speed up** reactions

Many reactions can be <u>speeded up</u> by adding a <u>catalyst</u>.

> A <u>catalyst</u> is a substance which <u>speeds up</u> a reaction,
> without being <u>changed</u> or <u>used up</u> in the reaction.

A <u>solid catalyst</u> works by giving the <u>reacting particles</u> a <u>surface</u> to <u>stick to</u>.
This increases the number of <u>successful collisions</u> (and so speeds the reaction up).

Catalysts help **reduce costs** in industrial reactions

1) Catalysts are <u>very important</u> for <u>commercial reasons</u> — most industrial reactions use them.

2) <u>Catalysts</u> increase the rate of the reaction, which saves a lot of <u>money</u> simply because the plant doesn't need to operate for <u>as long</u> to produce the <u>same amount</u> of stuff.

3) Alternatively, a catalyst will allow the reaction to work at a <u>much lower temperature</u>. That reduces the <u>energy</u> used up in the reaction (the <u>energy cost</u>), which is good for <u>sustainable development</u> (see page 101) and can save a lot of money too.

4) There are <u>disadvantages</u> to using catalysts, though.

5) They can be very expensive to buy, and often need to be removed from the product and cleaned. They never get <u>used up</u> in the reaction though, so once you've got them you can use them <u>over and over</u> again.

6) Different <u>reactions</u> use different <u>catalysts</u>, so if you make <u>more than one product</u> at your plant, you'll probably need to buy different catalysts for them.

7) Catalysts can be '<u>poisoned</u>' by impurities, so they <u>stop working</u>, e.g. sulfur impurities can poison the iron catalyst used in the Haber process (used to make ammonia for fertilisers). That means you have to keep your reaction mixture very <u>clean</u>.

A big advantage of catalysts is that they can be used over and over

And they're not only used in <u>industry</u>... every useful chemical reaction in the human body is catalysed by a <u>biological catalyst</u> (an enzyme). If the reactions in the body were just left to their own devices, they'd take so long to happen, we couldn't exist. Quite handy then, these catalysts.

Energy Transfer in Reactions

Whenever chemical reactions occur <u>energy</u> is <u>transferred to</u> or <u>from</u> the <u>surroundings</u>.

*In an **exothermic** reaction, heat is **given out***

An <u>EXOTHERMIC reaction</u> is one which <u>gives out energy</u> to the surroundings, usually in the form of <u>heat</u> and usually shown by a <u>rise in temperature</u>.

*1) **Burning** fuels*

The best example of an <u>exothermic</u> reaction is <u>burning fuels</u> — also called <u>COMBUSTION</u>. This gives out a lot of heat — it's very exothermic.

*2) **Neutralisation** reactions*

<u>Neutralisation reactions</u> (acid + alkali) are also exothermic — see page 120.

ACID

<u>Don't</u> do it like this!

ALKALI

*3) **Oxidation** reactions*

Many <u>oxidation reactions</u> are exothermic. For example:

Adding sodium to water <u>produces heat</u>, so it must be <u>exothermic</u> — see page 137. The sodium emits <u>heat</u> and moves about on the surface of the water as it is oxidised.

Exothermic reactions have lots of <u>everyday uses</u>. For example, some <u>hand warmers</u> use the exothermic <u>oxidation of iron</u> in air (with a salt solution catalyst) to generate <u>heat</u>. <u>Self heating cans</u> of hot chocolate and coffee also rely on exothermic reactions between <u>chemicals</u> in their bases.

Energy Transfer in Reactions

In an **endothermic** reaction, heat is **taken in**

An <u>ENDOTHERMIC reaction</u> is one which <u>takes in energy</u> from the surroundings, usually in the form of <u>heat</u> and is usually shown by a <u>fall in temperature</u>.

Endothermic reactions are much <u>less common</u>. <u>Thermal decompositions</u> are a good example:

> Heat must be supplied to make calcium carbonate <u>decompose</u> to make quicklime.
>
> $CaCO_3 \rightarrow CaO + CO_2$

Endothermic reactions also have everyday uses. For example, some <u>sports injury packs</u> use endothermic reactions — they <u>take in heat</u> and the pack becomes very <u>cold</u>. More <u>convenient</u> than carrying ice around.

Reversible reactions can be *endothermic* and *exothermic*

In reversible reactions (see page 101), if the reaction is <u>endothermic</u> in <u>one direction</u>, it will be <u>exothermic</u> in the <u>other direction</u>. The <u>energy absorbed</u> by the endothermic reaction is <u>equal</u> to the <u>energy released</u> during the exothermic reaction.

A good example is the <u>thermal decomposition of hydrated copper sulfate</u>.

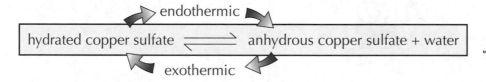

endothermic

hydrated copper sulfate ⇌ anhydrous copper sulfate + water

exothermic

"Anhydrous" just means "without water", and "hydrated" means "with water".

1) If you <u>heat blue hydrated</u> copper(II) sulfate crystals it drives the water off and leaves <u>white anhydrous</u> copper(II) sulfate powder. This is endothermic.

Water vapour

2) If you then <u>add</u> a couple of drops of <u>water</u> to the <u>white powder</u> you get the <u>blue crystals</u> back again. This is exothermic.

Right, so burning gives out heat — really...

This whole energy transfer thing is a fairly simple idea — don't be put off by the long words. Remember, "<u>exo-</u>" = <u>exit</u>, "<u>-thermic</u>" = <u>heat</u>, so an exothermic reaction is one that <u>gives out</u> heat. And "<u>endo-</u>" = erm... the other one. Okay, so there's no easy way to remember that one. Tough.

Warm-Up and Exam Questions

Here are some more questions to have a go at. If you can't do these ones then you won't be able to do the ones in the exam either. And you don't want that. If you're struggling, read the pages over again.

Warm-Up Questions

1) According to collision theory, what must happen in order for two particles to react?
2) Why does an increase in concentration of solutions increase the rate of a reaction?
3) Give a definition of a catalyst.
4) An endothermic reaction happens when ammonium nitrate is dissolved in water. Predict how the temperature of the solution will change during the reaction.

Exam Questions

1   *In this question you will be assessed on the quality of your English, the organisation of your ideas and your use of appropriate specialist vocabulary.*

Hydrogen and ethene react to form ethane. Nickel can be used as a catalyst for this reaction.

Using your knowledge of collision theory, suggest how the rate of this reaction can be increased.

(6 marks)

2   A student added hydrochloric acid to sodium hydroxide. He measured the temperature of the reaction mixture over the first 5 seconds and recorded his results in the table.

Time (s)	Temperature of the reaction mixture (°C)		
	1st run	2nd run	Average
0	22.0	22.0	
1	25.6	24.4	
2	28.3	28.1	
3	29.0	28.6	
4	28.8	28.8	
5	28.3	28.7	

(a) State the name given to this type of reaction.

(1 mark)

(b) Complete the table by calculating the average temperature of the reaction mixture during the two runs.

(2 marks)

(c) Calculate the maximum average increase in temperature during the reaction.

(1 mark)

(d) Is this reaction exothermic or endothermic? Explain your answer.

(2 marks)

Acids and Alkalis

Testing the pH of a solution means using an <u>indicator</u> — and that means pretty <u>colours</u>...

The **pH scale** goes from **0 to 14**

1) The <u>pH scale</u> is a measure of how <u>acidic</u> or <u>alkaline</u> a solution is.
2) The <u>strongest acid</u> has <u>pH 0</u>. The <u>strongest alkali</u> has <u>pH 14</u>.
3) A <u>neutral</u> substance has <u>pH 7</u> (e.g. pure water).

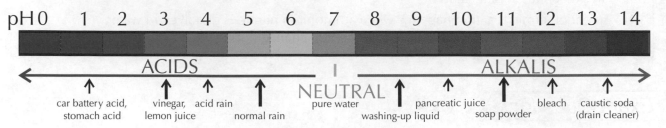

4) You can test the pH of a solution using an <u>indicator</u>.
5) The dye in an indicator <u>changes colour</u> depending on whether it's <u>above or below a certain pH</u>.
6) <u>Universal indicator</u> is a <u>combination of dyes</u> which gives the colours shown above.

Acids and *bases* neutralise each other

An <u>ACID</u> is a substance with a pH of less than 7. Acids form <u>H$^+$ ions</u> in <u>water</u>.
A <u>BASE</u> is a substance with a pH of greater than 7.
An <u>ALKALI</u> is a base that <u>dissolves in water</u>. Alkalis form <u>OH$^-$ ions</u> in <u>water</u>.
So, <u>H$^+$</u> ions make solutions <u>acidic</u> and <u>OH$^-$</u> ions make them <u>alkaline</u>.

The reaction between acids and bases is called <u>neutralisation</u>. Make sure you learn it:

$$acid \ + \ base \ \rightarrow \ salt \ + \ water$$

Neutralisation can also be seen in terms of <u>H$^+$</u> and <u>OH$^-$ ions</u> like this, so learn it too:

$$H^+_{(aq)} \ + \ OH^-_{(aq)} \ \rightarrow \ H_2O_{(l)}$$

Hydrogen (H$^+$) ions react with hydroxide (OH$^-$) ions to produce water.

When an acid neutralises a base (or vice versa), the <u>products</u> are <u>neutral</u>, i.e. they have a <u>pH of 7</u>.
An indicator can be used to show that a neutralisation reaction is over (Universal indicator will go green).

State symbols tell you what *physical state* it's in

These are easy enough, <u>so make sure you know them</u> — especially aq (aqueous).

| (s) — Solid | (l) — Liquid | (g) — Gas | (aq) — Dissolved in water |

E.g. $2Mg_{(s)} \ + \ O_{2\,(g)} \ \rightarrow \ 2MgO_{(s)}$

Interesting(ish) fact — your skin is slightly acidic (pH 5.5)...

That neutralisation reaction is important. Make sure you understand it in terms of the ions.

Acids Reacting With Metals

There are loads of different salts out there. Some of them are made when an <u>acid</u> reacts with a <u>metal</u>.

Metals react with acids to give salts

$$\boxed{\text{acid} \;+\; \text{metal} \;\rightarrow\; \text{salt} \;+\; \text{hydrogen}}$$

That's written big because it's really worth remembering. Here's the <u>typical experiment</u>:

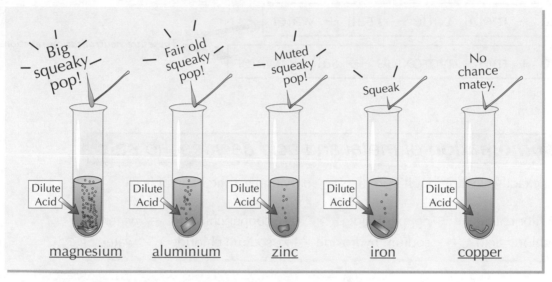

1) The more <u>reactive</u> the metal, the <u>faster</u> the reaction will go — very reactive metals (e.g. sodium) react <u>explosively</u>.

2) <u>Copper</u> does <u>not</u> react with dilute acids <u>at all</u> — because it's <u>less</u> reactive than <u>hydrogen</u>.

3) The <u>speed</u> of reaction is indicated by the <u>rate</u> at which the <u>bubbles</u> of hydrogen are given off.

4) The <u>hydrogen</u> is confirmed by the <u>burning splint test</u> giving the notorious 'squeaky pop'.

5) The <u>name</u> of the <u>salt</u> produced depends on which <u>metal</u> is used, and which <u>acid</u> is used:

Hydrochloric acid will always produce chloride salts:

$$2HCl + Mg \rightarrow MgCl_2 + H_2 \qquad \text{(Magnesium chloride)}$$
$$6HCl + 2Al \rightarrow 2AlCl_3 + 3H_2 \qquad \text{(Aluminium chloride)}$$
$$2HCl + Zn \rightarrow ZnCl_2 + H_2 \qquad \text{(Zinc chloride)}$$

Sulfuric acid will always produce sulfate salts:

$$H_2SO_4 + Mg \rightarrow MgSO_4 + H_2 \qquad \text{(Magnesium sulfate)}$$
$$3H_2SO_4 + 2Al \rightarrow Al_2(SO_4)_3 + 3H_2 \qquad \text{(Aluminium sulfate)}$$
$$H_2SO_4 + Zn \rightarrow ZnSO_4 + H_2 \qquad \text{(Zinc sulfate)}$$

Nitric acid produces nitrate salts when NEUTRALISED, but...

Nitric acid reacts fine with alkalis, to produce nitrates, but it can play silly devils with metals and produce nitrogen oxides instead, so we'll ignore it here.

Oxides, Hydroxides and Ammonia

I'm afraid there's more stuff on <u>neutralisation</u> reactions coming up...

Metal *oxides* and metal *hydroxides* are *bases*

1) Some <u>metal oxides</u> and <u>metal hydroxides</u> dissolve in <u>water</u>. These soluble compounds are <u>alkalis</u>.
2) Even bases that won't dissolve in water will still react with acids.
3) So, all <u>metal oxides</u> and <u>metal hydroxides</u> react with <u>acids</u> to form a <u>salt</u> and <u>water</u>.

> acid + metal oxide → salt + water

> acid + metal hydroxide → salt + water

These are neutralisation reactions.

The *combination* of metal and acid decides the *salt*

This isn't exactly exciting but it's pretty easy, so try and get the hang of it:

hydrochloric acid + copper oxide → copper chloride + water
hydrochloric acid + sodium hydroxide → sodium chloride + water

sulfuric acid + zinc oxide → zinc sulfate + water
sulfuric acid + calcium hydroxide → calcium sulfate + water

nitric acid + magnesium oxide → magnesium nitrate + water
nitric acid + potassium hydroxide → potassium nitrate + water

The symbol equations are all pretty much the same. Here are two of them:

$$H_2SO_{4\ (aq)} + ZnO_{(s)} \rightarrow ZnSO_{4\ (aq)} + H_2O_{(l)}$$
$$HNO_{3\ (aq)} + KOH_{(aq)} \rightarrow KNO_{3\ (aq)} + H_2O_{(l)}$$

Ammonia can be *neutralised* with HNO_3 to make *fertiliser*

<u>Ammonia</u> dissolves in water to make an <u>alkaline solution</u>.
When it reacts with <u>nitric acid</u>, you get a <u>neutral salt</u> — <u>ammonium nitrate</u>:

$$NH_{3\ (aq)} + HNO_{3\ (aq)} \rightarrow NH_4NO_{3\ (aq)}$$
ammonia + nitric acid → ammonium nitrate

This is a bit different from most neutralisation reactions because there's <u>NO WATER</u> produced — just the ammonium salt.

<u>Ammonium nitrate</u> is an especially good fertiliser because it has <u>nitrogen</u> from <u>two sources</u>, the ammonia and the nitric acid. Kind of a <u>double dose</u>. Plants need nitrogen to make <u>proteins</u>.

Making Salts

Most <u>chlorides</u>, <u>sulfates</u> and <u>nitrates</u> are <u>soluble</u> in water (the main exceptions are lead chloride, lead sulfate and silver chloride). Most <u>oxides</u> and <u>hydroxides</u> are <u>insoluble</u> in water.

The method you use to make a soluble salt depends on whether the <u>base</u> you use is <u>soluble</u> or <u>not</u>.

Making **soluble salts** using a **metal** or an **insoluble base**

1) You need to pick the right <u>acid</u>, plus a <u>metal</u> or an <u>insoluble base</u> (a <u>metal oxide</u> or <u>metal hydroxide</u>). E.g. if you want to make <u>copper chloride</u>, mix <u>hydrochloric acid</u> and <u>copper oxide</u>.

Remember some metals are unreactive and others are too reactive to use for this reaction (see page 121).

$$CuO_{(s)} + 2HCl_{(aq)} \rightarrow CuCl_{2\,(aq)} + H_2O_{(l)}$$

2) You add the <u>metal</u>, <u>metal oxide</u> or <u>hydroxide</u> to the <u>acid</u> — the solid will <u>dissolve</u> in the acid as it reacts. You will know when all the acid has been neutralised because the excess solid will just <u>sink</u> to the bottom of the flask.

3) Then <u>filter</u> out the <u>excess</u> metal, metal oxide or metal hydroxide to get the salt solution. To get <u>pure</u>, <u>solid</u> crystals of the <u>salt</u>, evaporate some of the water (to make the solution more concentrated) and then leave the rest to evaporate very <u>slowly</u>. This is called <u>crystallisation</u>.

filter paper

filter funnel

Making **soluble salts** using an **alkali**

1) You can't use the method above with <u>alkalis</u> (soluble bases) like <u>sodium</u>, <u>potassium</u> or <u>ammonium hydroxides</u>, because you can't tell whether the reaction has <u>finished</u> — you can't just add an <u>excess</u> to the acid and filter out what's left.

2) You have to add <u>exactly</u> the right amount of alkali to just <u>neutralise</u> the acid — you need to use an <u>indicator</u> (see page 120) to show when the reaction's finished. Then <u>repeat</u> using exactly the same volumes of alkali and acid so the salt isn't <u>contaminated</u> with indicator.

3) Then just <u>evaporate</u> off the water to <u>crystallise</u> the salt as normal.

Make sure you pick the right method...

Think very carefully in the exam if you are asked for the method to make a salt. You'll be throwing marks away if you write about <u>filtering the mixture</u> when you used a <u>soluble base</u> in the first place.

Making Salts

That last page was all about making <u>soluble salts</u>. This one's about making <u>insoluble salts</u>.

Making *insoluble* salts — *precipitation reactions*

1) If the salt you want to make is <u>insoluble</u>, you can use a <u>precipitation reaction</u>.

2) You just need to pick <u>two solutions</u> that contain the <u>ions</u> you need. E.g. to make <u>lead chloride</u> you need a solution which contains <u>lead ions</u> and one which contains <u>chloride ions</u>. So you can mix <u>lead nitrate solution</u> (most nitrates are soluble) with <u>sodium chloride solution</u> (all group 1 compounds are soluble).

$$\text{E.g.} \quad Pb(NO_3)_{2\,(aq)} + 2NaCl_{(aq)} \longrightarrow PbCl_{2\,(s)} + 2NaNO_{3\,(aq)}$$

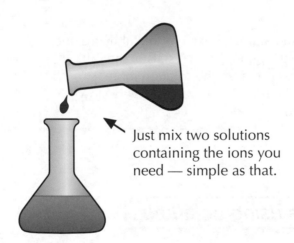

Just mix two solutions containing the ions you need — simple as that.

3) Once the salt has precipitated out (and is lying at the bottom of your flask), all you have to do is <u>filter</u> it from the solution, <u>wash</u> it and then <u>dry</u> it on filter paper.

4) <u>Precipitation reactions</u> can be used to remove <u>poisonous ions</u> (e.g. lead) from <u>drinking water</u>. <u>Calcium</u> and <u>magnesium</u> ions can also be removed from water this way — they make water "<u>hard</u>", which stops soap lathering properly. Another use of precipitation is in <u>treating effluent</u> (sewage) — again, <u>unwanted ions</u> can be removed.

Precipitation reaction — put up an umbrella...

In the exam you may get a question asking you to select <u>two solutions</u> to mix together to make a certain salt. All you need is two solutions that contain the <u>ions you need</u> and Bob's your uncle.

Warm-Up and Exam Questions

Now try these questions — you're less likely to get a nasty surprise in the exam if you do.

Warm-Up Questions

1) What name is given to the type of reaction in which an acid reacts with a base?
2) Which two substances are formed when an acid reacts with a metal such as zinc?
3) Which two substances are formed when nitric acid reacts with copper oxide?
4) Explain what you would do to make a dry sample of a soluble salt from an insoluble base.
5) Write down the word equation for the precipitation reaction between barium chloride and sodium sulfate.

Exam Questions

1 An experiment was carried out in which sodium hydroxide solution was added, 2 cm³ at a time, to 10 cm³ of sulfuric acid. The pH was estimated after each addition using universal indicator paper.

   The results are shown in the table.

Volume of sodium hydroxide added (cm³)	pH
0	1
2	1
4	2
6	4
8	12
10	13
12	13

   (a) Plot the results on a graph, with pH on the vertical axis and volume of sodium hydroxide added on the horizontal axis.

   Draw a best fit curve.

   (2 marks)

   (b) Estimate the volume of sodium hydroxide needed to neutralise the acid.

   (1 mark)

   (c) How do the results show that sulfuric acid is a strong acid?

   (1 mark)

   (d) Name the salt formed in the reaction.

   (1 mark)

2 Jenny wanted to make a dry sample of silver chloride, AgCl, by precipitation.

   (a) What property must a salt have to be made by precipitation?

   (1 mark)

   (b) Jenny looked up the solubilities of some compounds she might use.

   Write down a word equation using substances from the table that she could use to make silver chloride by precipitation.

Compound	Formula	Solubility
silver oxide	Ag_2O	insoluble
silver nitrate	$AgNO_3$	soluble
silver carbonate	$AgCO_3$	insoluble
sulfuric acid	H_2SO_4	soluble
nitric acid	HNO_3	soluble
hydrochloric acid	HCl	soluble

   (1 mark)

   (c) Outline the steps needed to give a pure dry sample of silver chloride after mixing the solutions.

   (3 marks)

Electrolysis

Examiners love <u>electrolysis</u>. It's just a shame that no one else does.

Electrolysis means "splitting up with electricity"

1) If you pass an <u>electric current</u> through an <u>ionic substance</u> that's <u>molten</u> or in <u>solution</u>, it breaks down into the <u>elements</u> it's made of. This is called <u>electrolysis</u>.

2) It requires a <u>liquid</u> to <u>conduct</u> the <u>electricity</u>, called the <u>electrolyte</u>.

3) Electrolytes contain <u>free ions</u> — they're usually the <u>molten</u> or <u>dissolved ionic substance</u>.

NaCl dissolved

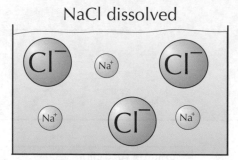

Molten NaCl

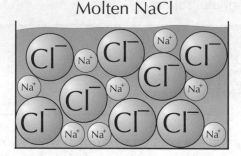

4) In either case it's the <u>free ions</u> which <u>conduct</u> the electricity and allow the whole thing to work.

5) For an electrical circuit to be complete, there's got to be a <u>flow of electrons</u>. <u>Electrons</u> are taken <u>away from</u> ions at the <u>positive electrode</u> and <u>given to</u> other ions at the <u>negative electrode</u>. As ions gain or lose electrons they become atoms or molecules and are released.

Electrolysis reactions involve oxidation and reduction

1) Back in Core Chemistry you learnt about <u>reduction</u> involving the <u>loss of oxygen</u>. However...

2) <u>Reduction</u> is also a <u>gain of electrons</u>.

3) On the other hand, <u>oxidation</u> is a gain of oxygen or a <u>loss of electrons</u>.

4) So "reduction" and "oxidation" don't have to involve <u>oxygen</u>.

5) Electrolysis <u>ALWAYS</u> involves an oxidation and a reduction.

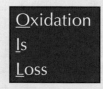

Remember it as OIL RIG.

Electrolysis needs a liquid to conduct the electricity

Before you electrolyse a substance it has to be <u>liquid</u>. This allows the ions to <u>move</u> towards the <u>positive</u> or <u>negative</u> electrode. The next few pages are about the electrolysis of different substances.

Electrolysis of Lead Bromide

Molten lead bromide can be broken down by electrolysis. You end up with lead and bromine.

The **electrolysis** of molten **lead bromide**

When a salt (e.g. lead bromide) is molten it will conduct electricity.

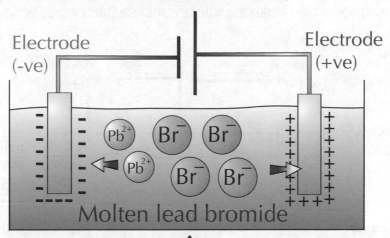

Electrode (-ve)　　　　　　　　　Electrode (+ve)

Molten lead bromide

HEAT

+ve ions are attracted
to the –ve electrode.
Here they gain
electrons (reduction).

–ve ions are attracted
to the +ve electrode.
Here they lose
electrons (oxidation).

Lead is produced
at the –ve electrode.

Bromine is produced
at the +ve electrode.

1) At the –ve electrode, one lead ion accepts two electrons to become one lead atom.

2) At the +ve electrode, two bromide ions lose one electron each
and become one bromine molecule.

Reactivity affects the **products** formed by **electrolysis**

1) Sometimes there are more than two free ions in the electrolyte.
For example, if a salt is dissolved in water there will also be some H^+ and OH^- ions.

2) At the negative electrode, if metal ions and H^+ ions are present, the metal ions will stay in solution
if the metal is more reactive than hydrogen. This is because the more reactive an element, the
keener it is to stay as ions. So, hydrogen will be produced unless the metal is less reactive than it.

3) At the positive electrode, if OH^- and halide ions (Cl^-, Br^-, I^-) are present then molecules of chlorine,
bromine or iodine will be formed. If no halide is present, then oxygen will be formed.

So, lead bromide splits into lead and bromine — I know, it's tricky

The electrolysis of lead bromide is pretty simple — bromine ions are oxidised so bromine is produced
at the positive electrode and lead ions are reduced so lead is produced at the negative electrode.
But when your substance is dissolved in water things get trickier — as you'll see on the next page.

Electrolysis of Sodium Chloride

You need to know about the electrolysis of salt (sodium chloride) solution. Get learning...

The **electrolysis** of **sodium chloride solution**

When common salt (sodium chloride) is dissolved in water and electrolysed, it produces three useful products — hydrogen, chlorine and sodium hydroxide.

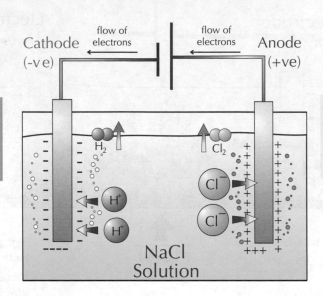

H⁺ ions are released from the water.

+ve ions are attracted to the –ve electrode. Here they gain electrons (reduction).

Hydrogen is produced at the –ve electrode.

–ve ions are attracted to the +ve electrode. Here they lose electrons (oxidation).

Chlorine is produced at the +ve electrode.

1) At the negative electrode, two hydrogen ions accept two electrons to become one hydrogen molecule.

2) At the positive electrode, two chloride (Cl⁻) ions lose their electrons and become one chlorine molecule.

3) The sodium ions stay in solution because they're more reactive than hydrogen. Hydroxide ions from water are also left behind. This means that sodium hydroxide (NaOH) is left in the solution.

The **half-equations** — make sure **the electrons balance**

1) Half equations show the reactions at the electrodes. The main thing is to make sure the number of electrons is the same for both half-equations.

2) For the electrolysis of sodium chloride the half-equations are:

You need to make sure the atoms are balanced too.

Negative Electrode: $2H^+ + 2e^- \rightarrow H_2$
Positive Electrode: $2Cl^- \rightarrow Cl_2 + 2e^-$
or $2Cl^- - 2e^- \rightarrow Cl_2$

For the electrolysis of molten lead bromide (previous page) the half equations would be:
$$Pb^{2+} + 2e^- \rightarrow Pb$$
and $2Br^- \rightarrow Br_2 + 2e^-$

Useful products from the **electrolysis of sodium chloride solution**

The products of the electrolysis of sodium chloride solution are pretty useful in industry.

1) Chlorine has many uses, e.g. in the production of bleach and plastics.

2) Sodium hydroxide is a very strong alkali and is used widely in the chemical industry, e.g. to make soap.

Electrolysis of Aluminium

OK — one more example to learn about. This is the electrolysis of <u>aluminium oxide</u>.

Electrolysis is used to remove aluminium from its ore

1) Aluminium's a very <u>abundant</u> metal, but it is always found naturally in <u>compounds</u>.

2) Its main ore is <u>bauxite</u>, and after mining and purifying, a <u>white powder</u> is left.

3) This is <u>pure</u> aluminium oxide, Al_2O_3.

4) The <u>aluminium</u> has to be extracted from this using <u>electrolysis</u>.

Cryolite is used to lower the temperature (and costs)

1) Al_2O_3 has a very <u>high melting point</u> of over <u>2000 °C</u> — so melting it would be very <u>expensive</u>.

2) <u>Instead</u> the aluminium oxide is <u>dissolved</u> in <u>molten cryolite</u> (a less common ore of aluminium).

3) This brings the <u>temperature down</u> to about <u>900 °C</u>, which makes it much <u>cheaper</u> and <u>easier</u>.

4) The <u>electrodes</u> are made of <u>carbon</u> (graphite), a good conductor of electricity (see page 85).

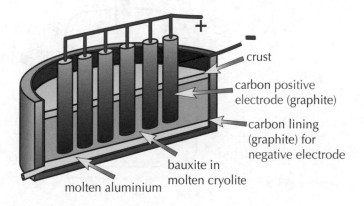

+ −

crust

carbon positive
electrode (graphite)

carbon lining
(graphite) for
negative electrode

bauxite in
molten cryolite

molten aluminium

| Negative Electrode: $Al^{3+} + 3e^- \rightarrow Al$ | Positive Electrode: $2O^{2-} \rightarrow O_2 + 4e^-$ |

5) <u>Aluminium</u> forms at the <u>negative electrode</u> and <u>oxygen</u> forms at the <u>positive electrode</u>.

6) The <u>oxygen</u> then reacts with the <u>carbon</u> in the electrode to produce <u>carbon dioxide</u>.
This means that the <u>positive electrodes</u> gradually get 'eaten away' and have to be <u>replaced</u>
every now and again.

It's all about lowering the cost...

The electrolysis of aluminium oxide may look <u>a bit different</u> to the examples on the other pages but
don't be fooled. It's the same story — the positive aluminium ions go to the <u>negative</u> electrode and the
negative oxygen ions are attracted to the <u>positive</u> electrode. Learn the whole lot before you turn over.

Electroplating

Electroplating coats one metal onto the surface of another. It's really useful...

Electroplating uses electrolysis

1) Electroplating uses electrolysis to <u>coat</u> the <u>surface of one metal</u> with <u>another metal</u>, e.g. you might want to electroplate silver onto a brass cup to make it look nice.

2) The <u>negative electrode</u> is the <u>metal object</u> you want to plate and the <u>positive electrode</u> is the <u>pure metal</u> you want it to be plated with. You also need the <u>electrolyte</u> to contain <u>ions</u> of the <u>plating metal</u>. (The ions that plate the metal object come from the solution, while the positive electrode keeps the solution 'topped up'.)

<u>Example</u>: To electroplate <u>silver</u> onto a <u>brass cup</u>, you'd make the <u>brass cup</u> the negative electrode (to attract the positive silver ions), a lump of <u>pure silver</u> the positive electrode and dip them in a solution of <u>silver ions</u>, e.g. silver nitrate.

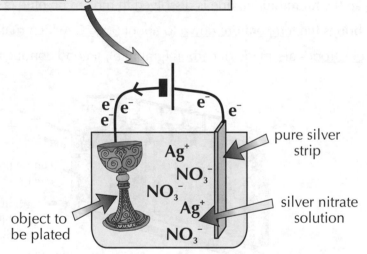

pure silver strip

silver nitrate solution

object to be plated

3) There are lots of different <u>uses</u> for electroplating:
   • <u>Decoration</u>: <u>Silver</u> is <u>attractive</u>, but very <u>expensive</u>. It's much <u>cheaper</u> to plate a brass cup with silver, than it is to make the cup out of solid silver — but it looks just as <u>pretty</u>.
   • <u>Conduction</u>: Metals like <u>copper</u> conduct <u>electricity</u> well — because of this they're often used to plate metals for <u>electronic circuits</u> and <u>computers</u>.

Silver electroplated text is worth a fortune...

There are loads of metals you can use for electroplating, but you just need to know about silver and copper plating. The tricky bit is remembering that the metal <u>object you want to plate</u> is the <u>negative electrode</u> and the <u>metal</u> you're plating it with is the <u>positive electrode</u>.

Warm-Up and Exam Questions

It's question time again. You know the drill. Off you go...

Warm-Up Questions

1) What state must an ionic compound be in if it's to be used as an electrolyte?
2) In electrolysis, what is meant by the terms oxidation and reduction?
3) At which electrode are metals deposited during electrolysis?
4) During the electrolysis of molten lead bromide, which gas is produced at the positive electrode?
5) An object requires electroplating. Which electrode should it be used as?

Exam Questions

1   When sodium chloride solution is electrolysed a gas is produced at each electrode.
   (a) (i)   What is the name of the gas produced at the negative electrode?

   (1 mark)

       (ii)   State the half equation for the reaction at the negative electrode.

   (1 mark)

   (b) (i)   What is the name of the gas produced at the positive electrode?

   (1 mark)

       (ii)   State the half equation for the reaction at the positive electrode.

   (1 mark)

       (iii) Suggest one use for the gas produced at the positive electrode.

   (1 mark)

   (c) Explain why sodium hydroxide is left in solution at the end of the reaction.

   (3 marks)

2   The diagram shows a cell used to extract aluminium from aluminium oxide.

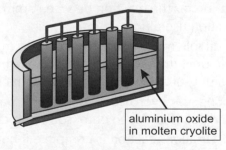

aluminium oxide
in molten cryolite

   (a) Explain why the aluminium oxide is dissolved in molten cryolite.

   (2 marks)

   (b) Complete the half-equation below for the reaction at the negative electrode.

       _____ + 3e⁻ → _____

   (1 mark)

   (c) The positive electrode is made out of carbon. Explain why it will need to be replaced over time.

   (3 marks)

Revision Summary for Chemistry 2b

Well, I don't think that was too bad, was it... Four things affect the rate of reactions, there are loads of ways to measure reaction rates and it's all explained by collision theory. Reactions can be endothermic or exothermic, and quite a few of them are reversible. And so on... Easy. Ahem. Well here are some more of those nice questions that you enjoy so much. If there are any you can't answer, go back to the appropriate page, do a bit more learning, then try again.

1) What are the four factors that affect the rate of a reaction?
2) Describe three different ways of measuring the rate of a reaction.
3) A student carries out an experiment to measure the effect of surface area on the reaction between marble and hydrochloric acid. He measures the amount of gas given off at regular intervals.
   a) What factors must he keep constant for it to be a fair test?
   b)*He uses four samples for his experiment:
       Sample A – 10 g of powdered marble
       Sample B – 10 g of small marble chips
       Sample C – 10 g of large marble chips
       Sample D – 5 g of powdered marble
     Sketch a typical set of graphs for this experiment.
4) Explain how higher temperature and larger surface area increase the frequency of successful collisions between particles.
5) What is activation energy?
6) Discuss the advantages and disadvantages of using catalysts in industrial processes.
7) What is an exothermic reaction? Give three examples.
8) The reaction to split ammonium chloride into ammonia and hydrogen chloride is endothermic. What can you say for certain about the reverse reaction?
9) What does the pH scale show?
10) What type of ions are always present in a) acids and   b) alkalis?
11) What is neutralisation? Write down the general equation for neutralisation in terms of ions.
12) Write down the state symbol that means 'dissolved in water'.
13) What is the general equation for reacting an acid with a metal?
14) Name a metal that doesn't react at all with dilute acids.
15) What type of salts do hydrochloric acid and sulfuric acid produce?
16) What type of reaction is "acid + metal oxide", or "acid + metal hydroxide"?
17) Write a balanced symbol equation for the reaction between ammonia and nitric acid. What is the product of this reaction useful for?
18) Suggest a suitable acid and a suitable metal oxide/hydroxide to mix to form the following salts.
   a) copper chloride   b) calcium nitrate   c) zinc sulfate
   d) magnesium nitrate   e) sodium sulfate   f) potassium chloride
19) Iron chloride can made by mixing iron hydroxide (an insoluble base) with hydrochloric acid. Describe the method you would use to produce pure, solid iron chloride in the lab.
20) How can you tell when a neutralisation reaction is complete if both the base and the salt are soluble in water?
21) Give a practical use of precipitation reactions.
22) What is electrolysis? Explain why only liquids can be electrolysed.
23) Draw a detailed diagram with half equations showing the electrolysis of sodium chloride.
24) Give one industrial use of sodium hydroxide and two uses of chlorine.
25) Why is cryolite used during the electrolysis of aluminium oxide?
26) Give two different uses of electroplating.

*Answers on page 220.

History of the Periodic Table

We haven't always known as much about Chemistry as we do now. Early chemists looked to try and understand patterns in the elements' properties to get a bit of understanding.

In the **early 1800s** they could only go on **atomic mass**

Until quite recently, there were two obvious ways to categorise elements:

> 1) Their physical and chemical properties   2) Their Relative Atomic Mass

1) Remember, they had no idea of atomic structure or of protons or electrons, so there was no such thing as atomic number to them. (It was only in the 20th century after protons and electrons were discovered that it was realised the elements were best arranged in order of atomic number.)

2) Back then, the only thing they could measure was relative atomic mass, and so the known elements were arranged in order of atomic mass. When this was done, a periodic pattern was noticed in the properties of the elements. This is where the name 'periodic table' comes from.

Newlands' law of octaves was the first good effort

A chap called Newlands had the first good stab at arranging things more usefully in 1864. He noticed that every eighth element had similar properties, and so he listed some of the known elements in rows of seven:

H	Li	Be	B	C	N	O
F	Na	Mg	Al	Si	P	S
Cl	K	Ca	Cr	Ti	Mn	Fe

These sets of eight were called Newlands' Octaves.
Unfortunately the pattern broke down on the third row, with transition metals like titanium (Ti) and iron (Fe) messing it up.

It was because he left no gaps that his work was ignored.
But he was getting pretty close, as you can see.

Newlands presented his ideas to the Chemical Society in 1865. But his work was criticised because:

1) His groups contained elements that didn't have similar properties, e.g. carbon and titanium.

2) He mixed up metals and non-metals, e.g. oxygen and iron.

3) He didn't leave any gaps for elements that hadn't been discovered yet.

History of the Periodic Table

Newland's wasn't the only one who had ideas about <u>classifying elements</u>.

Dmitri Mendeleev left gaps and predicted new elements

1) In <u>1869</u>, <u>Dmitri Mendeleev</u> in Russia, armed with about 50 known elements, arranged them into his Table of Elements — with various <u>gaps</u> as shown.

<u>Mendeleev's Table of the Elements</u>

H																	
Li	Be											B	C	N	O	F	
Na	Mg											Al	Si	P	S	Cl	
K	Ca	*	Ti	V	Cr	Mn	Fe	Co	Ni	Cu	Zn	*	*	As	Se	Br	
Rb	Sr	Y	Zr	Nb	Mo	*	Ru	Rh	Pd	Ag	Cd	In	Sn	Sb	Te	I	
Cs	Ba	*	*	Ta	W	*	Os	Ir	Pt	Au	Hg	Tl	Pb	Bi			

2) Mendeleev put the elements in order of <u>atomic mass</u> (like Newlands). But Mendeleev found he had to leave <u>gaps</u> in order to keep elements with <u>similar properties</u> in the same <u>vertical columns</u> (known as <u>groups</u>) — and he was prepared to leave some <u>very big gaps</u> in the first two rows before the transition metals come in on the <u>third</u> row.

3) The <u>gaps</u> were the really clever bit because they <u>predicted</u> the properties of so far <u>undiscovered elements</u>. When they were found and they <u>fitted the pattern</u> it was pretty smashing news for old Dmitri.

Not all scientists thought the periodic table was important

1) When the periodic table was first released, many scientists thought it was just a bit of <u>fun</u>. At that time, there wasn't all that much <u>evidence</u> to suggest that the elements really did fit together in that way — ideas don't get the scientific stamp of approval without evidence.

2) After Mendeleev released his work, <u>newly discovered elements</u> fitted into the <u>gaps</u> he left. This was convincing evidence in favour of the periodic table.

3) Once there was more evidence, many more scientists realised that the periodic table could be a <u>useful tool</u> for <u>predicting</u> properties of elements. It <u>really worked</u>.

4) In the late 19th century, scientists discovered protons, neutrons and electrons. The periodic table <u>matches up</u> very well to what's been discovered about the <u>structure</u> of the atom. Scientists now accept that it's a very important and useful <u>summary of the structure of atoms</u>.

Elementary my dear Mendeleev

You need to know about how <u>Mendeleev</u> tried to classify elements — and you need to be able to evaluate how well he got on. In the exam you might be given another example of the way someone has tried to classify elements and be asked to <u>compare</u> it with the ones you already know about.

The Modern Periodic Table

Chemists were getting pretty close to producing something useful.
The big breakthrough came when the <u>structure</u> of the <u>atom</u> was understood a bit better.

The *modern periodic table* is based on *electronic structure*

When <u>electrons</u>, <u>protons</u> and <u>neutrons</u> were discovered, the periodic table was arranged
in order of atomic number. All elements were put into <u>groups</u>.

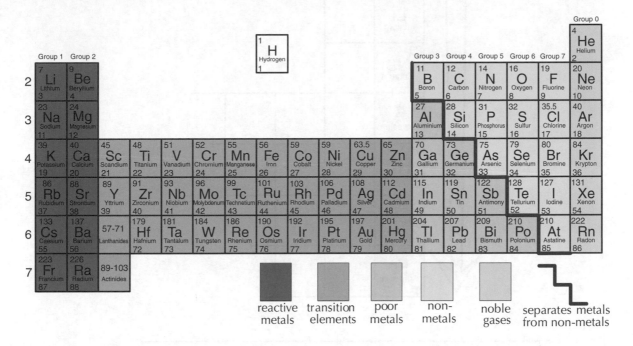

1) The elements in the periodic table can be seen as being arranged by their <u>electronic structure</u>.
   Using the electron arrangement, you can predict the element's <u>chemical properties</u>.

2) Electrons in an atom are set out in <u>shells</u> which each correspond to an <u>energy level</u>.

3) Apart from the transition metals, elements in the same group have the <u>same number of electrons</u>
   in their <u>highest occupied energy level</u> (outer shell).

4) The <u>group number</u> is <u>equal</u> to the <u>number of electrons</u> in the <u>highest occupied energy level</u>
   — e.g. Group 6 all have 6 electrons in the highest energy level.

5) The positive charge of the nucleus attracts electrons and holds them in place.
   The <u>further</u> from the nucleus the electron is, the <u>less the attraction</u>.

6) The attraction of the nucleus is <u>even less</u> when there are a lot of <u>inner electrons</u>.
   Inner electrons "get in the way" of the nuclear charge, reducing the attraction.
   This effect is known as <u>shielding</u>.

7) The combination of <u>increased distance</u> and <u>increased shielding</u> means that an electron
   in a higher energy level is <u>more easily lost</u> because there's <u>less attraction</u> from the nucleus
   holding it in place. That's why <u>Group 1 metals</u> get <u>more reactive</u> as you go down the group.

8) <u>Increased distance</u> and <u>shielding</u> also means that a higher energy level is <u>less likely</u>
   <u>to gain an electron</u> — there's less attraction from the nucleus pulling electrons into
   the atom. That's why <u>Group 7 elements</u> get <u>less reactive</u> going down the group.

Ahh, finally, the nice colourful periodic table in full...

This is a good example of how science often progresses — even now. A scientist has a <u>basically good</u>
(though incomplete) idea. Other scientists laugh and mock and generally deride. Eventually, the idea
is modified a bit to take account of the <u>available evidence</u>, and into the textbooks it goes.

Group 1 — The Alkali Metals

The alkali metals are <u>silvery solids</u> that have to be <u>stored in oil</u> and handled with <u>forceps</u> (they burn the skin).

Learn these *trends*:

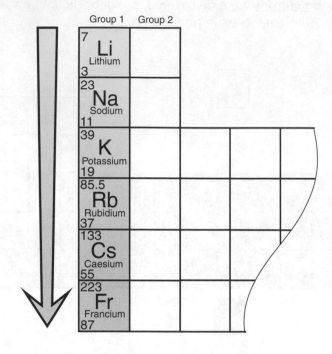

As you go <u>DOWN</u> Group 1, the alkali metals:

1) become <u>MORE REACTIVE</u>
   ...because the outer electron is <u>more easily lost</u>, because it's <u>further</u> from the nucleus.

2) have <u>LOWER MELTING AND BOILING POINTS</u>

The alkali metals have <u>LOW DENSITY</u>. In fact, the <u>first three</u> in the group are <u>less dense than water</u>.

1) They are: *lithium*, *sodium*, *potassium* *and a couple more*

Know those three names real well. They may also mention <u>rubidium</u> and <u>caesium</u>.

2) *The alkali metals all have* **one outer electron**

This makes them very <u>reactive</u> and gives them all similar <u>properties</u>.

Group 1 — The Alkali Metals

3) The alkali metals form *ionic compounds* with *non-metals*

1) They are <u>keen to lose</u> their one outer electron to form a <u>1⁺ ion</u>.

2) They are so keen to lose the outer electron there's <u>no way</u> they'd consider <u>sharing</u>, so covalent bonding is <u>out of the question</u>.

3) So they always form <u>ionic bonds</u> — and they produce <u>white compounds</u> that dissolve in water to form <u>colourless solutions</u>.

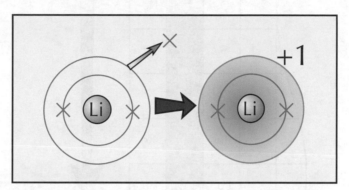

4) Reaction with water produces *hydrogen gas*

1) When <u>lithium</u>, <u>sodium</u> or <u>potassium</u> are put in <u>water</u>, they react very <u>vigorously</u>.

2) They <u>float</u> and <u>move</u> around the surface, <u>fizzing</u> furiously.

3) They produce <u>hydrogen</u>. Potassium gets hot enough to <u>ignite</u> it.
A lighted splint will <u>indicate</u> hydrogen by producing the notorious "<u>squeaky pop</u>" as the H_2 ignites.

4) They form <u>hydroxides</u> that <u>dissolve</u> in water to give <u>alkaline</u> solutions.

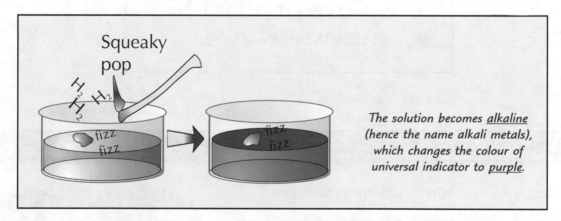

The solution becomes <u>alkaline</u> (hence the name alkali metals), which changes the colour of universal indicator to <u>purple</u>.

$$2Na_{(s)} + 2H_2O_{(l)} \rightarrow 2NaOH_{(aq)} + H_{2\,(g)}$$
$$2K_{(s)} + 2H_2O_{(l)} \rightarrow 2KOH_{(aq)} + H_{2\,(g)}$$

2 trends and 4 properties — not much to learn at all...

I'm no gambler, but I'd put money on a question like this in the exam: "Using your knowledge of the Group 1 metals, describe what would happen if a piece of caesium were put into water." Just use what you know about the <u>other</u> Group 1 metals... you're going to get H_2, and a pretty violent reaction.

Group 7 — The Halogens

The 'trend thing' happens in Group 7 as well — that shouldn't come as a surprise.
But some of the trends are kind of the opposite of the Group 1 trends. Remember that.

Learn these *trends*:

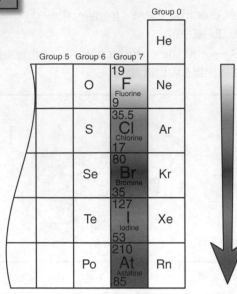

As you go <u>DOWN</u> Group 7, the <u>HALOGENS</u> have the following properties:

1) <u>LESS REACTIVE</u>
...because it's <u>harder to gain</u> an extra electron, because the outer shell's <u>further</u> from the nucleus.

2) <u>HIGHER MELTING POINT</u>

3) <u>HIGHER BOILING POINT</u>

1) The **halogens** are all **non-metals** with **coloured vapours**

<u>Fluorine</u> is a very reactive, poisonous <u>yellow gas</u>.

<u>Chlorine</u> is a fairly reactive, poisonous <u>dense green gas</u>.

<u>Bromine</u> is a dense, poisonous, <u>red-brown volatile liquid</u>.

<u>Iodine</u> is a <u>dark grey</u> crystalline <u>solid</u> or a <u>purple vapour</u>.

They all exist as molecules which are <u>pairs of atoms</u>:

Group 7 — The Halogens

2) The halogens form *ionic bonds* with *metals*

The halogens form 1⁻ ions called halides (F^-, Cl^-, Br^- and I^-)
when they bond with metals, for example Na^+Cl^- or $Fe^{3+}Br^-_3$.
The diagram shows the bonding in sodium chloride, NaCl.

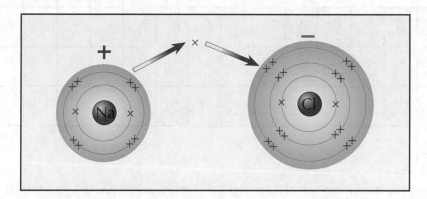

3) More reactive halogens will *displace* less reactive ones

A more reactive halogen can displace (kick out) a less reactive halogen
from an aqueous solution of its salt.

E.g. chlorine can displace bromine and iodine from an aqueous solution of its salt
(a bromide or iodide). Bromine will also displace iodine because of the trend in reactivity.

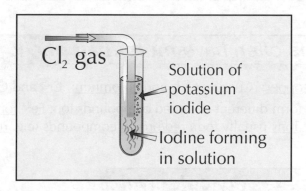

$$Cl_{2\,(g)} + 2KI_{(aq)} \rightarrow I_{2\,(aq)} + 2KCl_{(aq)}$$

$$Cl_{2\,(g)} + 2KBr_{(aq)} \rightarrow Br_{2\,(aq)} + 2KCl_{(aq)}$$

Polish that halo and get revising...

Once more, you don't have to be a mind-reader to be able to guess the kind of thing they're going
to ask you in the exam. My money's on something to do with displacement reactions — will iodine
displace bromine from some compound or other, for instance. Learn the facts... just learn the facts.

Transition Elements

Transition elements make up the big clump of metals in the middle of the periodic table.

| Group 1 | Group 2 | | | | | | | | | | | Group 3 | Group 4 | Group 5 | Group 6 | Group 7 | Group 0 |

Here they are, right in the middle of Group 2 and Group 3

		45 Sc Scandium 21	48 Ti Titanium 22	51 V Vanadium 23	52 Cr Chromium 24	55 Mn Manganese 25	56 Fe Iron 26	59 Co Cobalt 27	59 Ni Nickel 28	63.5 Cu Copper 29	65 Zn Zinc 30						
		89 Y Yttrium 39	91 Zr Zirconium 40	93 Nb Niobium 41	96 Mo Molybdenum 42	98 Tc Technetium 43	101 Ru Ruthenium 44	103 Rh Rhodium 45	106 Pd Palladium 46	108 Ag Silver 47	112 Cd Cadmium 48						
		57-71 Lanthanides	178 Hf Hafnium 72	181 Ta Tantalum 73	184 W Tungsten 74	186 Re Rhenium 75	190 Os Osmium 76	192 Ir Iridium 77	195 Pt Platinum 78	197 Au Gold 79	201 Hg Mercury 80						
		89-103 Actinides															

Transition elements (or transition metals) are <u>typical metals</u>, and have the properties you would expect of a 'proper' metal:

1) They're <u>good conductors</u> of heat and electricity.

2) They're very <u>dense</u>, <u>strong</u> and <u>shiny</u>.

3) Transition metals are much <u>less reactive</u> than Group 1 metals — they don't react as vigorously with <u>water</u> or <u>oxygen</u>, for example.

4) They're also much <u>denser</u>, <u>stronger</u> and <u>harder</u> than the Group 1 metals, and have much <u>higher melting points</u> (except for mercury, which is a liquid at room temperature). E.g. iron melts at 1500 °C, copper at 1100 °C and zinc at 400 °C.

Transition metals often have more than one ion, e.g. Fe^{2+}, Fe^{3+}

Two other examples are <u>copper</u>: Cu^+ and Cu^{2+} and <u>chromium</u>: Cr^{2+} and Cr^{3+}.

The <u>different ions</u> usually form different-coloured compounds too: $\underline{Fe^{2+}}$ <u>ions</u> usually give <u>green</u> compounds, whereas $\underline{Fe^{3+}}$ <u>ions</u> usually form <u>red/brown</u> compounds (e.g. <u>rust</u>).

The compounds are very colourful

1) The <u>compounds</u> are <u>colourful</u> due to the <u>transition metal ion</u> they contain, e.g. Potassium chromate(VI) is <u>yellow</u>. Potassium manganate(VII) is <u>purple</u>. Copper(II) sulfate is <u>blue</u>.

2) The colours in <u>gemstones</u>, like <u>blue sapphires</u> and <u>green emeralds</u>, and the colours in <u>pottery glazes</u> are all due to <u>transition metals</u>. And weathered <u>copper</u> is a lovely colourful <u>green</u>.

Transition metals and their compounds all make good catalysts

1) <u>Iron</u> is the <u>catalyst</u> used in the <u>Haber process</u> (see page 150) for making <u>ammonia</u>.

2) <u>Manganese(IV) oxide</u> is a good <u>catalyst</u> for the decomposition of <u>hydrogen peroxide</u>.

3) <u>Nickel</u> is useful for turning <u>oils into fats</u> for making margarine.

Remember, catalysts increase the rate of a reaction.

Warm-Up and Exam Questions

Question time again. Sit down at a table for a short period, and try these...

Warm-Up Questions

1) In Group 1, as you go down the periodic table, does the reactivity increase or decrease?
2) Which gas is produced when an alkali metal reacts with water?
3) Do halide ions have a positive or a negative charge?
4) Give three typical properties of transition metals.

Exam Questions

1   Newlands and Mendeleev both came up with a system for classifying elements.

   (a) Describe Newlands' system for classifying elements.

   (1 mark)

   (b) Explain why the work of Mendeleev was taken more seriously
        than that of Newlands.

   (4 marks)

2   The table shows some of the physical properties of four of the halogens.

Halogen	Atomic number	Colour	Physical state at room temperature	Boiling point
			Properties	
Fluorine	9	yellow		−188 °C
Chlorine	17	green		−34 °C
Bromine	35	red-brown		59 °C
Iodine	53	dark grey		185 °C

   (a) Complete the table to give the physical state at room temperature
        of all four halogens.

   (4 marks)

   (b) Draw an arrow next to the left hand side of the table to show the direction of
        increasing reactivity in the halogens.

   (1 mark)

   (c) This equation shows a reaction between chlorine and potassium iodide.

   $$Cl_2(g) + 2KI(aq) \rightarrow I_2(aq) + 2KCl(aq)$$

   (i)   What type of reaction is this?

   (1 mark)

   (ii) Which is the less reactive halogen in this reaction?

   (1 mark)

Exam Questions

3   Chlorine is a Group 7 element used in water purification. Its electron arrangement is shown in the diagram below.

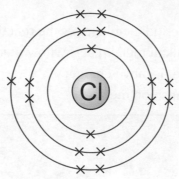

(a)   Chlorine is very reactive and forms compounds with metals.
What type of bonds form between chlorine and metals?

(1 mark)

(b)   Chlorine is more reactive than bromine. When chlorine is bubbled through potassium bromide solution a reaction occurs.

(i)   Write a word equation for the reaction.

(1 mark)

(ii)   Explain why chlorine atoms are more reactive than bromine atoms

(3 marks)

4   All the Group 1 metals react vigorously with water.
(a)   Explain why this is.

(1 mark)

(b)   The Group 1 metals all react with water at a different rate. Explain why this is.

(2 marks)

(c)   Give the two products formed in these reactions.

(2 marks)

(d)   During these reactions a solution is formed.
Is this solution acidic, neutral or alkaline?

(1 mark)

5   (a)   Iron is a transition metal. Sodium is a Group 1 metal.
(i)   Give two differences between the physical properties of iron and sodium.

(2 marks)

(ii)   Give one difference in the chemical properties of iron and sodium.

(1 mark)

(b)   Iron oxide can have the formula FeO or Fe_2O_3.
(i)   Suggest why this is.

(1 mark)

(ii)   These two types of iron oxide are not the same colour. Explain why this is.

(1 mark)

Hardness of Water

Water where you live might be <u>hard</u> or <u>soft</u>. It depends on the <u>rocks</u> your water meets on its way to you.

Hard water makes scum and scale

1) With <u>soft water</u>, you get a nice <u>lather</u> with soap. But with <u>hard water</u> you get a <u>nasty scum</u> instead — unless you're using a soapless detergent. The problem is dissolved <u>calcium ions</u> and <u>magnesium ions</u> in the water (see below) reacting with the soap to make <u>scum</u> which is insoluble. So to get a decent lather you need to use <u>more soap</u> — and because soap <u>isn't free</u>, that means <u>more money</u> going down the drain.

2) When <u>heated</u>, hard water also forms furring or <u>scale</u> (mostly calcium carbonate) on the insides of pipes, boilers and kettles. Badly scaled-up pipes and boilers reduce the <u>efficiency</u> of heating systems, and may need to be <u>replaced</u> — all of which costs money. Scale can even <u>eventually block pipes</u>.

3) <u>Scale</u> is also a bit of a <u>thermal insulator</u>. This means that a <u>kettle</u> with scale on the <u>heating element</u> takes <u>longer to boil</u> than a <u>clean</u> non-scaled-up kettle — so it becomes <u>less efficient</u>.

Hardness is caused by Ca^{2+} and Mg^{2+} Ions

1) Most hard water is hard because it contains lots of <u>calcium ions</u> and <u>magnesium ions</u>.

2) Rain falling on some types of rocks (e.g. <u>limestone</u>, <u>chalk</u> and <u>gypsum</u>) can dissolve compounds like <u>magnesium sulfate</u> (which is soluble), and <u>calcium sulfate</u> (which is also soluble, though only a bit).

Hard water isn't all bad

1) Ca^{2+} ions are good for healthy <u>teeth</u> and <u>bones</u>.

2) Studies have found that people who live in <u>hard water</u> areas are at <u>less risk</u> of developing <u>heart disease</u> than people who live in soft water areas. This could be to do with the <u>minerals</u> in hard water.

Hardness of Water

Remove the dissolved Ca²⁺ and Mg²⁺ ions to make hard water soft

There are two kinds of hardness — temporary and permanent.
Temporary hardness is caused by the hydrogencarbonate ion, HCO_3^-, in $Ca(HCO_3)_2$.
Permanent hardness is caused by dissolved calcium sulfate (among other things).

1) Temporary hardness is removed by boiling. When heated, the calcium hydrogencarbonate decomposes to form calcium carbonate which is insoluble. This solid is the 'limescale' on your kettle.

   e.g.

   calcium hydrogencarbonate → calcium carbonate + water + carbon dioxide
   $$Ca(HCO_3)_{2(aq)} \rightarrow CaCO_{3(s)} + H_2O_{(l)} + CO_{2(g)}$$

   This won't work for permanent hardness, though. Heating a sulfate ion does nowt.

2) Both types of hardness can be softened by adding washing soda (sodium carbonate, Na_2CO_3) to it. The added carbonate ions react with the Ca^{2+} and Mg^{2+} ions to make an insoluble precipitate of calcium carbonate and magnesium carbonate. The Ca^{2+} and Mg^{2+} ions are no longer dissolved in the water so they can't make it hard.

   e.g. $$Ca^{2+}_{(aq)} + CO_3^{2-}_{(aq)} \rightarrow CaCO_{3(s)}$$

3) Both types of hardness can also be removed by running water through 'ion exchange columns' which are sold in shops. The columns have lots of sodium ions (or hydrogen ions) and 'exchange' them for calcium or magnesium ions in the water that runs through them.

   e.g. $$Na_2Resin_{(s)} + Ca^{2+}_{(aq)} \rightarrow CaResin_{(s)} + 2Na^+_{(aq)}$$

   ('Resin' is a huge insoluble resin molecule.)

And if the water's really hard, you can chip your teeth...

Hard water — good thing or bad thing... Well, it provides minerals that are good for health, but it creates an awful lot of unnecessary expense. In hard water areas, you need more soap to get a lather, it takes longer (and therefore more electricity) to boil water (as heating elements get furred up), and you need to get your pipes replaced more often. It's a bit of a drag. But you still need to learn it.

Hardness of Water

With soft water, you get a nice <u>lather</u> with soap. Not so with hard water...

*You can use titration to **compare the hardness** of **water samples***

Method

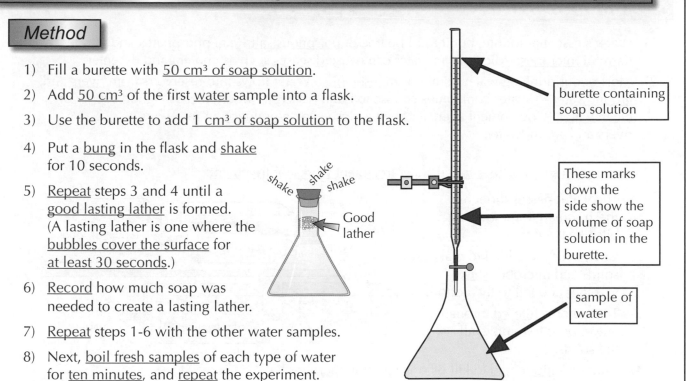

1) Fill a burette with <u>50 cm³ of soap solution</u>.

2) Add <u>50 cm³</u> of the first <u>water</u> sample into a flask.

3) Use the burette to add <u>1 cm³ of soap solution</u> to the flask.

4) Put a <u>bung</u> in the flask and <u>shake</u> for 10 seconds.

5) <u>Repeat</u> steps 3 and 4 until a <u>good lasting lather</u> is formed. (A lasting lather is one where the <u>bubbles cover the surface</u> for <u>at least 30 seconds</u>.)

6) <u>Record</u> how much soap was needed to create a lasting lather.

7) <u>Repeat</u> steps 1-6 with the other water samples.

8) Next, <u>boil fresh samples</u> of each type of water for <u>ten minutes</u>, and <u>repeat</u> the experiment.

burette containing soap solution

These marks down the side show the volume of soap solution in the burette.

sample of water

Good lather

shake shake shake

Results

This method was carried out on <u>3 different samples of water</u> — <u>distilled</u> water, <u>local tap water</u> and <u>imported tap water</u>. Here's the <u>table of results</u>:

Sample	Volume of soap solution needed to give a good lather	
	using unboiled water in cm³	using boiled water in cm³
Distilled	1	1
Local water	7	1
Imported water	14	8

The results tell you the following things about the water:

1) Distilled water contains little or no <u>hardness</u> — only the <u>minimum</u> amount of soap was needed.

2) The sample of <u>imported water</u> contains <u>more hardness</u> than <u>local water</u> — <u>more soap</u> was needed to produce a lather.

3) The local water contains only <u>temporary hardness</u> — all the hardness is <u>removed by boiling</u>. You can tell because the same amount of soap was needed for <u>boiled local water</u> as for <u>distilled water</u>.

4) The imported water contains both <u>temporary</u> and <u>permanent hardness</u>. 8 cm³ of soap is still needed to produce a lather after boiling.

5) If your brain's really switched on, you'll see that the local water and the imported water contain the <u>same amount</u> of <u>temporary hardness</u>. In both cases, the amount of soap needed in the <u>boiled</u> sample is <u>6 cm³ less</u> than in the <u>unboiled</u> sample.

Water Quality

It's easy to take water for granted... turn on the tap, and there it is — nice, clean water. The water you drink's been round the block a few times — so there's some <u>fancy chemistry</u> needed to make it drinkable.

Drinking water needs to be **good quality**

1) Water's essential for life, but it must be free of <u>poisonous salts</u> (e.g. phosphates and nitrates) and harmful <u>microbes</u>. Microbes in water can cause <u>diseases</u> such as cholera and dysentery.

2) Most of our drinking water comes from <u>reservoirs</u>. Water flows into reservoirs from <u>rivers</u> and <u>groundwater</u> — water companies choose to build reservoirs where there's a good supply of <u>clean water</u>. Government agencies keep a close eye on <u>pollution</u> in reservoirs, rivers and groundwater.

<u>Water from reservoirs goes to the water treatment works for treatment</u>:

1) The water passes though a <u>mesh screen</u> to remove big bits like twigs.

2) Chemicals are added to make solids and microbes <u>stick together</u> and fall to the bottom.

3) The water is <u>filtered</u> through gravel beds to remove all the solids.

4) Water is <u>chlorinated</u> to kill off any harmful <u>microbes</u> left.

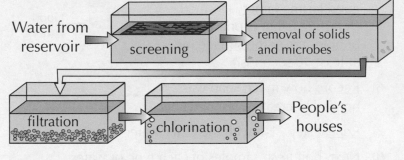

Some people <u>still aren't satisfied</u>. They buy filters that contain <u>carbon</u> or <u>silver</u> to remove substances from their tap water. Carbon in the filters removes <u>chlorine taste</u> and silver is supposed to kill bugs. Some people in hard water areas buy <u>water softeners</u> which contain <u>ion exchange resins</u> (see p. 144).

<u>Totally pure water</u> with <u>nothing</u> dissolved in it can be produced by <u>distillation</u> — boiling water to make steam and condensing the steam. This process is too <u>expensive</u> to produce tap water — bags of energy would be needed to boil all the water we use. Distilled water is used in <u>chemistry labs</u>.

You'd use pure water to make a solution of (say) KBr, because you wouldn't want any other ions mucking it up.

Adding **fluoride** and **chlorine** to water has **disadvantages**

1) <u>Fluoride</u> is added to drinking water in some parts of the country because it helps to <u>reduce tooth decay</u>. <u>Chlorine</u> is added to <u>prevent disease</u> (see above). So far so good. However...

2) Some studies have linked adding chlorine to water with an <u>increase</u> in certain <u>cancers</u>. Chlorine can <u>react</u> with other <u>natural substances</u> in water to produce <u>toxic by-products</u> which some people think could cause cancer.

3) In <u>high doses</u> fluoride can cause <u>cancer</u> and <u>bone problems</u> in humans, so some people believe that fluoride <u>shouldn't be added</u> to drinking water. There is also concern about whether it's right to 'mass medicate' — people can <u>choose</u> whether to use a <u>fluoride toothpaste</u>, but they can't choose whether their tap water has added fluoride.

4) <u>Levels of chemicals</u> added to drinking water need to be carefully <u>monitored</u>. For example, in some areas the water may already contain a lot of fluoride, so adding more could be harmful.

Warm-Up and Exam Questions

Just like day follows night, exam questions follow warm-up questions.

Warm-Up Questions

1) What is hard water?
2) What is scale?
3) Name the two types of water hardness.
4) How can totally pure water be produced?

Exam Questions

1 Hard water in many areas is caused by dissolved Ca^{2+} ions.

(a) Give two disadvantages of living in a hard water area.

(2 marks)

(b) Give two advantages of living in a hard water area.

(2 marks)

(c) Hard water can be caused by dissolved calcium hydrogencarbonate.

Explain how this type of hardness can be removed by boiling.

(2 marks)

d) Give two other methods that can be used to remove hardness.

(2 marks)

2 The diagram below shows how water in some parts of the UK is treated before it reaches people's homes.

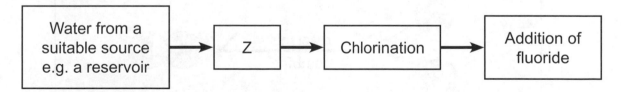

(a) Describe stage **Z** in the process.

(2 marks)

(b) *In this question you will be assessed on the quality of your English, the organisation of your ideas and your use of appropriate specialist vocabulary.*

Discuss the advantages and disadvantages of the treatment of water in this way.

(6 marks)

Reversible Reactions

A <u>reversible reaction</u> is one where the <u>products</u> of the reaction can <u>themselves react</u> to produce the <u>original reactants</u>

$$A + B \rightleftharpoons C + D$$

In other words, <u>the reaction can go both ways</u>.

Reversible reactions will reach **equilibrium**

1) If a reversible reaction takes place in a <u>closed system</u> then a state of <u>equilibrium</u> will always be reached.

2) <u>Equilibrium</u> means that the <u>amounts</u> of reactants and products will reach a certain <u>balance</u> and stay there. (A 'closed system' just means that none of the reactants or products can <u>escape</u>.)

3) The reactions are still taking place in <u>both directions</u>, but the <u>overall effect is nil</u> because the forward and reverse reactions <u>cancel</u> each other out. The reactions are taking place at <u>exactly the same rate</u> in both directions.

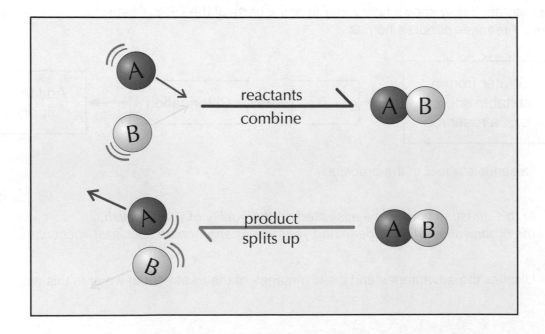

Reversible Reactions

Reversible reactions always reach equilibrium eventually, but by changing the <u>conditions</u> you can change the <u>position</u> of the equilibrium — i.e. shift it over so you end up with more products.

Changing *temperature* and *pressure* to get *more product*

1) In a reversible reaction the 'position of equilibrium' (the relative amounts of reactants and products) depends <u>very strongly</u> on the <u>temperature</u> and <u>pressure</u> surrounding the reaction.

2) If you <u>deliberately alter</u> the temperature and pressure you can <u>move</u> the 'position of equilibrium' to give <u>more product</u> and <u>less</u> reactants.

Temperature

All reactions are <u>exothermic</u> in one direction and <u>endothermic</u> in the other.

- If you <u>raise</u> the <u>temperature</u>, the <u>endothermic</u> reaction will increase to <u>use up</u> the extra heat.
- If you <u>reduce</u> the <u>temperature</u>, the <u>exothermic</u> reaction will increase to <u>give out</u> more heat.

Pressure

Many reactions have a <u>greater volume</u> on one side, either of <u>products</u> or <u>reactants</u> (greater volume means there are more gas molecules and less volume means there are fewer gas molecules).

- If you <u>raise</u> the <u>pressure</u> it will encourage the reaction which produces <u>less volume</u>.
- If you <u>lower</u> the <u>pressure</u> it will encourage the reaction which produces <u>more volume</u>.

<u>Adding a CATALYST doesn't change the equilibrium position</u>:

1) Catalysts speed up <u>both</u> the <u>forward</u> and <u>backward</u> reactions by the <u>same amount</u>.

2) So, adding a catalyst means the reaction reaches equilibrium <u>quicker</u>, but you end up with the <u>same amount</u> of product as you would without the catalyst.

Remember — catalysts DON'T affect the equilibrium position...

Changing the temperature <u>always</u> changes the equilibrium position, but that's not true of pressure. If your reaction has the same number of gas molecules on each side of the equation, changing the pressure won't change the equilibrium position at all (it still affects the <u>rate</u> of reaction though).

The Haber Process

This is an <u>important industrial process</u>. It produces <u>ammonia</u> (NH_3), which is used to make <u>fertilisers</u>.

Nitrogen and hydrogen are needed to make ammonia

$$N_2(g) \ + \ 3H_2(g) \ \rightleftharpoons \ 2NH_3(g) \ \ (+ \text{ heat})$$

These gases are first purified.

1) The <u>nitrogen</u> is obtained easily from the <u>air</u>, which is <u>78% nitrogen</u> (and 21% oxygen).

2) The <u>hydrogen</u> comes from <u>natural gas</u> or from <u>other sources</u> like crude oil.

3) Some of the nitrogen and hydrogen reacts to form <u>ammonia</u>. Because the reaction is <u>reversible</u> — it occurs in both directions — ammonia breaks down again into nitrogen and hydrogen. The reaction reaches an <u>equilibrium</u>.

> <u>**Industrial conditions**</u>: pressure = <u>200 atmospheres</u>; temperature = <u>450 °C</u>; catalyst: <u>iron</u>.

The reaction is reversible, so there's a compromise to be made:

1) <u>Higher pressures</u> favour the <u>forward</u> reaction (since there are four molecules of gas on the left-hand side, for every two molecules on the right — see the equation above).

2) So the pressure is set <u>as high as possible</u> to give the best % yield, without making the plant too expensive to build (it'd be too expensive to build a plant that'd stand pressures of over 1000 atmospheres, for example). Hence the <u>200 atmospheres</u> operating pressure.

3) The <u>forward reaction</u> is <u>exothermic</u>, which means that <u>increasing</u> the <u>temperature</u> will actually move the equilibrium the <u>wrong way</u> — away from ammonia and towards N_2 and H_2. So the yield of ammonia would be greater at <u>lower temperatures</u>.

4) The trouble is, <u>lower temperatures</u> mean a <u>lower rate of reaction</u>. So what they do is increase the temperature anyway, to get a much faster rate of reaction.

5) The 450 °C is a <u>compromise</u> between <u>maximum yield</u> and <u>speed of reaction</u>. It's better to wait just <u>20 seconds</u> for a <u>10% yield</u> than to have to wait <u>60 seconds</u> for a <u>20% yield</u>.

6) The <u>ammonia</u> is formed as a <u>gas</u> but as it cools in the condenser it <u>liquefies</u> and is <u>removed</u>.

7) The unused hydrogen (H_2) and nitrogen (N_2) are <u>recycled</u> so <u>nothing is wasted</u>.

H_2 and N_2 mixed in 3:1 ratio

Reaction vessel

Trays of iron catalyst

450 °C 200 atm

Unused H_2 and N_2 is recycled

Condenser

Liquid Ammonia

The iron catalyst speeds up the reaction and keeps costs down

1) The <u>iron catalyst</u> makes the reaction go <u>faster</u>, which gets it to the <u>equilibrium proportions</u> more quickly. But remember, the catalyst <u>doesn't</u> affect the <u>position</u> of equilibrium (i.e. the % yield).

2) <u>Without the catalyst</u> the temperature would have to be <u>raised even further</u> to get a <u>quick enough</u> reaction, and that would <u>reduce the % yield</u> even further. So the catalyst is very important.

Alcohols

This page is about different types of <u>alcohols</u> — and that's not just beer, wine and spirits.

Alcohols have an '-OH' functional group and end in '-ol'

1) The <u>general formula</u> of an alcohol is $C_nH_{2n+1}OH$.
   So an alcohol with 2 carbons has the formula C_2H_5OH.

2) All alcohols contain the same <u>-OH group</u>.
   You need to know the <u>first 3</u> in the homologous series:

> *A homologous series is a group of chemicals that react in a similar way because they have the same functional group (in alcohols it's the −OH group).*

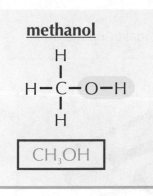

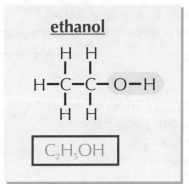

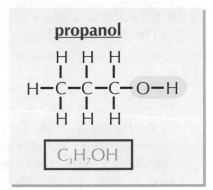

3) The basic <u>naming</u> system is the same as for alkanes — but replace the final '<u>-e</u>' with '<u>-ol</u>'.

4) Don't write CH_4O instead of CH_3OH — it doesn't show the <u>functional -OH group</u>.

The first three alcohols have similar properties

1) Alcohols are <u>flammable</u>. They burn in air to produce <u>carbon dioxide</u> and <u>water</u>.
   E.g.

   $$2CH_3OH_{(l)} + 3O_{2(g)} \rightarrow 2CO_{2(g)} + 4H_2O_{(g)}$$

2) The first three alcohols all <u>dissolve completely in water</u> to form <u>neutral solutions</u>.

3) They also react with <u>sodium</u> to give <u>hydrogen</u> and <u>alkoxides</u>,
   e.g. ethanol gives sodium ethoxide and H_2.
   E.g.

   $$2C_2H_5OH_{(l)} + 2Na_{(s)} \rightarrow 2C_2H_5ONa_{(aq)} + H_{2(g)}$$

4) <u>Ethanol</u> is the main alcohol in alcoholic drinks. It's not as <u>toxic</u> as methanol
   (which causes <u>blindness</u> if drunk) but it still damages the <u>liver</u> and <u>brain</u>.

Learn how to draw the first three alcohols

The examiner could ask you to draw any one of the <u>first three alcohols</u> in the homologous series
so make sure you can come up with the goods. You can't do it without knowing the <u>functional group</u>.

Alcohols

Here's another page of useful facts about alcohols.

Alcohols are used as solvents

1) Alcohols such as methanol and ethanol can <u>dissolve</u> most compounds that <u>water</u> dissolves, but they can also dissolve substances that <u>water can't dissolve</u> — e.g. hydrocarbons, oils and fats. This makes ethanol, methanol and propanol <u>very useful solvents</u> in industry.

2) <u>Ethanol</u> is the solvent for <u>perfumes</u> and <u>aftershave</u> lotions.
It can mix with both the <u>oils</u> (which give the smell) <u>and</u> the <u>water</u> (that makes up the bulk).

3) '<u>Methylated spirit</u>' (or 'meths') is <u>ethanol</u> with chemicals (e.g. methanol) added to it. It's used to <u>clean</u> paint brushes and as a <u>fuel</u> (among other things). It's <u>poisonous</u> to drink, so a <u>purply-blue dye</u> is also added (to stop people drinking it by mistake).

Alcohols are used as fuels

1) Ethanol is used as a fuel in <u>spirit burners</u> — it burns fairly cleanly and it's non-smelly.

2) Ethanol can also be mixed in with petrol and used as <u>fuel for cars</u>. Since pure ethanol is <u>clean burning</u>, the more ethanol in a petrol/ethanol mix, the less <u>pollution</u> is produced.

3) Some countries that have little or no oil deposits but plenty of land and sunshine (e.g. Brazil) grow loads of <u>sugar cane</u>, which they <u>ferment</u> to form ethanol.

4) A big advantage of this is that sugar cane is a <u>renewable resource</u> (unlike petrol, which will run out).

Quick tip — don't fill your car with single malt whisky...

The examiners will be happy if you know the <u>formulas</u>, the <u>structures</u>, the <u>properties</u> and the <u>reactions</u> on this page and the previous page. They might also give you some extra information about alcohols to evaluate... knowing the facts on these pages will help you be able to do that.

Carboxylic Acids

So what if carboxylic is a funny name — these are easy.

Carboxylic acids have the functional group -COOH

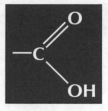

1) Carboxylic acids have '-COOH' as a functional group.

2) Their names end in '-anoic acid' (and start with the normal 'meth/eth/prop).

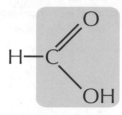

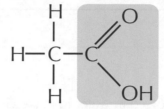

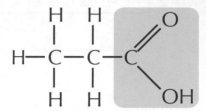

Methanoic acid
HCOOH

Ethanoic acid
CH_3COOH

Propanoic acid
C_2H_5COOH

Carboxylic acids react like other acids

1) They react just like any other acid with carbonates to produce carbon dioxide.

2) The salts formed in these reactions end in -anoate — e.g. methanoic acid will form a methanoate, ethanoic acid an ethanoate, etc. For example:

> ethanoic acid + sodium carbonate → carbon dioxide + sodium ethanoate

3) Carboxylic acids dissolve in water to produce acidic solutions. When they dissolve, they ionise and release H^+ ions which are responsible for making the solution acidic. But, because they don't ionise completely (not many H^+ ions are released), they just form weak acidic solutions. This means that they have a higher pH (less acidic) than aqueous solutions of strong acids with the same concentration.

The strength of an acid isn't the same as its concentration. Concentration is how watered down your acid is and strength is how well it has ionised in water.

Carboxylic acids are just like other acids

The trickiest bit on this page is probably the bit about carboxylic acids not ionising completely in water and being weak acids. But when it comes to carbonates, they just act like any old acid — easy.

Carboxylic Acids

Here are some of the wonderful things you can do with carboxylic acids.

Some **carboxylic acids** are fairly **common**

1) <u>Ethanoic acid</u> can be made by <u>oxidising ethanol</u>. Microbes, like yeast, cause the ethanol to ferment. Ethanol can also be oxidised using <u>oxidising agents</u>.

> ethanol + oxygen → ethanoic acid + water

If you leave wine open, the ethanol in it is oxidised — this is why it goes off.

2) <u>Ethanoic acid</u> can then be <u>dissolved in water</u> to make <u>vinegar</u>, which is used for <u>flavouring</u> and <u>preserving</u> foods.

3) <u>Citric acid</u> (another carboxylic acid) is present in <u>oranges</u> and <u>lemons</u>, and is manufactured in large quantities to make <u>fizzy drinks</u>. It's also used to get rid of <u>scale</u> (see page 143).

Carboxylic acids are used in industry to make **soaps** and **esters**

1) <u>Carboxylic acids</u> with <u>longer chains</u> of carbon atoms are used to make <u>soaps and detergents</u>.

2) Carboxylic acids are also used in the preparation of <u>esters</u> (see next page).

3) Ethanoic acid is a very good <u>solvent</u> for many organic molecules. But ethanoic acid isn't usually chosen as a solvent because it makes the solution <u>acidic</u>.

Ethanoic acid — it's not just for putting on your chips...

Bet you didn't think of <u>vinegar</u> or <u>fizzy drinks</u> when you first heard of carboxylic acids. It turns out they've got a fair few uses from <u>descaler</u> to <u>soaps</u>. Make sure you've learnt the ones on this page.

Esters

Mix an alcohol from page 151 and a carboxylic acid from page 153, and you get an ester.

Esters have the functional group *-COO-*

1) Esters are formed from an alcohol and a carboxylic acid.
2) An acid catalyst is usually used (e.g. concentrated sulfuric acid).

$$alcohol + carboxylic\ acid \rightarrow ester + water$$

| CH$_3$COOH | C$_2$H$_5$OH | CH$_3$COOC$_2$H$_5$ | H$_2$O |
| ethanoic acid | ethanol | ethyl ethanoate | water |

Their names end in '-oate'. The alcohol forms the first part of the ester's name, and the acid forms the second part.

ethanol + ethanoic acid → ethyl ethanoate + water
methanol + propanoic acid → methyl propanoate + water

Esters smell nice but *don't* mix well with *water*

1) Many esters have pleasant smells — often quite sweet and fruity. They're also volatile. This makes them ideal for perfumes (the evaporated molecules can be detected by smell receptors in your nose).
2) However, many esters are flammable (or even highly flammable). So their volatility also makes them potentially dangerous.
3) Esters don't mix very well with water. (They're not nearly as soluble as alcohols or carboxylic acids.)
4) But esters do mix well with alcohols and other organic solvents.

Esters are often used in *flavourings* and *perfumes*

1) Because many esters smell nice, they're used in perfumes.
2) Esters are also used to make flavourings and aromas — e.g. there are esters that smell or taste of rum, apple, orange, banana, grape, pineapple, etc.
3) Some esters are used in ointments (they give Deep Heat® its smell).
4) Other esters are used as solvents for paint, ink, glue and in nail varnish remover.

There are things you need to think about when using esters:

1) Inhaling the fumes from some esters irritates mucous membranes in the nose and mouth.
2) Ester fumes are heavier than air and very flammable. Flammable vapour + naked flame = flash fire.
3) Some esters are toxic, especially in large doses. Some people worry about health problems associated with synthetic food additives such as esters.
4) BUT... esters aren't as volatile or as toxic as some other organic solvents — they don't release nearly as many toxic fumes as some of them. In fact esters have replaced solvents such as toluene in many paints and varnishes.

Warm-Up and Exam Questions

Almost done with this section. Just a few more questions to get stuck into.

Warm-Up Questions

1) What can you say about the forward and backward reaction rates at equilibrium?
2) How does increasing the pressure alter the equilibrium position of a reaction which produces fewer moles of gas molecules in the forward direction?
3) Name the catalyst used in the Haber process.
4) What happens to leftover reactants that are not converted to product in the Haber process?
5) What is the general formula of an alcohol?
6) Name the first three carboxylic acids in the homologous series.

Exam Questions

1   When calcium carbonate is heated to a high temperature in a closed system, an equilibrium is reached:

$$CaCO_3 \text{ (s)} \rightleftharpoons CaO \text{ (s)} + CO_2 \text{ (g)}$$

The forwards reaction is endothermic.

(a)   Why is a closed system needed for this reaction to reach equilibrium?

(1 mark)

(b)   Give two ways in which the equilibrium could be changed to increase the proportion of products present.

(2 marks)

2   Ammonia, NH_3, is made by combining nitrogen and hydrogen at a pressure of 200 atm, a temperature of 450 °C and in the presence of a catalyst.
A flow diagram is shown for the reaction:

(a)   Write labels for boxes (i) and (ii) to show the sources of nitrogen and hydrogen.

(2 marks)

(b)   Write a balanced equation with state symbols for the reaction between nitrogen and hydrogen.

(3 marks)

(c)   The reaction is exothermic. Explain why a high temperature is still used.

(2 marks)

```
   (i)            (ii)
    |              |
    v              v
 hydrogen       nitrogen
    |              |
    v              v
  200 atm. pressure
  450 °C temperature
      catalyst
         |
         v
      ammonia
```

Exam Questions

3   Alcohols are an important group of organic chemicals. The most widely used alcohol is ethanol. Its displayed formula is shown in the box below.

$$
\begin{array}{ccc}
& H & H \\
& | & | \\
H - & C - C & - O - H \\
& | & | \\
& H & H
\end{array}
$$

(a)   Name two other chemicals in this homologous series.

(2 marks)

(b)   Write down the functional group of ethanol.

(1 mark)

(c)   Ethanol can be used as a fuel. Ethanol burns in oxygen to give carbon dioxide and water.
Write a balanced symbol equation for this reaction.

(2 marks)

(d)   Ethanol reacts with sodium to give sodium ethoxide and one other product.
Name this product.

(1 mark)

(e)   Ethanol can be used as a solvent.
Suggest one disadvantage of using ethanol as a solvent.

(1 mark)

4   Carboxylic acids are a widely used family of organic chemicals.

(a)   Ethanoic acid is better known by the name of its dilute solution — vinegar.
Draw its displayed (full structural) formula.

(2 marks)

(b)   One use of carboxylic acids is in the production of esters.

(i)   Name the ester formed when ethanoic acid is reacted with ethanol.

(1 mark)

(ii)   When carboxylic acids and alcohols react to form esters, one other product is formed.
Name this product.

(1 mark)

(iii)   Give one use of esters.

(1 mark)

(c)   Carboxylic acids are weak acids. Explain what this means.

(2 marks)

Revision Summary for Chemistry 3a

Bit of a mixed bag — one minute you're pondering the periodic table, the next you're worrying about whether fluoride in drinking water is bad for you. The one thing that's constant and unchanging is the need to learn it all for the exam you've got coming up. So test yourself on these little beauties.

1) Before 1800, how were elements classified?
2) Give two reasons why Newlands' Octaves were criticised.
3) Why did Mendeleev leave gaps in his Table of Elements?
4) How are the group number and the number of electrons in the outer shell related?
5) What is shielding?
6) Name the type of bonds Group 1 elements form.
7) Describe the density of the alkali metals.
8) Write down the balanced symbol equation for the reaction between sodium and water.
9) Explain why Group 7 elements get less reactive as you go down the group from fluorine to iodine.
10) What type of bonds do halogens form with metals?
11) Write down the balanced equation for the displacement of bromine from potassium bromide by chlorine.
12) Will the following reactions occur:
a) iodine with lithium chloride, b) chlorine with lithium bromide?
13) Describe the chemical properties of a typical transition metal.
14) Give an industrial use for transition metals.
15) What are the main ions that cause water hardness?
16) Describe how you could use titration to compare the hardness of two different water samples.
17) During water treatment, how are microbes killed so that the water is safe to drink?
18) Explain why tap water isn't purified by distillation.
19) What is a reversible reaction? Explain what is meant by an equilibrium.
20) How does changing the temperature and pressure of a reversible reaction alter the equilibrium position?
21) How does this influence the choice of pressure for the Haber process?
22) What determines the choice of operating temperature for the Haber process?
23) What effect does the iron catalyst have on the reaction between nitrogen and hydrogen?
24) Draw the structure of the first three alcohols.
25) When alcohols dissolve in water, is the solution acidic, neutral or alkaline?
26) Give two uses of alcohols.
27) What is the functional group in carboxylic acids?
28) Give two uses of carboxylic acids.
29) What two kinds of substance react together to form an ester?
What catalyst is used in the formation of esters?

Moles and Titration

This page is full of useful stuff about <u>moles</u> and <u>concentration</u>. There's also a nice little experiment you can do to find out how much alkali you need to <u>neutralise</u> an acid.

*"THE MOLE" is simply the name given to **a certain number***

Just like "<u>a million</u>" is this many: 1 000 000; or "<u>a billion</u>" is this many: 1 000 000 000, "<u>a mole</u>" is this many: 602 300 000 000 000 000 000 000 or 6.023×10^{23}.

1) And that's all it is. <u>Just a number</u>. But why is it such a long number with a six at the front?

2) The answer is that when you get <u>precisely that number</u> of atoms of <u>carbon-12</u> it weighs exactly <u>12 g</u>. So, get that number of atoms or molecules, <u>of any element or compound</u>, and conveniently, they <u>weigh</u> exactly the same number of <u>grams</u> as the relative atomic mass, A_r (or M_r) of the element or compound. This is arranged <u>on purpose</u> of course, to make things easier.

3) So, you can use <u>moles</u> as a <u>unit</u> of measurement when you're talking about an amount of a substance.

Concentration *is a measure of how* **crowded** *things are*

The <u>concentration</u> of a solution can be measured in <u>moles per dm³</u> (i.e. <u>moles per litre</u>). So 1 mole of stuff in 1 dm³ of solution has a concentration of <u>1 mole per dm³</u> (or 1 mol/dm³).

> The <u>more solute</u> you dissolve in a given volume, the <u>more crowded</u> the solute molecules are and the <u>more concentrated</u> the solution.

Concentration can also be measured in <u>grams per dm³</u>. So 56 grams of stuff dissolved in 1 dm³ of solution has a concentration of <u>56 grams per dm³</u>.

> 1 litre
> = 1000 cm³
> = 1 dm³

Titrations *are used to find out* **concentrations**

1) You met <u>titrations</u> on page 145. Titrations also allow you to find out <u>exactly</u> how much acid is needed to <u>neutralise</u> a quantity of alkali (or vice versa).

2) You put some <u>alkali</u> in a flask, along with some <u>indicator</u> — <u>phenolphthalein</u> or <u>methyl orange</u>. You don't use universal indicator as it changes colour gradually — and you want a <u>definite</u> colour change.

3) Add the <u>acid</u>, a bit at a time, to the alkali using a <u>burette</u> — giving the flask a regular <u>swirl</u>. Go especially <u>slowly</u> (a drop at a time) when you think the alkali's almost neutralised.

4) The indicator <u>changes colour</u> when <u>all</u> the alkali has been <u>neutralised</u> — phenolphthalein is <u>pink</u> in <u>alkalis</u> but <u>colourless</u> in <u>acids</u>, and methyl orange is <u>yellow</u> in <u>alkalis</u> but <u>red</u> in <u>acids</u>.

5) <u>Record</u> the amount of acid used to <u>neutralise</u> the alkali. It's best to <u>repeat</u> this process a few times, making sure you get (pretty much) the same answer each time.

6) You can then take the <u>mean</u> of your results.

You can also do titrations the other way round — adding alkali to acid.

burette containing acid

These marks down the side show the volume of acid used.

alkali and indicator

Repeating the experiment is really important

Repeating titrations and other experiments a few times helps to make sure your results are <u>reliable</u>. If you get the same result a number of times, you can have more faith in it than if it's a one-off.

Titration Calculations

In the exam you might be given the results of a <u>titration experiment</u> and asked to <u>calculate</u> the <u>concentration</u> of the <u>acid</u> when you know the <u>concentration</u> of the <u>alkali</u> (or vice versa).

*Example 1: If they ask for concentration in **MOLES** per dm³*

Say you start off with <u>25 cm³</u> of sodium hydroxide in your flask, and you know that its concentration is <u>0.1 moles per dm³</u>.

You then find from your titration that it takes <u>30 cm³</u> of sulfuric acid (whose concentration you don't know) to neutralise the sodium hydroxide.

You can work out the <u>concentration</u> of the acid in <u>moles per dm³</u>.

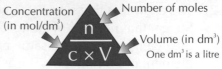

Concentration = moles ÷ volume, so you can make a handy formula triangle.

Concentration (in mol/dm³) — Number of moles — Volume (in dm³) One dm³ is a litre

$$\frac{n}{c \times V}$$

<u>Cover up</u> the thing you're trying to find — then what's left is the formula you need to use.

> Step 1: Work out how many <u>moles</u> of the "known" substance you have using this formula:
>
> Number of moles = concentration × volume
> = 0.1 mol/dm³ × (25 / 1000) dm³
> = <u>0.0025 moles of NaOH</u>
>
> *Remember: 1000 cm³ = 1 dm³*
>
> Step 2: Write down the <u>balanced equation</u> of the reaction...
> $2NaOH + H_2SO_4 \longrightarrow Na_2SO_4 + 2H_2O$
>
> ...and work out how many <u>moles</u> of the "<u>unknown</u>" stuff you must have had.
> Using the equation, you can see that for every <u>two moles</u> of sodium hydroxide you had...
> ...there was just <u>one mole</u> of sulfuric acid.
> So if you had <u>0.0025 moles</u> of sodium hydroxide...
> ...you must have had 0.0025 ÷ 2 = <u>0.00125 moles of sulfuric acid</u>.
>
> Step 3: Work out the concentration of the "<u>unknown</u>" stuff.
> *Don't forget to put the units.*
> Concentration = number of moles ÷ volume
> = 0.00125 mol ÷ (30 / 1000) dm³ = 0.041666... mol/dm³ = <u>0.0417 mol/dm³</u>

*Example 2: If they ask for concentration in **GRAMS** per dm³*

They might ask you to find out the acid concentration in <u>grams per cubic decimetre</u> (<u>grams per litre</u>). If they do, don't panic — you just need another formula triangle.

> Step 1: Work out the <u>relative formula mass</u> for the acid (you should be given the relative atomic masses, e.g. H = 1, S = 32, O = 16):
> So, H_2SO_4 = (1 × 2) + 32 + (16 × 4) = 98
>
> *Number of moles = mass ÷ relative formula mass.*
>
> Number of moles — Mass (in grams) — Relative formula mass
>
> $$\frac{m}{n \times M_r}$$
>
> Step 2: Convert the concentration in <u>moles</u> (that you've already worked out) into concentration in <u>grams</u>. So, in 1 dm³:
> Mass in grams = moles × relative formula mass
> = 0.041666... × 98 = 4.08333... g
> So the <u>concentration in g/dm³ = 4.08 g/dm³</u>

Warm-Up and Exam Questions

Come on now, don't look at me like that. They're for your own good — I promise.

Warm-Up Questions

1) What is the mass of one mole of oxygen gas?
2) Briefly describe how you'd carry out an acid-base titration.
3) How many moles of hydrochloric acid are there in 25 cm³ of a 0.1 mol/dm³ solution?
4) A solution of sodium carbonate, Na_2CO_3, has a concentration of 0.025 mol/dm³.
   What is the concentration of this solution in g/dm³?

Exam Questions

1 In a titration, 30.3 cm³ of a solution of 1.00 mol/dm³ sodium hydroxide was
   required to neutralise 25.0 cm³ of a solution of sulfuric acid.

   (a) Calculate the number of moles of sodium hydroxide used in the titration.

   (2 marks)

   (b) Work out the number of moles of sulfuric acid used in the titration.

   The equation is: $2NaOH$ (aq) $+$ H_2SO_4 (aq) $\rightarrow$ Na_2SO_4 (aq) $+$ $2H_2O$ (l)

   (1 mark)

   (c) Calculate the concentration of the sulfuric acid solution.

   (2 marks)

2 Jonah is concerned about the amount of acid in soft drinks. He decides to use a
   titration method to find the acid content of his favourite lemonade. He uses a solution
   of 0.1 mol/dm³ sodium hydroxide in titrations with 25 cm³ samples of the lemonade.
   His results are shown in the table.

	Initial burette reading (cm³)	Final burette reading (cm³)	Vol. of NaOH needed (cm³)
1	0.0	9.4	9.4
2	9.4	18.4	9.0
3	18.4	27.4	9.0

   Jonah calculates that the average volume of 0.1 mol/dm³ NaOH needed is 9.0 cm³.

   (a) The first titration value was not included in calculating the average. Why not?

   (1 mark)

   (b) The equation for the reaction in the titration can be written:

   $HA + NaOH \rightarrow NaA + H_2O$, where HA is the acid present in the lemonade.
   Calculate the concentration of acid HA present in the lemonade.

   (3 marks)

Energy

Whenever chemical reactions occur, there are changes in <u>energy</u>. Changes in energy during a chemical reaction can be explained by <u>making bonds</u> or <u>breaking bonds</u>.

Reactions are **exothermic** or **endothermic**

See pages 117-118 for more info on exothermic and endothermic reactions.

An **<u>EXOTHERMIC</u> reaction** is one which **<u>gives out energy</u>** to the surroundings, usually in the form of **<u>heat</u>** and usually shown by a **<u>rise in temperature</u>**.

E.g. <u>fuels burning</u> or <u>neutralisation reactions</u>.

An **<u>ENDOTHERMIC</u> reaction** is one which **<u>takes in energy</u>** from the surroundings, usually in the form of **<u>heat</u>** and usually shown by a **<u>fall in temperature</u>**.

E.g. <u>photosynthesis</u>.

Energy must always be **supplied** to **break bonds**...
...and energy is always **released** when **bonds form**

1) During a chemical reaction, <u>old bonds</u> are <u>broken</u> and <u>new bonds</u> are <u>formed</u>.

2) Energy must be <u>supplied</u> to break <u>existing bonds</u> — so bond breaking is an <u>endothermic</u> process. Energy is <u>released</u> when new bonds are <u>formed</u> — so bond formation is an <u>exothermic</u> process.

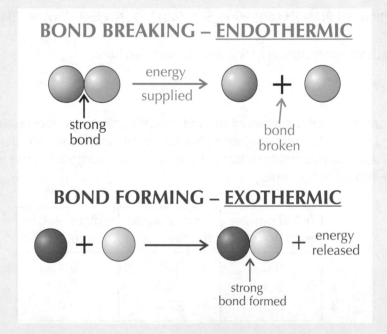

3) In an <u>endothermic</u> reaction, the energy <u>required</u> to break old bonds is <u>greater</u> than the energy <u>released</u> when <u>new bonds</u> are formed.

4) In an <u>exothermic</u> reaction, the energy <u>released</u> in bond formation is <u>greater</u> than the energy used in <u>breaking</u> old bonds.

Save energy — break fewer bonds...

You can get <u>cooling packs</u> that use an <u>endothermic</u> reaction to draw heat from an injury. The pack contains two compartments with different chemicals in. When you use it, you snap the partition and the chemicals <u>mix</u> and <u>react</u>, taking in <u>heat</u> — pretty cool, I reckon (no pun intended).

Energy

The <u>fuels</u> we use are great because they release <u>loads of energy</u> when they burn.
But they cause a few <u>problems</u> as well — none bigger than <u>global warming</u>.

Energy transfer can be measured

1) You can measure the amount of <u>energy released</u> by a <u>chemical reaction</u> (in solution) by taking
the <u>temperature of the reagents</u> (making sure they're the same), <u>mixing</u> them in a <u>polystyrene
cup</u> and measuring the <u>temperature of the solution</u> at the <u>end</u> of the reaction. Easy.

2) The biggest <u>problem</u> with energy measurements is the amount of energy <u>lost to the surroundings</u>.

3) You can reduce it a bit by putting the polystyrene cup into a <u>beaker of cotton wool</u> to give
<u>more insulation</u>, and putting a <u>lid</u> on the cup to reduce energy lost by <u>evaporation</u>.

4) This method works for reactions of <u>solids with water</u> (e.g. dissolving ammonium nitrate in water)
as well as for <u>neutralisation</u> reactions.

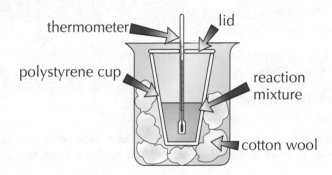

thermometer   lid

polystyrene cup

reaction
mixture

cotton wool

<u>Example:</u>
1) Place 25 cm³ of dilute hydrochloric acid in a polystyrene cup, and record its temperature.
2) Put 25 cm³ of dilute sodium hydroxide in a measuring cylinder and record its temperature.
3) As long as they're at the same temperature, add the alkali to the acid and stir.
4) Take the temperature of the mixture every 30 seconds, and record the highest temperature
it reaches.

5) This method can also be used where <u>energy</u> is being <u>absorbed</u> — there will be a <u>fall</u> in temperature.

Fuels provide energy — but there are consequences

1) Fuels release <u>energy</u> which we use in loads of ways — e.g. to generate electricity and to power cars.

2) Burning fuels has various effects on the <u>environment</u>. For example, burning fossil fuels releases CO_2,
a greenhouse gas. This causes <u>global warming</u> and other types of <u>climate change</u>.

3) It'll be <u>expensive</u> to slow down these effects, and to put things right. Developing alternative energy
sources (e.g. tidal power) costs money.

4) Crude oil is <u>running out</u>. We use <u>a lot of fuels</u> made from crude oil (e.g. <u>petrol and diesel</u>) and as it
runs out it will get more expensive. This means that everything that's <u>transported</u> by lorry, train or
plane gets more expensive too. So the <u>price of crude oil</u> has a big economic effect.

Crude oil — using it is bad, but we can't do without it

There's no hiding from it — finding the fuels to meet our energy needs really is a <u>huge challenge</u>.
But before you set about saving the world, learn the experiment for <u>measuring energy transfer</u> at the
top of the page. It's not too tricky, so it'd be silly to throw away marks if it comes up on the exam.

Energy and Fuels

Burning <u>fuels</u> releases <u>energy</u>. Just how much energy you can find using <u>calorimetry</u>. Bet you can't wait.

*Fuel energy is **calculated** using **calorimetry***

Different fuels produce <u>different amounts of energy</u>. To measure the amount of energy released when a fuel is burnt, you can simply burn the fuel and use the flame to <u>heat up some water</u>. Of course, this has to have a fancy chemistry name — <u>calorimetry</u>. Calorimetry uses a <u>glass</u> or <u>metal container</u> (it's usually made of <u>copper</u> because copper conducts heat so well).

<u>Method</u>:

1) Put 50 g of water in the copper can and <u>record its temperature</u>.

2) <u>Weigh the spirit burner</u> and lid.

3) Put the spirit burner underneath the can, and light the wick. Heat the water, <u>stirring constantly</u>, until the temperature reaches about <u>50 °C</u>.

4) <u>Put out the flame</u> using the burner lid, and measure the <u>final temperature</u> of the water.

5) <u>Weigh</u> the spirit burner and lid <u>again</u>.

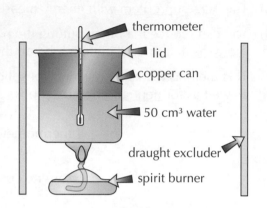

You can use pretty much the same method to calculate the amount of energy produced by <u>foods</u>. The only problem is that when you set food on fire, it tends to <u>go out</u> after a bit.

<u>Example: to work out the energy per gram of methylated spirit (meths)</u>:

1) Mass of spirit burner + lid before heating = 68.75 g → Mass of meths burnt = 0.9 g

2) Mass of spirit burner + lid after heating = 67.85 g

3) Temperature of water in copper can before heating = 21.5 °C → Temperature change in 50 g of water due to heating = 31.0 °C

4) Temperature of water in copper can after heating = 52.5 °C

5) So 0.9 g of fuel produces enough energy to heat up 50 g of water by 31 °C.

6) It takes 4.2 joules of energy to heat up 1 g of water by 1 °C. This is known as the specific heat capacity of water. ← *You'll be told this in the exam.*

$Q = mc\Delta T$ →

ENERGY TRANSFERRED (in J)	=	MASS OF WATER (in g)	×	SPECIFIC HEAT CAPACITY OF WATER (= 4.2)	×	TEMPERATURE CHANGE (in °C)
Q		m		c		ΔT

7) Therefore, the energy produced in this experiment = 50 × 4.2 × 31 = <u>6510 joules</u>.

8) So 0.9 g of meths produces 6510 joules of energy...
... meaning 1 g of meths produces 6510/0.9 = <u>7233 J or 7.233 kJ</u> ← *Energy's wasted heating the can, air, etc. — so this figure will often be much lower than the <u>actual</u> energy content.*

Energy from fuels — it's a burning issue...

Energy values are sometimes measured in <u>calories</u> instead of joules (1 calorie = 4.2 joules).
But more importantly, make sure you're familiar with the equation $Q = mc\Delta T$ — you might need it.

Bond Energies

Remember — chemical reactions involve a change in energy. <u>Energy level diagrams</u> show this change.

Energy level diagrams show if it's exo- or endo-thermic

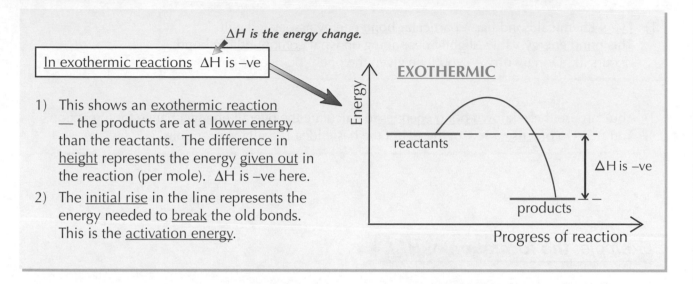

ΔH is the energy change.

In exothermic reactions ΔH is –ve

1) This shows an <u>exothermic reaction</u> — the products are at a <u>lower energy</u> than the reactants. The difference in <u>height</u> represents the energy <u>given out</u> in the reaction (per mole). ΔH is –ve here.

2) The <u>initial rise</u> in the line represents the energy needed to <u>break</u> the old bonds. This is the <u>activation energy</u>.

EXOTHERMIC

ΔH is –ve

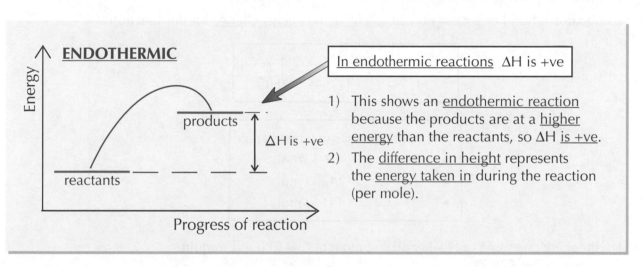

ENDOTHERMIC

In endothermic reactions ΔH is +ve

1) This shows an <u>endothermic reaction</u> because the products are at a <u>higher energy</u> than the reactants, so ΔH <u>is +ve</u>.

2) The <u>difference in height</u> represents the <u>energy taken in</u> during the reaction (per mole).

ΔH is +ve

The activation energy is lowered by catalysts

1) The <u>activation energy</u> represents the <u>minimum energy</u> needed by reacting particles to <u>break their bonds</u>.

2) A <u>catalyst</u> provides a <u>different pathway</u> for a reaction that has a <u>lower activation energy</u> (so the reaction happens more easily and more quickly).

3) This is represented by the <u>lower curve</u> on the diagram showing a <u>lower activation energy</u>.

4) The <u>overall energy change</u> for the reaction, ΔH, <u>remains the same</u> though.

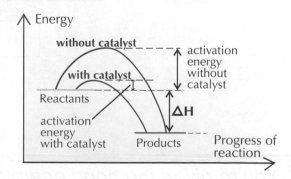

Bond Energies

You need to be able to <u>work out</u> ΔH for a particular reaction.

Bond energy calculations — need to be practised

1) <u>Every</u> chemical bond has a particular <u>bond energy</u> associated with it. This <u>bond energy</u> varies slightly depending on what <u>compound</u> the bond occurs in. Don't worry — you'll be given the ones you need.

2) You can use these <u>known bond energies</u> to calculate the <u>overall energy change</u> for a reaction. You need to <u>practise</u> a few of these, but the basic idea is really very simple...

Example: the formation of HCl

Using known bond energies you can <u>calculate</u> the <u>energy change</u> for this reaction:

$$H — H + Cl — Cl \rightarrow 2H — Cl$$
$$H_2 + Cl_2 \rightarrow 2HCl$$

The bond energies you need are:
- H—H: +436 kJ/mol
- Cl—Cl: +242 kJ/mol
- H—Cl: +431 kJ/mol

1) <u>Breaking</u> one mole of H—H and one mole of Cl—Cl bonds <u>requires</u>: 436 + 242 = <u>678 kJ</u>

2) <u>Forming</u> <u>two</u> moles of H—Cl bonds <u>releases</u> 2 × 431 = <u>862 kJ</u>

3) <u>Overall</u> more energy is <u>released</u> than is used to form the products: 862 – 678 = <u>184 kJ/mol</u> released.

4) Since this is energy <u>released</u>, if we wanted to show ΔH we'd need to put a <u>negative sign</u> in front of it to indicate that it's an <u>exothermic</u> reaction, like this:

$$\Delta H = -184 \text{ kJ/mol}$$

You're given the bond energies, but you must know how to use them

I admit — it's a bit like maths, this. But think how many times you've heard <u>energy efficiency</u> mentioned over the last few years. Well, this kind of calculation is used in working out whether we're using resources efficiently or not. So even if it's not exciting, it's useful at least.

Hydrogen Fuel Cells

Hydrogen can be used as a fuel by <u>burning</u> it in an engine or by using it in a <u>fuel cell</u>.

*Hydrogen and **oxygen** give out **energy** when they **react***

1) <u>Hydrogen and oxygen react</u> to produce <u>water</u> — which isn't a pollutant.
2) The reaction between hydrogen and oxygen is <u>exothermic</u> — it <u>releases energy</u>.
3) Put these two facts together, and you get <u>something useful</u>: you can get <u>energy</u> by reacting hydrogen and oxygen — either in a <u>combustion engine</u> or in a <u>fuel cell</u>.

*Hydrogen gas can be **burnt** to **power vehicles***

1) <u>Hydrogen gas</u> can be burnt in oxygen as a fuel in the <u>combustion engines</u> of vehicles.
2) <u>Pros</u>: Hydrogen combines with oxygen in the air to form <u>just water</u> — so it's <u>very clean</u>.

$$\text{hydrogen} + \text{oxygen} \longrightarrow \text{water}$$

3) <u>Cons</u>: You need a <u>special, expensive engine</u>. Although hydrogen can be made from <u>water</u>, which there's plenty of, you still need to use <u>energy</u> from <u>another source</u> to make it. Also, hydrogen's hard to <u>store safely</u> — it's very explosive.

*Fuel cells use **fuel** and **oxygen** to produce **electrical energy***

> A fuel cell is an electrical cell that's supplied with a <u>fuel</u> and <u>oxygen</u> and uses <u>energy</u> from the reaction between them to generate <u>electricity</u>.

1) Hydrogen can be used in a <u>hydrogen-oxygen fuel cell</u>.
2) Fuel cells were developed in the 1960s as part of the <u>space programme</u>, to provide electrical power on spacecraft — they were <u>more practical than solar cells</u> and <u>safer than nuclear power</u>. (They're still used on the Space Shuttle missions.)
3) Unlike a battery, a fuel cell <u>doesn't run down</u> or <u>need recharging</u> from the mains. It'll produce energy in the form of electricity and heat <u>as long as fuel is supplied</u>.

*The **car industry** is **developing fuel cells***

1) The car industry is developing <u>fuel cells</u> to replace conventional petrol/diesel engines.
2) Fuel cell vehicles don't produce any conventional pollutants — no <u>greenhouse gases</u>, no <u>nitrogen oxides</u>, no <u>sulfur dioxide</u>, no <u>carbon monoxide</u>. The only by-products are <u>water</u> and <u>heat</u>. This would be a major advantage in <u>cities</u>, where air pollution from traffic is a big problem.
3) Fuel cells could eventually help countries to become <u>less dependent on crude oil</u>.
4) However, they're <u>not likely</u> to mean the end of either <u>conventional power stations</u> or our dependence on <u>fossil fuels</u>. That's because:

- hydrogen is a <u>gas</u> so it takes up loads more <u>space</u> to <u>store</u> than liquid fuels like petrol.
- it's very <u>explosive</u> so it's difficult to store <u>safely</u>.
- the hydrogen fuel is often made either from <u>hydrocarbons</u> (from <u>fossil fuels</u>), or by electrolysis of water, which <u>uses electricity</u> (and that electricity's got to be generated <u>somehow</u> — usually this involves fossil fuels).

Warm-Up and Exam Questions

1) Describe the type of energy change that happens when new chemical bonds form.
2) Which symbol is used to represent the energy change in a reaction?
3) What is the effect of a catalyst on the activation energy of a reaction?
4) Explain how hydrogen fuel cells produce energy.

Exam Questions

1   When methane burns in air it produces carbon dioxide and water, as shown in the diagram:

$$H-\overset{\displaystyle H}{\underset{\displaystyle H}{\overset{|}{\underset{|}{C}}}}-H \; + \; \begin{array}{c} O=O \\ O=O \end{array} \;\rightarrow\; O=C=O \; + \; \begin{array}{c} H-O-H \\ H-O-H \end{array}$$

The bond energies for each bond in the above molecules are given below.

Bond energies (kJ/mol):   C–H 414   O=O 494   C=O 800   O–H 459

(a) Which two types of bond are broken during the reaction?

(1 mark)

(b) Calculate an energy value (in kJ/mol) for:
(i)   the total bonds broken.

(1 mark)

(ii) the total bonds formed.

(1 mark)

(iii) the difference between the bonds formed and the bonds broken.

(1 mark)

(c) Use the values from part (b) to explain why the reaction is exothermic.

(1 mark)

2   The amount of energy produced by two different fuels was compared.
1 g of each fuel was burned and the heat produced was used to increase the
temperature of 100 cm³ of water. The temperature rise for fuel A was 21 °C
and for fuel B it was 32 °C. (The specific heat capacity of water is 4.2 J/g/K.)

(a) Why must the same volume of water be used each time?

(1 mark)

(b) Calculate the heat energy transferred to the water from Fuel A, if the water
weighs 100 g.

(2 marks)

(c) Complete the diagrams to compare the energy changes caused by the two fuels.

(2 marks)

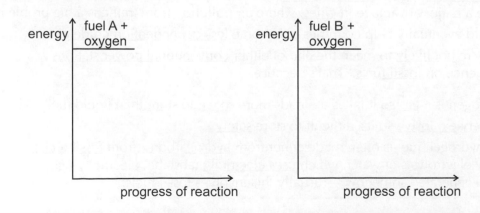

Tests for Positive Ions

Forensic science involves a lot of chemical tests, which is what these next two pages are about. Imagine you have a mystery substance — you don't know what it is, but you need to find out. If it's an ionic compound it'll have a positive and a negative part. So, first off, some tests for positive ions.

Flame tests identify metal ions

Compounds of some metals burn with a characteristic colour, as you see every November 5th when a firework explodes. So, remember, remember...

1) You can test for various metal ions by putting your substance in a flame and seeing what colour the flame goes.

Remember, metals always form positive ions.

> Lithium, Li$^+$, gives a crimson flame.
> Sodium, Na$^+$, gives a yellow flame.
> Potassium, K$^+$, gives a lilac flame.
> Calcium, Ca^{2+}, gives a red flame.
> Barium, Ba^{2+}, gives a green flame.

2) To flame-test a compound in the lab, dip a clean wire loop into a sample of the compound, and put the wire loop in the clear blue part of the Bunsen flame (the hottest bit). First make sure the wire loop is really clean by dipping it into hydrochloric acid and rinsing it with distilled water.

Some metal ions form a coloured precipitate with NaOH

This is also a test for metal ions, but it's slightly more involved. Concentrate now...

1) Many metal hydroxides are insoluble and precipitate out of solution when formed. Some of these hydroxides have a characteristic colour.

2) So in this test you add a few drops of sodium hydroxide solution to a solution of your mystery compound — all in the hope of forming an insoluble hydroxide.

3) If you get a coloured insoluble hydroxide you can then tell which metal was in the compound.

"Metal"	Colour of precipitate	Ionic Reaction
Calcium, Ca^{2+}	White	$Ca^{2+}_{(aq)} + 2OH^-_{(aq)} \rightarrow Ca(OH)_{2\,(s)}$
Copper(II), Cu^{2+}	Blue	$Cu^{2+}_{(aq)} + 2OH^-_{(aq)} \rightarrow Cu(OH)_{2\,(s)}$
Iron(II), Fe^{2+}	Green	$Fe^{2+}_{(aq)} + 2OH^-_{(aq)} \rightarrow Fe(OH)_{2\,(s)}$
Iron(III), Fe^{3+}	Brown	$Fe^{3+}_{(aq)} + 3OH^-_{(aq)} \rightarrow Fe(OH)_{3\,(s)}$
Aluminium, Al^{3+}	White at first. But then redissolves in excess NaOH to form a colourless solution.	$Al^{3+}_{(aq)} + 3OH^-_{(aq)} \rightarrow Al(OH)_{3\,(s)}$ then $Al(OH)_{3\,(s)} + OH^-_{(aq)} \rightarrow Al(OH)_4^-_{(aq)}$
Magnesium, Mg^{2+}	White	$Mg^{2+}_{(aq)} + 2OH^-_{(aq)} \rightarrow Mg(OH)_{2\,(s)}$

Testing metals is flaming useful...

Remember... your metal ion is your positive ion. To find out what your mystery ion is, start off with a flame test. If that doesn't give you an answer, then go on and try the sodium hydroxide test. Learn all the colours on this page and the metal ions they match up to — you might need them in the exam.

Tests for Negative Ions

So now maybe you know what the <u>positive</u> part of your mystery substance is (see previous page). Now it's time to test for the <u>negative</u> bit.

Testing for *carbonates* — check for CO_2

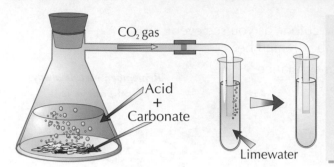

First things first — the test for carbon dioxide (CO_2).

1) You can test to see if a gas is <u>carbon dioxide</u> by bubbling it through <u>limewater</u>. If it is <u>carbon dioxide</u>, the <u>limewater turns cloudy</u>.

2) You can use this to test for <u>carbonate</u> ions (CO_3^{2-}), since carbonates react with <u>dilute acids</u> to form <u>carbon dioxide</u>.

$$\text{acid + carbonate} \rightarrow \text{salt + water + carbon dioxide}$$

Tests for *halides* and *sulfates*

You can test for certain ions by seeing if a <u>precipitate</u> is formed after these reactions...

Halide ions

To test for <u>chloride</u> (Cl^-), <u>bromide</u> (Br^-) or <u>iodide</u> (I^-) ions, add <u>dilute nitric acid</u> (HNO_3), followed by <u>silver nitrate solution</u> ($AgNO_3$).

A <u>chloride</u> gives a white precipitate of <u>silver chloride</u>.

$$Ag^+_{(aq)} + Cl^-_{(aq)} \longrightarrow AgCl_{(s)}$$

A <u>bromide</u> gives a cream precipitate of <u>silver bromide</u>.

$$Ag^+_{(aq)} + Br^-_{(aq)} \longrightarrow AgBr_{(s)}$$

An <u>iodide</u> gives a yellow precipitate of <u>silver iodide</u>.

$$Ag^+_{(aq)} + I^-_{(aq)} \longrightarrow AgI_{(s)}$$

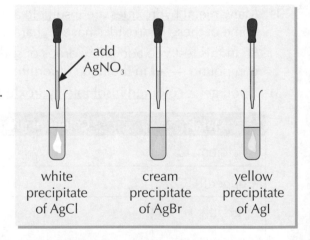

add $AgNO_3$

white precipitate of AgCl

cream precipitate of AgBr

yellow precipitate of AgI

Sulfate ions

1) To test for a <u>sulfate</u> ion (SO_4^{2-}), <u>add dilute HCl</u>, followed by <u>barium chloride solution</u>, $BaCl_2$.

2) A <u>white</u> precipitate of <u>barium sulfate</u> means the original compound was a sulfate.

$$Ba^{2+}_{(aq)} + SO_4^{2-}_{(aq)} \longrightarrow BaSO_{4(s)}$$

It may need loads of tests to work out what a substance is...

This is the kind of stuff <u>exam questions</u> are made of, by the way, so be warned. They might give you the <u>results</u> from several chemical tests, and you have to say what the substance is.

Warm-Up and Exam Questions

Lots of tests to remember on the last two pages. Try these questions to test your memory.

Warm-Up Questions

1) What metal ions would produce a lilac flame when burnt?
2) What colour is the precipitate formed when sodium hydroxide is added to a solution of copper(II) ions?
3) How would you test for carbon dioxide?

Exam Questions

1   Kelly carried out flame tests on compounds of four different metal ions.
    Complete the table below showing her results.

Flame colour	Metal ion
green	
	Li^+
yellow	
	Ca^{2+}

(4 marks)

2   A bottle of a chemical solution is labelled 'iron(II) sulfate'.
    (a) Describe a chemical test to confirm that the solution contains iron(II) ions.

(2 marks)

    (b) Describe a chemical test to confirm that the solution contains sulfate ions.

(2 marks)

3   The table below shows the results of a series of chemical tests conducted on two unknown compounds, X and Y.

TEST	OBSERVATION	
	COMPOUND X	COMPOUND Y
sodium hydroxide solution	white precipitate	no precipitate
hydrochloric acid & barium chloride solution	no precipitate	no precipitate
flame test	red flame	lilac flame
nitric acid & silver nitrate solution	white precipitate	yellow precipitate

    (a) What is the chemical name of compound X?

(2 marks)

    (b) What is the chemical name of compound Y?

(2 marks)

Revision Summary for Chemistry 3b

Whenever anything at all happens, energy is either taken in or released. So it's amazingly important. If that doesn't inspire you to learn the stuff about it, the fact that you're likely to get exam questions on it should. There's also titration and bagloads of chemical tests in this section too. There's no easy way to remember it all — you just have to do some good old-fashioned memorising. Anyway, enough words of wisdom, try these questions:

1) Name a suitable indicator you could use in the titration of sulfuric acid and sodium hydroxide.

2) In a titration, 49 cm³ of hydrochloric acid was required to neutralise 25 cm³ of sodium hydroxide with a concentration of 0.2 moles per dm³. Calculate the concentration of the hydrochloric acid in: a) mol/dm³   b) g/dm³

3) Is energy released when bonds are formed or when bonds are broken?

4) An acid and an alkali were mixed in a polystyrene cup, as shown to the right. The acid and alkali were each at 20 °C before they were mixed. After they were mixed, the temperature of the solution reached 24 °C.
   a) State whether this reaction is exothermic or endothermic.
   b) Explain why the cotton wool is used.

20 cm³ of dilute sulfuric acid + 20 cm³ of dilute sodium hydroxide

cotton wool

5) Explain why the price of bananas might rise if we keep burning so much fuel.

6) The apparatus below is used to measure how much energy is released when pentane is burnt. It takes 4.2 joules of energy to heat 1 g of water by 1 °C.

   a)*Using the following data, and the equation Q = mc ΔT, calculate the amount of energy per gram of pentane.

Mass of empty copper can	64 g
Mass of copper can + water	116 g

Initial temperature of water	17 °C
Final temperature of water	47 °C

Mass of spirit burner + pentane before burning	97.72 g
Mass of spirit burner + pentane after burning	97.37 g

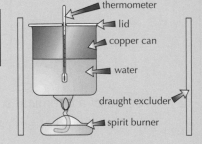

thermometer
lid
copper can
water
draught excluder
spirit burner

   b) A data book says that pentane has 49 kJ/g of energy. Why is the amount you calculated different?

7) a) Draw energy level diagrams for exothermic and endothermic reactions.
   b) Explain how bond breaking and forming relate to these diagrams.

8) What is the activation energy for a reaction? Mark it on your exothermic energy level diagram from Q7.

9) How does a catalyst affect overall energy change for a reaction?

10) Give an advantage of using hydrogen as a fuel in a car engine.

11) Give a disadvantage of using hydrogen as a fuel in a car engine.

12) What is a fuel cell?

13) Why is the car industry researching fuel cells?

14) Describe two ways of testing for metal ions.

15) How would you distinguish between solutions of:
    a) magnesium sulfate and aluminium sulfate,
    b) sodium bromide and sodium iodide,
    c) copper nitrate and copper sulfate?

* Answer on page 222.

Practice Exams

Once you've been through all the questions in this book, you should feel pretty confident about the exam.
As final preparation, here is a **practice exam** to really get you set for the real thing. The total time allowed for each
paper is 60 minutes. These papers are designed to give you the best possible preparation for your exams.

GCSE AQA Science

Unit Chemistry 1

Higher Tier

CGP Practice Exam Paper
GCSE Chemistry

In addition to this paper you should have:
• A ruler.
• A calculator.

Centre name				
Centre number				
Candidate number				

Time allowed:
• 60 minutes

Surname
Other names
Candidate signature

Instructions to candidates
• Write your name and other details in the spaces provided above.
• Answer **all** questions in the spaces provided.
• Do all rough work on the paper.

Information for candidates
• The marks available are given in brackets at the end of each question.
• There are 8 questions in this paper.
• There are 60 marks available for this paper.
• You are allowed to use a calculator.
• You should answer Questions 4 (c) and 7 (b) with continuous prose.
  You will be assessed on the quality of your English, the organisation
  of your ideas and your use of appropriate specialist vocabulary.

For examiner's use

Q	Attempt Nº			Q	Attempt Nº		
	1	2	3		1	2	3
1				5			
2				6			
3				7			
4				8			
Total							

Advice to candidates
• In calculations show clearly how you worked out your answers.

Answer **all** questions in the spaces provided

1   The diagram shows how a student extracted copper from copper ore by heating
     the ore with carbon in a crucible. The copper ore is mainly copper carbonate.

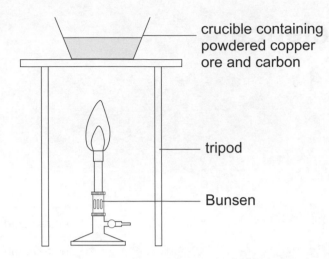

crucible containing
powdered copper
ore and carbon

tripod

Bunsen

1 (a)   Suggest **two** safety precautions the student should take when doing
          this experiment.

          ....

          ....
                                                                                              (2 marks)

1 (b)   What is an ore?

          ....

          ....
                                                                                              (1 mark)

1 (c)   Two reactions happen during the experiment.
Complete the two balanced chemical equations below.

Reaction A

copper carbonate → copper oxide + carbon dioxide

$CuCO_3$ → .... + CO_2

Reaction B

copper oxide + carbon → copper + carbon dioxide

.... + C → $2Cu$ + CO_2

(2 marks)

1 (d)   Copper ore can be obtained by mining from the ground.
Give **three** ways that mining copper ore can affect the environment.

1.   ....

2.   ....

3.   ....

(3 marks)

1 (e)   Copper is a transition metal.
Describe **two** physical properties that are characteristic of transition metals.

....

....

(2 marks)

$\boxed{\dfrac{}{10}}$

Turn over for the next question

2   A student did an experiment to study how effectively gases trap heat.
He assembled the equipment as shown in the diagram.

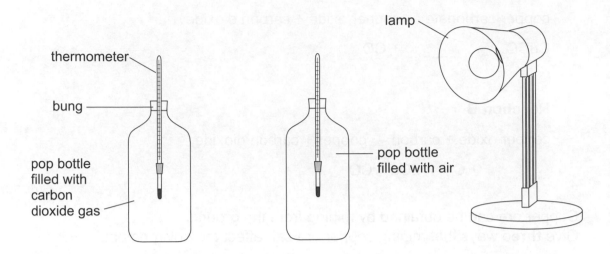

The student recorded the temperature of each bottle every 5 minutes for
25 minutes. The student plotted a graph to show how the temperature
of the bottles increased during the experiment.

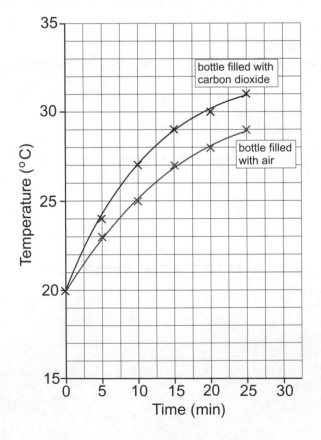

2 (a) How long did it take the bottle of air to reach 27 °C?

.... minutes

(1 mark)

2 (b) Based on the graph, suggest a valid conclusion that could be drawn from this experiment.

....

....

(1 mark)

2 (c) Suggest **one** thing the student should have done to ensure that the test was fair.

....

....

(1 mark)

2 (d) The student repeated the experiment using a bottle filled with methane. The student found that the bottle filled with methane had a final temperature of 36 °C.

Which gas (air, carbon dioxide or methane) is the most effective at trapping heat?

....

Explain your answer.

....

....

....

(2 marks)

5

Turn over for the next question

Turn over ▶

3 Carbon can be added to iron to produce steel.

Look at the graph below.

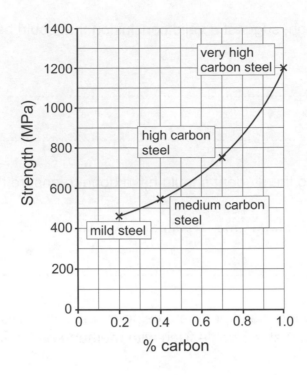

3 (a) (i) Which type of steel shown on the graph would be the easiest to shape?

....

(1 mark)

3 (a) (ii) Suggest an appropriate use for very high carbon steel.

....

....

(1 mark)

3 (b) Describe how the composition of steel differs from blast furnace iron.

....

....

....

....

(2 marks)

3 (c) Stainless steel is an alloy of iron which can be used to make cutlery and kitchen utensils. Suggest why iron is not used for this purpose.

....

....

(1 mark)

5

Turn over for the next question

Turn over▶

4 Alkanes are hydrocarbon compounds found in crude oil. The table shows how the boiling points of some alkanes change as the molecules get bigger.

Alkane	Molecular formula	Boiling point (°C)
Propane	C_3H_8	− 42
Butane	C_4H_{10}	0.5
Pentane	C_5H_{12}	
Hexane	C_6H_{14}	69
Heptane	C_7H_{16}	98

4 (a) (i) Plot a graph of the number of carbon atoms in an alkane molecule against boiling point, for the data in the table. Draw a smooth curve.

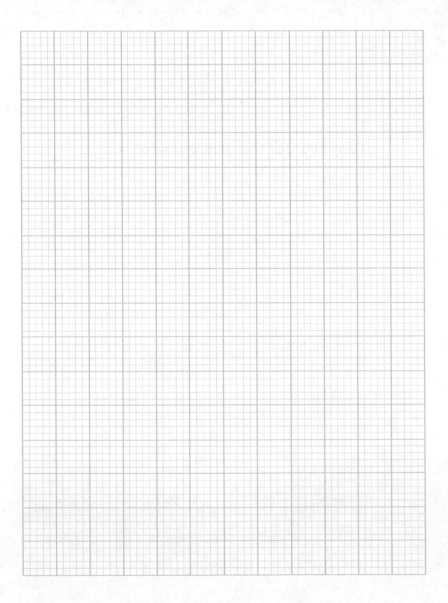

(2 marks)

4 (a) (ii) Use your graph to estimate the boiling point of pentane. .... °C

(1 mark)

4 (b) Describe what the graph shows about the size of alkane molecules and their boiling points.

....

(1 mark)

4 (c) *In this question you will be assessed on the quality of your English, the organisation of your ideas and your use of appropriate specialist vocabulary.*

Biofuels such as biodiesel contain hydrocarbon compounds. They can be used to power cars. Outline the advantages and disadvantages of using biofuels.

....

....

....

....

....

....

....

....

....

....

....

....

(6 marks)

10

Turn over for the next question

Turn over ▶

5 The map below shows the distribution of some recent volcanoes and earthquakes. It also shows plate boundaries.

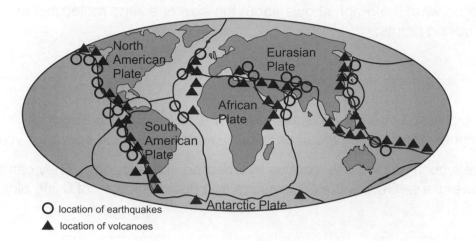

5 (a) Describe the distribution of volcanoes in relation to the plate boundaries.

....

....

(1 mark)

5 (b) Scientists cannot accurately predict when earthquakes will occur. Explain why.

....

....

(1 mark)

5 (c) Tectonic plates typically move by about 2-5 centimetres per year.
Explain what causes tectonic plates to move.

....

....

....

(2 marks)

5 (d) The South American Plate and the African Plate are moving away from each other at a rate of 5 cm per year. One heavy marker is placed on each plate at the plate boundary. If the sea level remains the same, how far apart will the two markers be in 8000 years' time? Give your answer in kilometres (km).

....

....

(2 marks)

6   The diagram shows the displayed formula of a long-chain molecule.

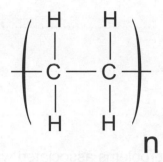

6 (a)   What name is given to long-chain molecules like this?

....
(1 mark)

6 (b)   Draw the displayed formula of the monomer used to make this compound.

(1 mark)

Question 6 continues on the next page

Turn over▶

184

6 (c)   One use of long-chain molecules like these is in memory foam mattresses.
Give **three** other uses of these long-chain molecules.

1. ....

2. ....

3. ....

(3 marks)

6 (d)   Describe **two** environmental problems associated with these
long-chain molecules.

1. ....

....

2. ....

....

(2 marks)

7

7   Natural fats and oils are used as raw materials in the food and chemical industries.

7 (a)   Explain, in terms of carbon bonds, the difference between saturated and unsaturated fats.

....

....

(1 mark)

7 (b)   Olive oil is a type of plant oil whereas butter is made from animal fats.

Butter
Fat/oil per 100 g:
Saturates 51 g
Unsaturates 24 g

Olive Oil
Fat/oil per 100 g:
Saturates 14 g
Unsaturates 84 g

In this question you will be assessed on the quality of your English, the organisation of your ideas and your use of appropriate specialist vocabulary.

Use the information above and your own knowledge to evaluate the benefits and drawbacks of frying food in butter and in olive oil.

....

....

....

....

....

....

....

....

....

(6 marks)

Question 7 continues on the next page

Turn over ▶

7 (c)   A chemical process is used to turn unsaturated fats into saturated fats.
Give the name of this process and briefly describe it.

Name of process ....

Description ....

....

....

....

....

(4 marks)

11

8 The pie charts below show the composition of Earth's atmosphere how we think it was 4 billion years ago, and how it is at the present time.

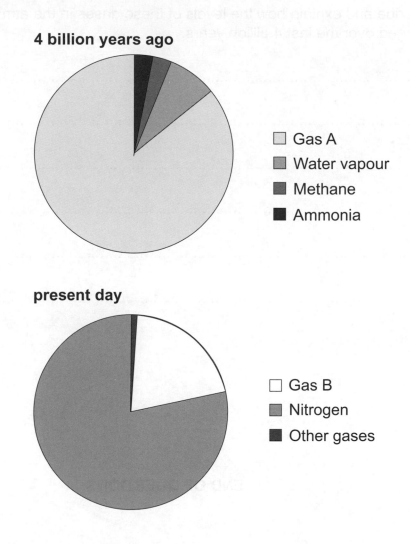

4 billion years ago

☐ Gas A
■ Water vapour
■ Methane
■ Ammonia

present day

☐ Gas B
■ Nitrogen
■ Other gases

8 (a) Name Gas A.

....

(1 mark)

8 (b) Name Gas B.

....

(1 mark)

Question 8 continues on the next page

Turn over▶

188

8 (c) In the present day, Gas A makes up only a very tiny percentage of the atmosphere. 4 billion years ago, Gas B was not present in the atmosphere at all.

Describe and explain how the levels of these gases in the atmosphere have changed over the last 4 billion years.

....

....

....

....

....

....

(4 marks)

6

END OF QUESTIONS

CGP Practice Exam Paper
GCSE Chemistry

GCSE AQA Science

Unit Chemistry 2

Higher Tier

In addition to this paper you should have:
- A ruler.
- A calculator.

Centre name					
Centre number					
Candidate number					

Time allowed:
- 60 minutes

Surname	
Other names	
Candidate signature	

Instructions to candidates
- Write your name and other details in the spaces provided above.
- Answer **all** questions in the spaces provided.
- Do all rough work on the paper.

Information for candidates
- The marks available are given in brackets at the end of each question.
- There are 9 questions in this paper.
- There are 60 marks available for this paper.
- You are allowed to use a calculator.
- You should answer Question 4 (a) and 6 with continuous prose.
  You will be assessed on the quality of your English, the organisation
  of your ideas and your use of appropriate specialist vocabulary.

Advice to candidates
- In calculations show clearly how you worked out your answers.

For examiner's use							
Q	Attempt Nº			Q	Attempt Nº		
	1	2	3		1	2	3
1				6			
2				7			
3				8			
4				9			
5							
	Total						

Answer **all** questions in the spaces provided

1   Read the information in the box and answer the questions that follow.

Ammonium nitrate (NH_4NO_3) is an ionic substance.

Relative atomic masses: H = 1, N = 14, O = 16.

1 (a)   Calculate the relative formula mass of ammonium nitrate.

Show clearly how you work out your answer.

....

....

Relative formula mass = ...

(2 marks)

1 (b)   Calculate the percentage of nitrogen in ammonium nitrate.

Show clearly how you work out your answer.

....

....

Percentage of nitrogen = ...%

(1 mark)

1 (c)   Describe the physical properties you would expect ammonium nitrate to have.

....

....

....

....

(4 marks)

7

2 Silver is a metallic element which occurs naturally as two isotopes, Ag-107 and Ag-109.

2 (a) The relative atomic mass of silver is 108.

Explain what is meant by the term 'relative atomic mass'.

....

....

....

(2 marks)

2 (b) All metallic elements have a similar structure that is determined by the way in which the atoms bond.

Draw a labelled diagram to represent the bonding within silver.

(1 mark)

Question 2 continues on the next page

Turn over ▶

192

2 (c) How does the structure of silver explain the following properties?

2 (c)(i) High thermal conductivity.

....

....
(1 mark)

2 (c)(ii) Ability to be bent and shaped.

....

....
(1 mark)

2 (d) Silver nanoparticles have been found to have an antibacterial action.

What are nanoparticles?

....
(1 mark)

6

3 (a)   Fullerenes are covalent substances that consist purely of carbon atoms.

Give **two** uses of fullerenes.

....

....

(2 marks)

3 (b)(i)   Graphite is also a covalent substance that contains only carbon atoms.

Explain why graphite can conduct electricity.

....

....

(1 mark)

3 (b)(ii)   Graphite is soft and slippery. Explain why.

....

....

(1 mark)

3 (c)   Give **one** other covalent substance that only contains carbon atoms
and explain how its structure is different from graphite and from fullerenes.

....

....

....

....

....

(3 marks)

7

Turn over for the next question

194

4 (a) *In this question you will be assessed on the quality of your English, the organisation of your ideas and your use of appropriate specialist vocabulary.*

Thermosetting and thermosoftening polymers have different properties.

Describe and explain the properties of thermosetting and thermosoftening polymers.

....

....

....

....

....

....

....

....

....

....

....

....

(6 marks)

4 (b) The table below shows the properties of three different polymers, **A-C**.

Polymer	Properties of polymer
A	low melting point and flexible
B	high melting point and rigid
C	high melting point and flexible

4 (b)(i) Give the polymer that is most suitable for use for insulation around an electric lead.

....
(1 mark)

4 (b)(ii) Give the polymer that is most suitable to make a work surface.

....
(1 mark)

4 (b)(iii) Polymers **A-C** are made using a polymerisation reaction.

Give **two** factors that can be changed during the reaction to give polymers with different properties.

1. ....

2. ....
(2 marks)

10

Turn over for the next question

5   Self-heating cans use **exothermic** chemical reactions to heat up their contents.
When a seal is broken two chemicals mix and react, heating up the can.
Calcium oxide and water can be used to heat up drinks in this way.

5 (a)   What is an exothermic reaction?

....

(1 mark)

5 (b)   A student wanted to test the reaction of different substances with water
to see if they could be used to cool drinks down.

Outline an experiment the student could carry out to test different substances.

....

....

....

....

(2 marks)

5 (c)   Describe what an endothermic reaction is.

....

....

(1 mark)

$\overline{4}$

6   *In this question you will be assessed on the quality of your English, the organisation of your ideas and your use of appropriate specialist vocabulary.*

A chemicals business has just appointed a new director. The business has been making product X for 10 years without the use of a catalyst. The new director has decided to introduce a catalyst into the process.

Describe the advantages and disadvantages of this decision.

....

....

....

....

....

....

....

....

....

....

....

(6 marks)

$\overline{6}$

Turn over for the next question

Turn over ▶

7   The graph shows the volume of gas produced over time when lumps of zinc are reacted with dilute sulfuric acid.

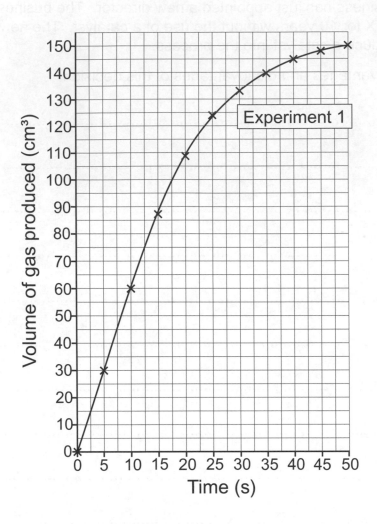

7 (a)   Calculate the rate of reaction (in cm^3/s) for the reaction during the first ten seconds.

....

(1 mark)

In a second experiment, some copper sulfate catalyst was added to the acid.
The same amounts of zinc and dilute sulfuric acid were used as before.
The results are shown in the table.

Time (secs)	Volume of gas formed (cm³) Experiment 2
0	0
5	50
10	100
15	130
20	143
25	148
30	150
35	150
40	150
45	150
50	150

7 (b)   Plot the results of the second experiment on the graph.

Draw a curve of best fit through the points. Label the line 'Experiment 2'.

(2 marks)

7 (c)   How long does it take to form half of the total amount of gas collected
in the second experiment?

....

(1 mark)

7 (d)   What do the curves show about how the rate of reaction changes as
the reaction proceeds?

....

(1 mark)

7 (e)   How does the catalyst affect the reaction rate? ....

How can you tell this from the graph?

....

....

(1 mark)

6

Turn over for the next question

Turn over ▶

8 Tiffany is doing an experiment to investigate the electrolysis of sodium chloride solution.

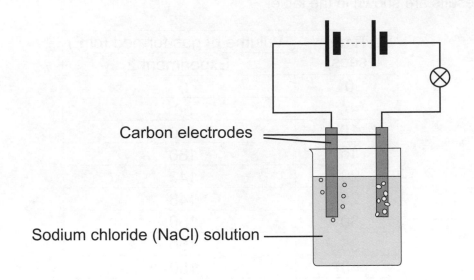

Carbon electrodes

Sodium chloride (NaCl) solution

8 (a) The reaction at each electrode can be described by a half equation.

Complete the half equations for the reaction occurring at each electrode.

positive electrode .... $Cl^- \rightarrow Cl_2 +$ ....

negative electrode .... $H^+ +$ .... $\rightarrow H_2$

(2 marks)

8 (b) At the end of her experiment, Tiffany is left with three products.

8 (b)(i) Name the product that is left in the solution.

....

(1 mark)

8 (b)(ii) Give **one** industrial use for this product.

....

(1 mark)

8 (b)(iii) Give **two** industrial uses for the chlorine produced.

....

(2 marks)

8 (c) Electrolysis can also be used in a process called electroplating.

What is electroplating?

....

(1 mark)

7

9   Soluble salts can be made by reacting an acid with an insoluble base or an alkali.

9 (a) (i) An excess of zinc oxide is added to a beaker of dilute hydrochloric acid.
The mixture is stirred and the acid is neutralised.

dilute hydrochloric acid

excess of zinc oxide

How could you tell when all the acid has been neutralised?

....
(1 mark)

9 (a) (ii) Give the products of this reaction.

....
(2 marks)

9 (b)   Describe how you could obtain pure, dry crystals of potassium chloride
from the alkali potassium hydroxide and dilute hydrochloric acid.

....

....

....

....
(4 marks)

7

END OF QUESTIONS

GCSE AQA Science
Unit Chemistry 3
Higher Tier

In addition to this paper you should have:
• A ruler.
• A calculator.

Centre name				
Centre number				
Candidate number				

Time allowed:
• 60 minutes

Surname
Other names
Candidate signature

Instructions to candidates
• Write your name and other details in the spaces provided above.
• Answer **all** questions in the spaces provided.
• Do all rough work on the paper.

Information for candidates
• The marks available are given in brackets at the end of each question.
• There are 8 questions in this paper.
• There are 60 marks available for this paper.
• You are allowed to use a calculator.
• You should answer Question 7 (c) with continuous prose.
   You will be assessed on the quality of your English, the organisation
   of your ideas and your use of appropriate specialist vocabulary.

Advice to candidates
• In calculations show clearly how you worked out your answers.

For examiner's use

Q	Attempt Nº			Q	Attempt Nº		
	1	2	3		1	2	3
1				5			
2				6			
3				7			
4				8			
			Total				

Answer **all** questions in the spaces provided

1   The Haber process is used to make ammonia from nitrogen and hydrogen. The chemical equation for the reaction that takes place in the Haber process is shown below.

$$N_{2(g)} + 3H_{2(g)} \rightleftharpoons 2NH_{3(g)}$$

1 (a)   The Haber process reaction reaches equilibrium. What does this mean?

....

....

(1 mark)

1 (b)   Give the temperature at which the Haber process is carried out.

....

(1 mark)

1 (c)   The reaction between nitrogen and hydrogen is exothermic.

Explain what will happen to the yield of ammonia if the temperature is increased.

....

....

....

(2 marks)

Question 1 continues on the next page

Turn over ▶

1 (d)   Give the pressure at which the Haber process is carried out.

....

(1 mark)

1 (e)   Explain what will happen to the yield of ammonia if the pressure
is decreased.

....

....

....

(2 marks)

1 (f)   What catalyst is used in the Haber process?

....

(1 mark)

$\overline{8}$

2 A student investigates the reactions of the Group 1 metals, lithium, sodium and potassium, with water. His observations are recorded in the table below.

Metal	Observations
lithium	Fizzes, moves across surface
sodium	Fizzes strongly, moves quickly across surface
potassium	Fizzes violently, moves very quickly across surface, flame seen

He decides that the order of reactivity of the three metals is:

- potassium (most reactive)
- sodium
- lithium (least reactive)

2 (a) Give **two** pieces of evidence from the table that support the student's conclusion.

1. ....

....

2. ....

....

(2 marks)

Question 2 continues on the next page

Turn over▶

2 (b) Explain the pattern of reactivity that the student has noticed in terms of the outer electrons of the atoms.

....

....

....

....

(2 marks)

2 (c) The reactions produce a metal hydroxide and one other product.
Name this product.

....

(1 mark)

2 (d) Complete and balance the chemical equation for the reaction between lithium and water.

.... Li + ... H_2O → .... + ...

(2 marks)

2 (e) For each of the physical properties below, describe briefly how sodium compares to most other metals:

2 (e) (i) hardness

....

(1 mark)

2 (e) (ii) melting point

....

(1 mark)

9

3   In an experiment to compare the **hardness** of three different water sources, soap solution was added to samples using a burette. 1 cm^3 of soap solution was added at a time, until it formed a good lather on shaking. Fresh samples of the water were boiled and the experiment was then repeated.

The results for 5 cm^3 samples of water from the three different sources are shown below.

Source	Volume of soap needed to form a good lather (cm^3) with unboiled sample	Volume of soap needed to form a good lather (cm^3) with boiled sample
A	8	5
B	8	1
C	1	1

3 (a)   What is initially formed when soap solution is added to hard water?

....
(1 mark)

3 (b)   Look at the results in the table above. Which water source is soft water?

....
(1 mark)

3 (c)   Which sample contains permanent hardness? ....

Explain why you chose this sample.

....

....

....
(3 marks)

Question 3 continues on the next page

Turn over ▶

3 (d)   Describe and explain **two** ways in which permanent hardness can be removed
from water.

1. ....

....

2. ....

....

(4 marks)

3 (e)   Give **two** disadvantages of hard water.

....

....

....

....

(2 marks)

11

4 Analytical tests can be used to identify different substances for forensic, environmental and health reasons.

4 (a) Suggest tests that could be used to distinguish between the following pairs of compounds in solution. You should describe the tests and results expected for each solution.

Solution A	Solution B	Description of test	Observations	
			Solution A	Solution B
Iron(II) chloride	Iron(III) chloride			
Sodium chloride	Sodium iodide			

(4 marks)

4 (b) When an unknown compound is placed in a Bunsen flame, it gives a yellow colour. If dilute acid is added to the compound, a gas is produced. When this gas is bubbled through limewater, the limewater goes cloudy.

Identify the compound by its chemical name.

....

(2 marks)

6

Turn over for the next question

Turn over▶

5   Hydrogen can be burned in oxygen and used as a fuel.

5 (a)   Use the bond energies provided and the diagram of the bonds involved during combustion to calculate the energy change for the reaction.

Bond energy values kJ/mol:

O=O   +498

H–H   +436

O–H   +464

$$ \begin{matrix} H-H \\ H-H \end{matrix} \quad + \quad O=O \quad \rightarrow \quad \begin{matrix} H-O-H \\ H-O-H \end{matrix} $$

....

....

....

Energy change = ... kJ/mol

(4 marks)

5 (b)   Is the reaction above exothermic or endothermic?
Explain your answer in terms of bond energies.

....

....

(2 marks)

6

6   Titration with 0.05 mol/dm³ sulfuric acid was used to determine the concentration of calcium hydroxide solution. In the titration, 8.8 cm³ of sulfuric acid was needed to neutralise 10 cm³ of the calcium hydroxide solution.

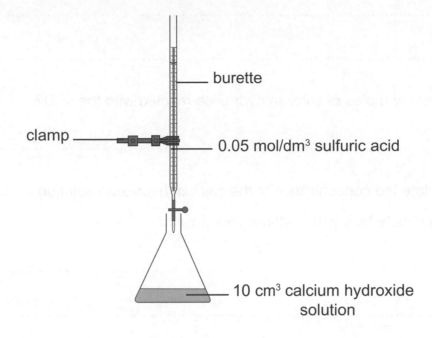

burette

clamp

0.05 mol/dm³ sulfuric acid

10 cm³ calcium hydroxide solution

6 (a)   Name a suitable indicator for the titration.

....

(1 mark)

6 (b)   Complete and balance the equation for this reaction below.

$H_2SO_4(aq)$ + $Ca(OH)_2(aq)$ → ....(aq) + ...$H_2O(l)$

(1 mark)

Question 6 continues on the next page

Turn over▶

6 (c) (i) How many moles of sulfuric acid reacted with the calcium hydroxide in the titration?

....

....

(1 mark)

6 (c) (ii) How many moles of calcium hydroxide reacted with the acid?

....

(1 mark)

6 (c) (iii) Calculate the concentration of the calcium hydroxide solution in mol/dm^3.

Show clearly how you work out your answer.

....

....

Concentration = ... mol/dm^3

(1 mark)

6 (c) (iv) Calculate the concentration of the calcium hydroxide solution in g/dm^3.
The M_r for calcium hydroxide is 74.

Show clearly how you work out your answer.

....

....

Concentration = ... g/dm^3

(1 mark)

6

7   The car industry is developing fuel cells.

7 (a)   What is a hydrogen fuel cell?

....

....

(1 mark)

7 (b)   Write down a word equation for the reaction that takes place in a
hydrogen fuel cell.

....

(1 mark)

7 (c)   *In this question you will be assessed on the quality of your English,
the organisation of your ideas and your use of appropriate specialist vocabulary.*

Evaluate the use of hydrogen fuel cells to power cars compared to other fuels.

....

....

....

....

....

....

....

....

....

....

....

....

(6 marks)

8

Turn over for the next question

Turn over▶

214

8   Ethanoic acid (CH_3COOH) is the acid found in vinegar.

8 (a)   In the box below, draw the structure of ethanoic acid.

(1 mark)

8 (b)   Describe how ethanoic acid can be made from ethanol.

....

....

....

(2 marks)

8 (c)   Ethanoic acid can be used to produce esters.
Write a word equation for the formation of ethyl ethanoate from ethanoic acid.

....

(1 mark)

8 (d)   Give the functional group of ethyl ethanoate.

....

(1 mark)

8 (e)   Esters are pleasant smelling compounds.
Give **one** use of esters that makes use of this property.

....

(1 mark)

END OF QUESTIONS

Pages 28-29
Warm-Up Questions

1) An element is a substance that consists of only one type of atom. There are about 100 elements.

2) a) 2
   b) 8

3) ions

4) covalent bonds

5) $C_6H_{12}O_6 + 6O_2 \rightarrow 6CO_2 + 6H_2O$

6) Cement is limestone that has been heated with clay. Mortar is cement mixed with sand (and water).

7) Any one of: e.g. makes huge holes / causes lots of dust / destroys habitats / causes noise / causes pollution / leads to unsightly tips.

Exam Questions

1 (a) 7 *(1 mark)*

  (b) N *(1 mark)*

  (c) non-metal *(1 mark)*

  (d) Any one of: e.g. phosphorous / arsenic / antimony / bismuth *(1 mark)*. It's in the same group as nitrogen so it will have the same number of electrons in its outer shell *(1 mark)* which gives it similar chemical properties *(1 mark)*.

2 (a) Nothing/it stays the same *(1 mark)*.

  (b) 17 – 4 = 13 g
      (1 mark for correct working, 1 mark for correct answer)

  (c) ionic bonding *(1 mark)*

3 (a) 11 *(1 mark)*

  (b) Any one of: lithium / potassium / rubidium / caesium / francium *(1 mark)*

  (c) 1 *(1 mark)*

4 (a) sulfuric acid + ammonia $\rightarrow$ ammonium sulfate *(1 mark)*

  (b) $H_2SO_4 + 2NH_3 \rightarrow (NH_4)_2SO_4$ *(1 mark for correct products and reactants, 1 mark for correctly balancing the equation)*

  (c) 15 *(1 mark)*
      There are eight atoms of hydrogen, one atom of sulfur, four atoms of oxygen, and two atoms of nitrogen.

5 (a) $CaCO_3 \rightarrow CaO + CO_2$ *(1 mark for the correct products and reactants, 1 mark for correctly balancing the equation)*

  (b) A Bunsen burner can't reach a high enough temperature to thermally decompose all carbonates of Group 1 metals *(1 mark)*.

  (c) Calcium carbonate in the limestone reacts with the acid in acid rain *(1 mark)* to form a calcium salt, carbon dioxide and water *(1 mark)*.

6 (a) Powdered limestone is heated in a kiln with powdered clay. *(1 mark for limestone and clay, 1 mark for heating in a kiln)*

  (b) Limestone is made into cement and then mixed with sand and aggregate (water and gravel). *(1 mark for making into cement, 1 mark for sand and aggregate)*

Pages 36-37
Warm-Up Questions

1) A rock which contains enough metal to make it worthwhile extracting the metal from it.

2) Any one of: e.g. zinc / iron / tin / copper.

3) It uses a lot of energy.

4) electrolysis

5) Phytomining involves growing plants in soil that contains copper. The plants can't use or get rid of the copper so it builds up in the leaves. The plants can be harvested, dried and burned. The copper is then collected from the ash.

Exam Questions

1 (a) It can be extracted by reduction with carbon *(1 mark)*, which is cheaper than electrolysis *(1 mark)*.

  (b) The Cu^{2+} ions move towards the negative electrode *(1 mark)*.

2 (a) E.g. the supply of copper-rich ores is limited / demand for copper is growing *(1 mark)*.

  (b) (i) bioleaching *(1 mark)*

      (ii) Bacteria produce a (leachate) solution that contains copper *(1 mark)*.

      (iii) E.g. this method has a much smaller impact on the environment *(1 mark)*.

      (iv) E.g. it's slow *(1 mark)*.

3 How to grade your answer:

   0 marks: No positive effects and negative effects are given.

   1-2 marks: Brief description of at least one positive effect and one negative effect is given.

   3-4 marks: At least two positive effects and two negative effects are given. The answer has a logical structure and spelling, grammar and punctuation are mostly correct.

   5-6 marks: The answer gives at least three positive effects and three negative effects. The answer has a logical structure and uses correct spelling, grammar and punctuation.

   Here are some points your answer may include:

   Positive Effects:

   Mining metal ores allows useful products to be made from the metal.

   The mines provide jobs for workers.

   Mining brings money into the local area.

   Negative Effects:

   Mining can be very noisy.

   Mines scar the landscape.

   Mining can lead to a loss of wildlife habitats.

   Abandoned mine shafts can be dangerous.

4 (a) Any one of: e.g. potassium / sodium / calcium / magnesium / aluminium (any metal above carbon in the reactivity series) *(1 mark)*.

  (b) (i) removal of oxygen *(1 mark)*

      (ii) zinc oxide + carbon $\rightarrow$ zinc + carbon dioxide *(1 mark)*

  (c) $2Fe_2O_3 + 3C \rightarrow 4Fe + 3CO_2$ *(1 mark for the correct products and reactants, 1 mark for correctly balancing the equation)*

  (d) (i) B *(1 mark)*

      (ii) Iron is more reactive than copper *(1 mark)*, so iron will displace copper *(1 mark)*.

  (e) E.g. extracting metals uses energy from fossil fuels *(1 mark)*. Recycling saves fossil fuels which are running out by saving energy *(1 mark)*. Using less fossil fuels means less pollution *(1 mark)*. Using less energy means recycling saves money *(1 mark)*. Recycling means less metals get sent to landfill sites *(1 mark)*. There's a finite amount of metal in the Earth so recycling will conserve these resources *(1 mark)*.

Page 42
Warm-Up Questions

1) Any three of: e.g. strong / hard to break / can be bent or hammered into different shapes / conduct heat / conduct electricity.

2) In the centre block.

3) It is brittle.

4) A mixture of metals, or a mixture of a metal and a non-metal.

5) alloys

Exam Questions

1 (a) E.g. it's corrosion-resistant *(1 mark)*, it has a low density *(1 mark)*.

  (b) It can be turned into an alloy by mixing it with other metals *(1 mark)*.

2 (a) E.g. it doesn't corrode / it has a low density *(1 mark each)*.

  (b) E.g. it conducts electricity / it conducts heat *(1 mark)*.

3 (a) E.g. high carbon steel is inflexible/very hard *(1 mark)* but low carbon steel is easily shaped *(1 mark)*.

  (b) High carbon steel — e.g. blades for cutting tools / bridges *(1 mark)* Low carbon steel — e.g. car bodies *(1 mark)*

(c) (i)   stainless steel *(1 mark)*

(ii) E.g. cutlery / containers for corrosive substances *(1 mark)*.

(d) Scientists now know a lot about the properties of metals so alloys can be designed for specific uses *(1 mark)*.

Pages 51-52
Warm-Up Questions

1) Two (or more) elements or compounds that aren't chemically bonded together.

2) carbon and hydrogen only

3) methane, ethane and propane

4) Any three of: e.g. transport / electricity generation / making chemicals including plastics / heating.

Exam Questions

1 (a) C_4H_{10} *(1 mark)*

(b)
```
    H   H   H   H
    |   |   |   |
H — C — C — C — C — H
    |   |   |   |
    H   H   H   H          (1 mark)
```

2 (a) (i)   There should be an M in the bottom box *(1 mark)*.

(ii) There should be a B in the top box *(1 mark)*.

Fractions with longer molecules have a higher boiling point, so condense at the higher temperatures at the bottom of the column. Fractions with shorter molecules have a lower boiling point, so don't condense until they reach the top of the column.

(b) The crude oil is heated and piped in at the bottom *(1 mark)*. The vaporised oil rises up the column *(1 mark)* and the fractions are tapped off at the different levels where they condense *(1 mark)*.

3 (a) global warming *(1 mark)*

(b) (i)   Sulfur dioxide produced from burning fossil fuels mixes with clouds *(1 mark)* and forms dilute sulfuric acid *(1 mark)*. This then falls as acid rain *(1 mark)*.

(ii) Any one of: e.g. makes lakes acidic and many plants and animals die as a result / damages limestone buildings and stone statues *(1 mark)*.

(c) (i)   Global dimming is the reduction in the amount of sunlight reaching the Earth's surface *(1 mark)*.

(ii) Global dimming is caused by particles of soot and ash produced when fossil fuels are burnt that reflect light back into space *(1 mark)*.

(d) Any two of: e.g. engines need to be converted to work with ethanol. / Ethanol is not widely available. / It may increase food prices if farmers switch to growing crops to make ethanol from growing crops to make food *(1 mark each, up to 2 marks)*.

4 (a) vegetable oils *(1 mark)*

(b) (i)   Global warming is caused by an increase in carbon dioxide *(1 mark)*. The carbon dioxide released when biodiesel is burnt was taken in when the plants were grown to make it *(1 mark)*. So there's no increase in carbon dioxide in the atmosphere *(1 mark)*.

(ii) Any two of: e.g. produces less sulfur dioxide than diesel or petrol / doesn't release as many particulates as diesel or petrol / it's made from a renewable resource / engines don't need to be converted *(1 mark each, up to 2 marks)*.

(c) Any two of: e.g. it's expensive to make / we're unable to make enough biodiesel to completely replace regular diesel / it could increase food prices if farmers switch from growing food crops to growing crops to make biodiesel *(1 mark each, up to 2 marks)*.

5 (a) It's made from the electrolysis of water *(1 mark)*.

(b) It's a clean fuel — it combines with oxygen to form just water *(1 mark)*.

(c) It's explosive *(1 mark)*.

(d) Any one of: e.g. you would need a special expensive engine / hydrogen isn't widely available / you still need energy from another source to make hydrogen *(1 mark)*.

Revision Summary for Chemistry 1a
(page 53)

3) Calcium

7) a)

Could be hydrogen/oxygen/nitrogen (or any other diatomic gaseous element).

b)

Could be carbon dioxide (water molecules are bent).

8) a) $CaCO_3 + 2HCl \rightarrow CaCl_2 + H_2O + CO_2$

b) $Ca + 2H_2O \rightarrow Ca(OH)_2 + H_2$

28) Propane — the fuel needs to be a gas at –10 °C to work in a camping stove.

Page 59
Warm-Up Questions

1) Long-chain hydrocarbons are cracked to make more useful products.

2) High temperature and a catalyst.

3) They contain carbon-carbon double bonds — the double bonds can open up, allowing the carbon atoms to bond with other atoms.

4) Ethene is reacted with steam in the presence of a catalyst.

5) Many ethene molecules are joined together.

Exam Questions

1 (a)
```
    ⎛   H       H   ⎞            ⎛ H   H ⎞
  n ⎜    C = C      ⎟   ──────→  ⎜  C — C  ⎟
    ⎝   H      CH₃  ⎠            ⎝ H   CH₃⎠ n    (1 mark)
```

(b)
```
   H        H
    \      /
     C  =  C
    /      \
   H        ⬡       (1 mark)
```

2 (a) ethanol *(1 mark)*

(b) (i) By fermentation *(1 mark)* of sugar using yeast *(1 mark)*.

(ii) Any one of: e.g. the process needs a lower temperature / the process needs simpler equipment / the raw material (sugar) is a renewable resource *(1 mark)*.

Page 64
Warm-Up Questions

1) They provide a lot of energy.

2) A nickel catalyst, and a temperature of about 60 °C.

3) They reduce the amount of cholesterol in the blood.

4) An emulsion is a mixture of oil and water.

Exam Questions

1 (a) The plant material is crushed *(1 mark)*. The crushed plant material is pressed between metal plates to squash the oil out *(1 mark)*. The oil can be separated from the crushed plant material by a centrifuge or by using solvents *(1 mark)*. The oil is distilled to refine it *(1 mark)*.

(b) E.g. vegetable oils have higher boiling points than water so they can be used to cook foods at higher temperatures and at faster speeds *(1 mark)*. They give food a different flavour *(1 mark)*. They increase the amount of energy we get from food *(1 mark)*.

2 (a) hydrophilic —●〰〰— hydrophobic *(1 mark)*

(b) Hydrophobic means that part of the molecule is attracted to oil molecules *(1 mark)*. Hydrophilic means that part of the molecule is attracted to water molecules *(1 mark)*.

1Bc.l.arge...

(c) *(1 mark)*

(d) They prevent the mayonnaise emulsion separating into its component liquids / they keep the oil and water mixed well together. *(1 mark)*

Page 70
Warm-Up Questions

1) E.g. scientists thought that it was impossible that continents could plough through the sea bed. Wegener used inaccurate data in his calculations. Wegener wasn't a geologist.

2) volcano

   Earthquakes occur at plate boundaries but they aren't a geological feature.

3) volcanic activity

4) fractional distillation

Exam Questions

1 (a) The diagram should be labelled:
   A – crust *(1 mark)*
   B – mantle *(1 mark)*
   C – core *(1 mark)*

   (b) (i) tectonic plates *(1 mark)*

   (ii) Radioactive decay takes place in the mantle *(1 mark)*. This produces heat which causes the mantle to flow in convection currents *(1 mark)*. These currents cause the plates to drift *(1 mark)*.

2 (a) There have been large variations in temperature and CO_2 concentration over the last 250 000 years *(1 mark)*. There is a positive correlation between CO_2 concentration and temperature *(1 mark)*.

   The question's worth two marks, so you have to make two points.

   (b) The X should be drawn at 25 000 years ago *(1 mark)*.

Revision Summary for Chemistry 1b (page 71)

21)b) 2 cm
   c) 3.5 years

Pages 79-80
Warm-Up Questions

1) Mass number is the sum of the number of protons and the number of neutrons in an atom. Atomic number is the number of protons in an atom.

2) isotopes

3) A high boiling point.

4) When ionic compounds are dissolved the ions separate and are free to move in the solution. These free-moving charged particles allow the solution to carry electric current.

5) positive ions

6) negative ions

7) $Al(OH)_3$

Exam Questions

1 (a) An isotope is a different atomic form of the same element *(1 mark)*, which has the same number of protons *(1 mark)* but a different number of neutrons *(1 mark)*.

   (b)
   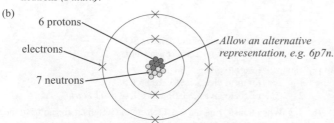

   Allow an alternative representation, e.g. 6p7n.

   (1 mark each for the correct number and placement of protons, neutrons and electrons)

(c) It has a different atomic number from carbon *(1 mark)*.

2 (a) 1 *(1 mark)*

   (b) The relative mass of electrons is very small *(1 mark)*.

3 (a) lithium oxide *(1 mark)*

   (b) (i) and (ii)

   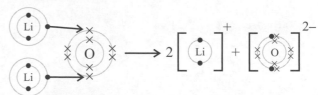

   (1 mark for arrows shown correctly, 1 mark for correct electron arrangement and charge on lithium ion, 1 mark for correct electron arrangement and charge on oxygen ion).

4 (a)

   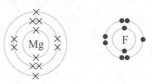

   (1 mark)   *(1 mark)*

   (b) Mg^{2+} *(1 mark)* and F^- *(1 mark)*

   (c) MgF_2 *(1 mark)*

   (d) There are electrostatic forces of attraction between the ions *(1 mark)*.

   (e) (i) There are strong electrostatic forces between the ions *(1 mark)* so a large amount of energy is needed to break these bonds/overcome these forces *(1 mark)*.

   (ii) When the magnesium fluoride is molten the ions can move about and carry charge (i.e. conduct a current) through the liquid *(1 mark)*.

5 (a)

	Potassium atom, K	Potassium ion, K^+	Chlorine atom, Cl	Chloride ion, Cl^-
Number of electrons	19	**18**	17	**18**
Electron arrangement	2, 8, 8, 1	**2, 8, 8**	2, 8, 7	**2, 8, 8**

   (1 mark for each correct column, maximum 3 marks)

   (b)

   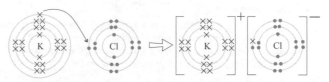

   (2 marks — 1 mark for correct electron arrangements, 1 mark for correct arrow and charges on ions)

Page 87
Example

A is simple molecular, B is giant metallic,
C is giant covalent, D is giant ionic

Pages 88-89
Warm-Up Questions

1) In a covalent bond, the atoms share electrons. In an ionic bond, one of the atoms donates electrons to the other atom.

2) E.g. diamond is very hard and graphite is fairly soft. Graphite conducts electricity and diamond doesn't.

3) E.g. silicon dioxide/silica

4) Because the intermolecular forces between the chlorine molecules are very weak.

Exam Questions

1

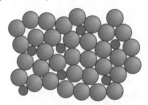

*(1 mark for bonds shown correctly,
1 mark for correct number of atoms shown)*

2 (a) (i) giant covalent *(1 mark)*

(ii) giant covalent *(1 mark)*

(iii) simple molecular *(1 mark)*

(b) It doesn't contain any ions to carry the charge *(1 mark)*.

(c) Each carbon atom has a delocalised electron that's able to carry the charge *(1 mark)*.

(d) All of the atoms in silicon dioxide and in graphite are held together by strong covalent bonds *(1 mark)*. In bromine, each molecule is held together with a strong covalent bond but the forces between these molecules are weak *(1 mark)*.

In order to melt, a substance has to overcome the forces holding its particles tightly together in the rigid structure of a solid. If the forces between the particles are weak, this is easy to do and doesn't take much energy at all. But if the forces are really strong, like in a giant covalent structure, you have to provide loads of heat to give the particles enough energy to break free.

3 (a) E.g:

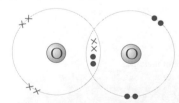

(1 mark for showing two different sizes of atoms, 1 mark for showing irregular arrangement)

(b) The regular arrangement of atoms in iron means that they can slide over each other meaning iron can be bent *(1 mark)*. Steel contains different sized atoms which distorts the layers of iron atoms *(1 mark)* making it more difficult for them to slide over each other *(1 mark)*.

4 (a) solid *(1 mark)*

(b) (i) giant covalent *(1 mark)*

(ii) giant ionic *(1 mark)*

(c) (i)

*(1 mark for correct number of electrons in each shell,
1 mark for showing covalent bond correctly)*

(ii) Oxygen has weak intermolecular forces between its molecules *(1 mark)*. It doesn't take much energy to separate the molecules *(1 mark)*.

(d) (i) It has delocalised electrons *(1 mark)* which are free to move through the whole structure and carry an electrical charge *(1 mark)*.

(ii) yes *(1 mark)*

Page 94
Warm-Up Questions

1) A shape memory alloy (about half nickel and half titanium) / a smart material

2) The higher the melting point the stronger the forces holding the polymer chains together.

3) crosslinks

4) E.g. the starting materials and the reaction conditions.

Exam Questions

1 (a) (i) nm *(1 mark)*

(ii) surface area *(1 mark)*, volume *(1 mark)*

(b) (i) The CNTs provide strength *(1 mark)* and lightness/low density *(1 mark)*.

(ii) fullerenes *(1 mark)*

(c) Any one of: e.g. in computer chips / in sensors / as catalysts / delivering drugs / in cosmetics / in lubricants *(1 mark)*.

2 (a) B *(1 mark)*

(b) C (accept A) *(1 mark)*

(c) A *(1 mark)*

Page 96
Top Tip

a) 30.0%

b) 88.9%

c) 48.0%

d) 65.3%

Page 97
Top Tip

CH_4

Page 99
Warm-Up Questions

1) The relative atomic mass.

2) The relative formula mass.

3) A mole is the relative formula mass of a substance, in grams.

4) One mole of O_2 weighs $16 \times 2 = 32$ g.

Exam Questions

1 (a) (i) Relative atomic mass *(1 mark)*.

(ii) Boron-11 has one more neutron in its nucleus than boron-10 *(1 mark)*.

(iii) Boron-11 must be the most abundant *(1 mark)*. The A_r value takes into account how much there is of each isotope, and in the case of boron it is closer to 11 than to 10 *(1 mark)*.

(b) (i) M_r of $BF_3 = 11 + (19 \times 3) = 68$ *(1 mark)*

(ii) M_r of $B(OH)_3 = 11 + (17 \times 3) = 62$ *(1 mark)*

2 (a) $100 - 60 = 40\%$ *(1 mark)*

(b) 40 g of sulfur combine with 60 g of oxygen.

S = 40	O = 60
$40 \div 32$	$60 \div 16$
= 1.25	= 3.75
$1.25 \div 1.25 = 1$	$3.75 \div 1.25 = 3$

Therefore, the formula of the oxide is SO_3
(2 marks — 1 mark for correct working)

3 (a) 100g .... reacts to give ... 56 g
1 g .... reacts to give ... $56 \div 100 = 0.56$ g
2 g .... reacts to give ... $0.56 \times 2 = 1.12$ g *(1 mark)*

(b) E.g. When transferring the $CaCO_3$ from the weighing apparatus to the test tube, or the CaO from the test tube to the weighing apparatus some of the solid may be left behind *(1 mark)*.

Page 104
Warm-Up Questions

1) Because a low product yield means that resources are wasted rather than being saved for future generations.

2) Instrumental methods are very sensitive, very fast and very accurate.

3) A gas chromatography machine can be attached to a mass spectrometer (GC-MS). The relative molecular mass of a substance can then be read off from the molecular ion peak on the graph the mass spectrometer draws.

Exam Questions

1 (a) From the equation, 4 moles of CuO → 4 moles of Cu
so 1 mole CuO → 1 mole Cu *(1 mark)*

$63.5 + 16 = 79.5$ g CuO → 63.5 g Cu *(1 mark)*

1 g CuO → $63.5 ÷ 79.5 = 0.8$ g (1 d.p.)

4 g CuO → $0.8 × 4 = 3.2$ g *(1 mark)*

(b) Percentage yield = $(2.8 ÷ 3.2) × 100$ *(1 mark)*

$= 87.5\%$ *(1 mark)*

(c) E.g. there may have been unexpected reactions (which used up the reactants so that there wasn't as much left to make the copper) *(1 mark)*. Some of the copper may have been left behind when it was scraped out into the beaker *(1 mark)*. Some of the copper may have been left on the filter paper *(1 mark)*.

2 (a) 4 *(1 mark)*

(b) 1 *(1 mark)*

(c) 3 *(1 mark)*

(d) 2 *(1 mark)*

Revision Summary for Chemistry 2a (page 105)

9) a) KCl   b) $CaCl_2$

10)

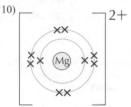

16) A: giant metallic, B: giant covalent, C: giant ionic

21) a) 40 b) 108 c) 44 d) 84 e) 106 f) 81 g) 56 h) 17

23) a) i) 12.0%   ii) 27.3%   iii) 75.0%

    b) i) 74.2%   ii) 70.0%   iii) 52.9%

24) $MgSO_4$

25) 80.3 g

Page 113
Warm-Up Questions

1) E.g. the corrosion of iron is a reaction that happens very slowly. Explosions are very fast reactions.

2) Increase the temperature (of the acid).
Use smaller pieces of/powdered magnesium.
Increase the acid concentration.
Use a catalyst.

3) Measure the volume of gas given off by collecting it in a gas syringe/monitor the mass of a reaction flask from which the gas escapes.

4) It would increase the time taken (i.e. reduce the rate of reaction).

5) By keeping the milk cool/storing it in a fridge.

Exam Questions

1 (a) Any two from: e.g. the concentration of sodium thiosulfate/hydrochloric acid / the person judging when the black cross is obscured / the black cross used (size, darkness etc.) *(1 mark each)*.

Judging when a cross is completely obscured is quite subjective — two people might not agree on exactly when it happens. You can try to limit this problem by using the same person each time, but you can't remove the problem completely. The person might have changed their mind slightly by the time they do the next experiment — or be looking at it from a different angle, be a bit more bored, etc.

(b)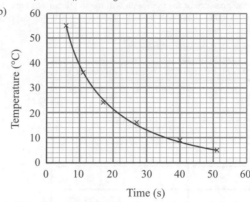

(1 mark for all points plotted correctly, 1 mark for best-fit curve)

(c) As the temperature increases the time decreases, meaning that the reaction is happening faster *(1 mark)*.

(d) Each of the reactions would happen more slowly *(1 mark)*, although they would still vary with temperature in the same way *(1 mark)*.

(e) E.g. by repeating the experiment and taking an average of the results *(1 mark)*.

2 (a) A gas/carbon dioxide is produced and leaves the flask *(1 mark)*.

(b) The same volume and concentration of acid was used each time, with excess marble *(1 mark)*.

(c) E.g. the marble chips were smaller/the temperature was higher *(1 mark)*.

(d) The concentration of the acid is greatest at this point, before it starts being converted into products *(1 mark)*.

Page 119
Warm-Up Questions

1) They must collide with enough energy.

2) There will be more frequent collisions so the rate of reaction will increase.

3) A catalyst is a substance which speeds up a reaction, without being used up in the reaction.

4) The temperature will decrease.

Exam Questions

1   How to grade your answer:

0 marks:	No ways of increasing the rate given.
1-2 marks:	One or two ways of increasing the rate are given. No discussion of collision theory is provided.
3-4 marks:	At least two ways of increasing the rate are given. There is some relevant discussion of collision theory. The answer has a logical structure and spelling, grammar and punctuation are mostly correct.
5-6 marks:	Detailed discussion of ways of increasing the rate and relevant collision theory is given. The answer has a logical structure and uses correct spelling, grammar and punctuation.

Here are some points your answer may include:

Collision theory says that the rate of reaction depends on how often and how hard the reacting particles collide with each other. If the particles collide hard enough (with enough energy) they will react.

Increasing the temperature makes particles move faster, so they collide more often and with greater energy. This will increase the rate of reaction.

If the surface area of the catalyst is increased then the particles around it will have more area to work on. This increases the frequency of successful collisions and will increase the rate of reaction.

Increasing the pressure of the hydrogen will mean the particles are more squashed up together. This will increase the frequency of the collisions and increase the rate of reaction.

2 (a) Neutralisation / Exothermic *(1 mark)*.

(b)

Time (s)	Temperature of the reaction mixture (°C)		
	1st run	2nd run	Average
0	22	22	22.0
1	25.6	24.4	25.0
2	28.3	28.1	28.2
3	29.0	28.6	28.8
4	28.8	28.8	28.8
5	28.3	28.7	28.5

(2 marks if all correct, 1 mark for 4 or 5 correct)

(c) (28.8 − 22.0 =) 6.8 °C *(1 mark)*

Don't get caught off guard — the maximum average change is just the highest average temperature minus the lowest average temperature.

(d) Exothermic *(1 mark)* because heat is given out to the surroundings/the temperature of the reaction mixture increases *(1 mark)*.

Page 125
Warm-Up Questions

1) Neutralisation.

2) A salt and hydrogen gas.

3) Copper nitrate and water.

4) Add the insoluble base to an acid until all the acid is neutralised and the excess base can be seen on the bottom of the flask. Then filter out the excess base and evaporate off the water to leave a pure, dry sample.

5) barium chloride + sodium sulfate → barium sulfate + sodium chloride

Exam Questions

1 (a)

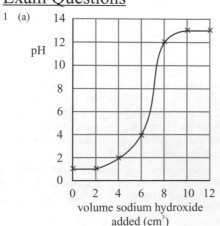

(1 mark for points plotted correctly, 1 mark for best fit curve)

(b) 7 cm³ (also accept answers between 6 and 8, depending on best fit curve at pH 7) *(1 mark)*.

(c) Because the starting pH is pH 1 *(1 mark)*.

This is the kind of question that can somehow trip you up, even if it seems obvious once you know the answer. So it's lucky you've come across it now rather than in the exam, isn't it? The pH before any alkali is added has to be the pH of the acid, and a pH of 1 means a very strong acid. See? Obvious.

(d) sodium sulfate *(1 mark)*

2 (a) It must be insoluble *(1 mark)*.

(b) silver nitrate + hydrochloric acid → silver chloride + nitric acid *(1 mark)*.

(c) First, filter the solution to remove the salt which has precipitated out *(1 mark)*. Then wash the insoluble salt *(1 mark)* and then leave it to dry on filter paper *(1 mark)*.

Page 131
Warm-Up Questions

1) It must be molten or dissolved in water.

2) Oxidation is loss of electrons and reduction is gain of electrons.

3) At the negative electrode.

4) Bromine.

5) The negative electrode.

Exam Questions

1 (a) (i) hydrogen *(1 mark)*

(ii) $2H^+ + 2e^- \rightarrow H_2$ *(1 mark)*

(b) (i) chlorine *(1 mark)*

(ii) $2Cl^- \rightarrow Cl_2 + 2e^- / 2Cl^- - 2e^- \rightarrow Cl_2$ *(1 mark)*

(iii) E.g. production of bleach / production of plastics *(1 mark)*.

(c) Sodium is more reactive than hydrogen, so sodium ions stay in solution *(1 mark)*. Hydroxide ions from water are also left behind *(1 mark)*. This means that sodium hydroxide is left in the solution *(1 mark)*.

2 (a) To lower the temperature that electrolysis can take place at *(1 mark)*. This makes it cheaper *(1 mark)*.

(b) $Al^{3+} + 3e^- \rightarrow Al$ *(1 mark)*

(c) Oxygen is made at the positive electrode *(1 mark)*. The oxygen will react with the carbon in the electrode to make carbon dioxide *(1 mark)*. This will gradually wear the electrode away *(1 mark)*.

Revision Summary for Chemistry 2b (page 132)

3 b)

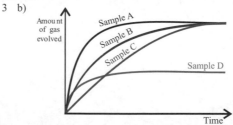

Pages 141-142
Warm-Up Questions

1) it increases

2) hydrogen

3) negative

4) Any three of: e.g. more than one ion (with different charges) / coloured compounds / make useful catalysts / good conductors of heat/electricity / dense / strong / shiny / hard / have high melting points.

Exam Questions

1 (a) Newlands listed elements in rows of seven in order of their relative atomic mass *(1 mark)*.

   (b) E.g. Newlands' groups contained elements that didn't have similar properties, e.g. carbon and titanium *(1 mark)*. He mixed up metals and non-metals, e.g. oxygen and iron *(1 mark)*. He didn't leave any gaps for elements that hadn't been discovered yet unlike Mendeleev *(1 mark)*. This meant that Newlands' Octaves broke down on the third row *(1 mark)*.

2 (a) Fluorine — gas *(1 mark)*

   Chlorine — gas *(1 mark)*

   Bromine — liquid *(1 mark)*

   Iodine — solid *(1 mark)*

   (b) Arrow should be pointing upwards. *(1 mark)*

   (c) (i) displacement *(1 mark)*

   Chlorine is displacing iodine.

   (ii) iodine/I/I_2 *(1 mark)*

3 (a) ionic bond *(1 mark)*.

   (b) (i) chlorine + potassium bromide → bromine + potassium chloride *(1 mark)*

   (ii) Chlorine has a stronger attraction for electrons *(1 mark)* because the outer shell is closer to the nucleus *(1 mark)* and is less shielded from the nucleus *(1 mark)*.

   Atoms react by gaining or losing electrons. Bromine is less able to attract an extra electron as its outer shell is further from the nucleus than chlorine's.

4 (a) They have a single outer electron which is easily lost so they are very reactive *(1 mark)*.

   (b) As you go down Group 1, the outer electron is further from the nucleus *(1 mark)*. It is more shielded from the nucleus so the outer electron is more easily lost and the alkali metal is more reactive *(1 mark)*.

   (c) hydrogen *(1 mark)* and a hydroxide *(1 mark)*

   (d) alkaline *(1 mark)*

5 (a) (i) Any two of: e.g. iron has a higher melting point / iron is stronger / iron is harder / iron is denser *(1 mark each)*.

   (ii) Any one of: e.g. iron is less reactive / iron forms more than one ion (Fe^{2+}, Fe^{3+}) *(1 mark)*.

   (b) (i) Transition metals can form ions with different charges *(1 mark)*.

   (ii) The different ions of transition metals usually form different coloured compounds *(1 mark)*.

Page 147
Warm-Up Questions

1) Water that doesn't form a lather with soap / Water that forms scale on the inside of pipes / Water that contains a lot of calcium and magnesium ions.

2) A furring on the inside of pipes, boilers and kettles that is mostly calcium carbonate.

3) temporary hardness and permanent hardness

4) By distillation (boiling water and condensing the steam).

Exam Questions

1 (a) Any two of: e.g. Forms scum with soap. / Requires more soap for cleaning. / Forms scale on heating systems/kettles, etc. / May block pipes. *(1 mark each)*.

   (b) Calcium ions are good for healthy teeth and bones.
   Studies have found that people who live in hard water areas are at less risk of developing heart disease than people who live in soft water areas. *(1 mark each)*

   (c) When heated, the calcium hydrogencarbonate decomposes to form calcium carbonate *(1 mark)* which is insoluble *(1 mark)*.

   (d) Adding sodium carbonate/washing soda *(1 mark)*.
   Using an ion exchange column *(1 mark)*.

2 (a) Filtration *(1 mark)* to remove solids *(1 mark)*.

   (b) How to grade your answer:

   0 marks: No advantages and disadvantages are given.

   1-2 marks: Brief description of one advantage and one disadvantage is given.

   3-4 marks: At least two advantages and two disadvantages are given. The answer has a logical structure and spelling, grammar and punctuation are mostly correct.

   5-6 marks: The answer gives at least three advantages and three disadvantages. The answer has a logical structure and uses correct spelling, grammar and punctuation.

   Here are some points your answer may include:

   Advantages:

   Water treated in this way has low levels of dissolved salts and no microbes.

   Adding chlorine to water reduces the risk of getting a disease from drinking it.

   This makes it suitable for humans to drink.

   Adding fluoride to water reduces tooth decay.

   Disadvantages:

   Chlorine can react with other natural substances in the water to produce toxic by-products which some people think could cause cancer.

   In high doses, fluoride can cause cancer and bone problems.

   There are concerns about whether it's right to 'mass medicate' people as they have no say about what chemicals are used to treat their water.

Pages 156-157
Warm-Up Questions

1) They are the same.

2) It increases the amount/concentration/yield of products / shifts the position of equilibrium to the right.

3) iron

4) They are recycled and used to produce more product.

5) $C_nH_{2n+1}OH$

6) Methanoic acid, ethanoic acid and propanoic acid.

Exam Questions

1 (a) Because the CO_2 gas that's produced would escape if the system wasn't closed. This would cause the equilibrium to shift *(1 mark)*.

   (b) Increasing the temperature *(1 mark)* and reducing the pressure *(1 mark)*.

2 (a) (i) E.g. crude oil/natural gas *(1 mark)*

   (ii) air *(1 mark)*

   (b) $3H_2(g) + N_2(g) \rightleftharpoons 2NH_3(g)$

   (1 mark for correct formula, 1 mark if correctly balanced, 1 mark for correct state symbols).

   (c) A high temperature reduces the equilibrium yield but increases the rate of the reaction *(1 mark)*. If the temperature was any lower, the product would be formed too slowly *(1 mark)*.

   Remember, it's better to get a yield of 10% after 20 seconds than a yield of 20% after 60 seconds.

3 (a) E.g. methanol, propanol *(1 mark each)*

   (b) -OH group *(1 mark)*

   (c) $C_2H_5OH + 3O_2 \rightarrow 2CO_2 + 3H_2O$

   (1 mark for correct reactants and products, 1 mark for correctly balancing equation)

   (d) hydrogen *(1 mark)*

   (e) Ethanol is flammable/it catches fire easily *(1 mark)*.

4 (a)

   (1 mark for showing the –COOH functional group correctly, 1 mark for showing two carbons in total and correct hydrogens.)

(b) (i) ethyl ethanoate *(1 mark)*

(ii) water *(1 mark)*

(iii) Any one of: e.g. perfumes/flavouring/ointments/solvents *(1 mark)*.

(c) Carboxylic acids don't ionise completely in water *(1 mark)* so not many H^+ ions are released *(1 mark)*.

Page 161
Warm-Up Questions

1) One mole of O_2 weighs $16 \times 2 = 32$ g.

2) E.g. put an accurately measured volume of alkali in a flask. Add a few drops of indicator. Fill a burette with acid and record the volume. Add the acid to the alkali a bit at a time whilst giving the flask a regular swirl. Stop the reaction as soon as the indicator changes colour and record the volume of acid used to neutralise the alkali.

3) $n = c \times V = 0.1 \times (25/1000) = 0.0025$ mol

4) $M_r = (2 \times 23) + 12 + (3 \times 16) = 106$

Concentration in grams per $dm^3 = 0.025 \times 106 = 2.65$ g/dm^3

Exam Questions

1 (a) $n = c \times V$ *(1 mark)*

$n = 1.00 \times (30.3/1000) = 0.0303$ mol *(1 mark)*

(b) H_2SO_4 and NaOH react in a 1:2 ratio, so number of moles of H_2SO_4 $= 0.0303 \div 2 = 0.01515 = 0.0152$ mol (3 s.f.) *(1 mark)*

(c) $c = n \div V$ *(1 mark)*

$V = 25/1000 = 0.025$

$c = 0.01515 \div 0.025 = 0.606$ mol/dm^3 *(1 mark)*

2 (a) Any one from: e.g. it was an anomalous result/an outlier / the first titration is often a 'rough' titration and its result is not accurate *(1 mark)*.

(b) Moles of NaOH $= c \times V$ $= 0.1 \times (9.0/1000) = 0.0009$ mol *(1 mark)*

HA and NaOH react in a 1:1 ratio, so moles of HA $= 0.0009$ moles *(1 mark)*

Concentration of HA $= n \div V$

$V = 25/1000 = 0.025$

Concentration of HA $= 0.0009 \div 0.025 = 0.036$ mol/dm^3 *(1 mark)*

Page 168
Warm-Up Questions

1) Energy is given out — it's exothermic.

2) ΔH

3) A catalyst lowers the activation energy (by providing a different pathway for the reaction).

4) A hydrogen fuel cell uses the reaction between hydrogen and oxygen which makes water. The reaction is exothermic so energy is given out.

Exam Questions

1 (a) C—H and O = O *(1 mark)*

(b) (i) $(4 \times 414) + (2 \times 494) = 2644$ kJ/mol *(1 mark)*

(ii) $(2 \times 800) + (4 \times 459) = 3436$ kJ/mol *(1 mark)*

(iii) $3436 - 2644 = 792$ kJ/mole *(1 mark)*

(c) The energy released when the new bonds are formed is greater than the energy needed to break the original bonds, so overall energy is given out *(1 mark)*.

2 (a) E.g. so that the temperature rise is proportional to the amount of heat produced *(1 mark)*.

(b) $100 \times 4.2 \times 21$ *(1 mark)* $= 8820$ J/8.82 kJ *(1 mark — units needed)*.

This gives you the energy transferred (in J) and normally you would then have to divide this by the mass of fuel burned (in g) to find the heat energy transferred per gram of fuel. But in this case only 1 g of fuel was burned anyway. So you're done.

(c)

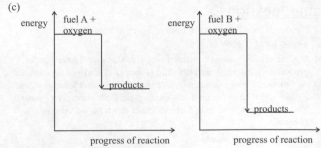

(1 mark for showing products lower than reactants, 1 mark if products are shown at a lower level for fuel B than for A.)

Page 171
Warm-Up Questions

1) K^+

2) Blue.

3) Bubble the gas through limewater — the limewater will turn milky if it's carbon dioxide.

Exam Questions

1

Flame colour	Metal ion
green	Ba^{2+}
crimson	Li^+
yellow	Na^+
red	Ca^{2+}

(1 mark each)

2 (a) Add sodium hydroxide solution *(1 mark)*. A green precipitate indicates iron(II) ions *(1 mark)*.

(b) Add dilute hydrochloric acid and then barium chloride solution *(1 mark)*. A white precipitate indicates sulfate ions *(1 mark)*.

3 (a) Calcium chloride *(1 mark for calcium, 1 mark for chloride)*.

(b) Potassium iodide *(1 mark for potassium, 1 mark for iodide)*.

Revision Summary for Chemistry 3b (page 172)

6 a) Mass of water heated $= 116$ g $- 64$ g $= 52$ g
Temperature rise of water $= 47$ °C $- 17$ °C $= 30$ °C
Mass of pentane burnt $= 97.72$ g $- 97.37$ g $= 0.35$ g

So 0.35 g of pentane provides enough energy to heat up 52 g of water by 30 °C.

It takes 4.2 joules of energy to heat up 1 g of water by 1 °C.

Therefore, the energy produced in this experiment is $4.2 \times 52 \times 30 = 6552$ joules.

So, 0.35 g of pentane produces 6552 joules of energy...
... meaning 1 g of pentane produces 6552/0.35
$= 18\,720$ J or 18.720 kJ

Exam Paper — Unit Chemistry 1

1 (a) Any two of: e.g. wear safety goggles / use a heatproof mat under the apparatus / wear a lab coat *(2 marks)*.

(b) An ore is a mineral/rock that contains enough of a metal to make it worth extracting *(1 mark)*.

(c) $CuCO_3 \rightarrow CuO + CO_2$,
$2CuO + C \rightarrow 2Cu + CO_2$
(1 mark for CuO, 1 mark for correctly balancing the equations)

(d) Any three of: e.g. it causes loss of habitats / it can scar the landscape / it creates noise / lorries used for transportation can cause pollution / waste may be dumped in tips / mining may leave behind ugly holes and dangerous mine shafts *(3 marks)*.

(e) Any two of: e.g. high melting/boiling point / good electrical conductor / good thermal conductor / high density / strong / hard / shiny *(2 marks)*.

15 minutes *(1 mark)*.

(b) The temperature of the carbon dioxide increased more (and more quickly) than the temperature of the air *(1 mark)*.

The line showing the temperature of the carbon dioxide reaches a higher point on the graph.

(c) E.g. he should have made sure the bottles were the same distance away from the lamp *(1 mark)*.

This would ensure that the bottles were receiving the same amount of heat from the lamp.

(d) Methane *(1 mark)*. The bottle containing methane has a higher final temperature than the other two bottles *(1 mark)*.

3 (a) (i) mild steel *(1 mark)*

It has the lowest strength out of the alloys shown on the graph.

(ii) E.g. for making cutting tools, such as drills *(1 mark)*.

This steel has the greatest strength, which is a property needed in tools.

(b) E.g. iron from the blast furnace is about 96% iron with 4% impurities *(1 mark)*. Steel is an alloy that is made up of iron and up to 1% carbon *(1 mark)*.

(c) E.g. iron corrodes very easily / iron is brittle *(1 mark)*.

4 (a) (i)

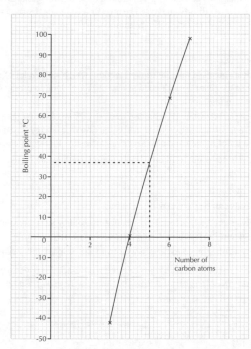

Be careful when you plot graphs and draw curves. You'll lose marks if your graph isn't accurate and other parts of the question may depend on it.*

(1 mark for correctly plotted points, 1 mark for a smooth curve that passes through all the points)

Be careful when you plot graphs and draw curves. You'll lose marks if your graph isn't accurate and other parts of the question may depend on it.

(ii) Pentane contains 5 carbon atoms. On the graph, this gives a boiling point within the range 34 - 38 °C *(1 mark)*.

(b) The larger the alkane molecule, the higher its boiling point / the smaller the alkane, the lower its boiling point *(1 mark)*.

(c) How to grade your answer:

0 marks: No advantages and disadvantages are given.

1-2 marks: Brief description of at least one advantage and one disadvantage.

3-4 marks: At least two advantages and two disadvantages are given. The answer has a logical structure and spelling, grammar and punctuation are mostly correct.

5-6 marks: Answer gives at least three advantages and three disadvantages. The answer has a logical structure and uses correct spelling, grammar and punctuation.

Here are some points your answer may include:

<u>Advantages:</u>

Biofuels are carbon neutral — the carbon dioxide made when they're burned was taken in by the plants used to make the biofuel.

Biodiesel releases much less sulfur dioxide and particulates than ordinary diesel or petrol.

Diesel engines don't have to be converted to use biodiesel.

<u>Disadvantages:</u>

Demand for biofuels could lead to farmers switching from growing crops to make food to growing crops to make biofuels. This may cause a shortage of food.

Biodiesel is expensive to make.

Engines have to be converted to run on biofuels such as ethanol.

5 (a) Most of the volcanoes are found on or near plate boundaries *(1 mark)*.

(b) E.g. earthquakes are sudden movements / there are very few clues to tell scientists when an earthquake is likely to happen *(1 mark)*.

(c) Heat from radioactive decay in the mantle causes the mantle to flow in convection currents *(1 mark)*. These convection currents cause the plates to drift *(1 mark)*.

(d) 8000 × 5 = 40 000 cm *(1 mark)*.
40 000 cm = 0.4 km *(1 mark)*.

6 (a) polymer *(1 mark)*

(b)

(1 mark)

(c) Any three of: e.g. plastic bags / waterproof coatings for fabrics / tooth fillings / hydrogel wound dressings / LYCRA® *(3 marks)*.

(d) Any two of: e.g. plastics are non-biodegradable so it is very hard to dispose of them / many plastics are buried in landfill sites, which waste valuable land / when burnt, plastics produce toxic gases / recycling plastics is difficult / plastics can pose a hazard to wildlife *(2 marks)*.

7 (a) Unsaturated fats contain some double carbon-carbon bonds and saturated fats contain only single carbon-carbon bonds *(1 mark)*.

(b) How to grade your answer:

0 marks: No benefits and drawbacks of using butter or olive oil given.

1-2 marks: One or two benefits and drawbacks are suggested but these are not fully evaluated.

3-4 marks: A number of benefits and drawbacks of using butter and olive oil are suggested but these are not fully evaluated. The answer has a logical structure and spelling, grammar and punctuation are mostly correct.

5-6 marks: A number of benefits and drawbacks of using butter and olive oil are given and these are fully evaluated. The answer has a logical structure and uses correct spelling, grammar and punctuation.

Here are some points your answer may include:

Butter and olive oil are used for frying food because they allow the food to be cooked at a higher temperature and at a faster speed. They also improve the flavour of the food.

Both butter and olive oil contain fats, which can make food more unhealthy. However, olive oil has more fat per 100 g than butter does. Butter has 75 g of fat per 100 g whilst olive oil has 98 g of fat per 100 g.

A major benefit of using olive oil is that it has a lower proportion of saturated fats than butter does. Eating more saturated fats increases the amount of cholesterol in the blood. This means that olive oil is more healthy than butter even though it has a higher level of fat overall.

There's no doubting it — this is a tricky 'un. The question has given you lots of useful information but just stating the facts isn't enough. For example, you can't just say that olive oil has less saturated fat than butter. To get the top marks you need to evaluate why this means it's beneficial for you (e.g. because it's more healthy).

(c) Hydrogenation *(1 mark)*. The unsaturated fats are reacted with hydrogen *(1 mark)* using a nickel catalyst at about 60 °C *(1 mark)*. The hydrogen opens out the double bonds to make a saturated fat *(1 mark)*.

8 (a) carbon dioxide *(1 mark)*

(b) oxygen *(1 mark)*

(c) In the early atmosphere there was a lot of carbon dioxide released from active volcanoes *(1 mark)*. As the Earth cooled, the oceans formed, dissolving a lot of carbon dioxide *(1 mark)*. Green plants and algae evolved, which removed more carbon dioxide *(1 mark)* and added oxygen to the air *(1 mark)* by photosynthesis.

Exam Paper — Unit Chemistry 2

1 (a) $14 + (1 \times 4) + 14 + (16 \times 3) = 80$ *(2 marks for correct answer, otherwise 1 mark for correct substitution)*

(b) $[(14 + 14) \div 80] \times 100 = 35\%$ *(1 mark)*

(c) E.g. high boiling point *(1 mark)*, high melting point *(1 mark)*, dissolves easily in water *(1 mark)*, conducts electricity when melted or dissolved in water *(1 mark)*.

2 (a) The relative atomic mass of an element is the mass of one atom of that element compared with an atom of carbon-12 *(1 mark)*. It is an average value for the isotopes of that element *(1 mark)*.

(b) E.g.

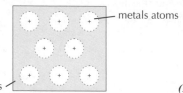

— metals atoms

delocalised electrons ⟍   *(1 mark)*

The question asks for a labelled diagram, so if you don't label it, you don't get the mark.

(c) (i) The delocalised electrons within silver are able to move so heat is easily conducted across the metal *(1 mark)*.

(ii) The layers of atoms within silver are able to slide over each other *(1 mark)*.

(d) Particles that are 1-100 nm across *(1 mark)*.

3 (a) Any two of: e.g. reinforcing graphite in tennis rackets / lubricant coatings / drug delivery in medicines / as catalysts *(2 marks)*.

(b) (i) Each carbon atom has one delocalised (free) electron and it's these free electrons that conduct electricity *(1 mark)*.

(ii) Each carbon atom only forms three covalent bonds. This creates layers which are free to slide over each other *(1 mark)*.

(c) E.g. diamond *(1 mark)*. Each carbon atom forms four covalent bonds in a very rigid giant structure, unlike graphite *(1 mark)*. Fullerenes have carbon atoms arranged in hexagonal rings that form hollow balls or tubes, unlike in diamond *(1 mark)*.

4 (a) How to grade your answer:

0 marks: No clear description or explanation of the properties of thermosetting or thermosoftening polymers.

1-2 marks: Some attempt to describe the properties of thermosetting and thermosoftening polymers, but these are not explained.

3-4 marks: The properties of thermosetting and thermosoftening polymers are described and some explanation is given. The answer has a logical structure and spelling, grammar and punctuation are mostly correct.

5-6 marks: The properties of thermosetting and thermosoftening polymers are described and full explanations are given. The answer has a logical structure and uses correct spelling, grammar and punctuation.

Here are some points your answer may include:

Thermosoftening polymers are easy to melt.

When they cool, thermosoftening polymers harden into a new shape, so these plastics can be melted and remoulded.

Polymers are made up of lots of molecules joined together in long chains. Thermosoftening polymers don't have cross-linking between chains.

The forces between the chains in thermosoftening polymers are really easy to overcome, so it's easy to melt the plastic.

Thermosetting polymers are strong, hard and rigid.

Thermosetting polymers don't soften when they're heated.

Thermosetting polymers have crosslinks which hold the chains together in a solid structure.

(b) (i) C *(1 mark)*

(ii) B *(1 mark)*

(iii) Any two from: e.g. catalyst used, reaction conditions, starting materials *(2 marks)*.

5 (a) A reaction that gives out energy (usually heat) to the surroundings *(1 mark)*.

(b) E.g. measure the temperature of some water, add the solid and stir, then measure the temperature again *(1 mark)*. Repeat the experiment with other solids to determine which is the most effective. The same volume of water and mass of solid should be used for each experiment *(1 mark)*.

(c) A reaction that takes in energy (usually heat) from the surroundings *(1 mark)*.

6 How to grade your answer:

0 marks: No advantages and disadvantages are given.

1-2 marks: Brief description of at least one advantage and one disadvantage is given.

3-4 marks: At least two advantages and two disadvantages are given. The answer has a logical structure and spelling, grammar and punctuation are mostly correct.

5-6 marks: The answer gives at least three advantages and three disadvantages. The answer has a logical structure and uses correct spelling, grammar and punctuation.

Here are some points your answer may include:

Advantages:

Catalysts increase the rate of the reaction, which saves a lot of money because the plant doesn't need to operate for as long to produce the same amount of product.

A catalyst will allow the reaction to work at a much lower temperature. That reduces the energy used in the reaction (the energy cost), which can save a lot of money and also saves resources for future generations.

Catalysts never get used up in the reaction, so they can be used again and again.

Disadvantages:

Catalysts can be very expensive to buy.

Catalysts can be 'poisoned' by impurities, so they stop working. This means the reaction mixture must be kept very clean.

Catalysts often need to be removed from the product and cleaned.

If you're asked for advantages and disadvantages, then ideally you should give an equal number of both. That way you're giving a balanced view.

7 (a) $60 \div 10 = 6$ cm³/s *(1 mark)*

(b)

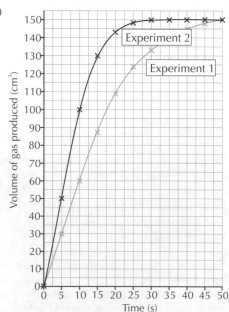

(1 mark for correctly plotted points, 1 mark for a good curve of best fit)

(c) 6-8 seconds (to collect 75 cm³) *(1 mark)*

The total volume is 150 cm³, so you need to read off the value from 75 cm³ on your graph.

(d) The rate of reaction decreases as the reaction proceeds *(1 mark)*.

It increases the rate of the reaction. The graph for experiment 2 has a steeper slope at the beginning. / The reaction is complete in less time *(1 mark)*.

  (a) $2Cl^- \rightarrow Cl_2 + 2e^-$ *(1 mark)*
     $2H^+ + 2e^- \rightarrow H_2$ *(1 mark)*

  (b) (i) sodium hydroxide/NaOH *(1 mark)*

     (ii) E.g. the production of soap *(1 mark)*

     (iii) E.g. the production of bleach *(1 mark)* and plastics *(1 mark)*

  (c) Coating of the surface of one metal with another metal using electricity *(1 mark)*.

9 (a) (i) The excess solid will just sink to the bottom of the flask *(1 mark)*.

     (ii) zinc chloride *(1 mark)* and water *(1 mark)*.

  (b) E.g. using an indicator to show when the reaction's finished *(1 mark)*, add exactly the right amount of potassium hydroxide to just neutralise the hydrochloric acid *(1 mark)*. Then repeat the reaction using exactly the same volumes of alkali and acid so the salt isn't contaminated with indicator *(1 mark)*. Slowly evaporate off the water to crystallise the salt *(1 mark)*.

Exam Paper — Unit Chemistry 3

1 (a) This means that the forward and reverse reactions happen at exactly the same rate *(1 mark)*.

  (b) 450 °C *(1 mark)*

  (c) The yield of ammonia will decrease *(1 mark)*. Increasing the temperature will favour the reverse reaction which takes in energy *(1 mark)*.

  (d) 200 atmospheres

  (e) The yield of ammonia will decrease *(1 mark)*. This is because lower pressures favour the reverse reaction (since there are four molecules of gas on the left-hand side, for every two molecules on the right) *(1 mark)*.

  (f) iron *(1 mark)*

2 (a) Any two of: e.g. potassium fizzes more than sodium, which fizzes more than lithium / potassium moves more quickly than sodium, which moves more quickly than lithium / a flame is only seen with potassium *(2 marks)*.

  (b) E.g. Group 1 elements further down the group have an outer electron that is further from the nucleus *(1 mark)*. The electron in the highest energy level is more easily lost because there's less attraction from the nucleus holding it in place *(1 mark)*.

  (c) hydrogen *(1 mark)*

  (d) $2Li + 2H_2O \rightarrow 2LiOH + H_2$ *(1 mark for products, 1 for balancing)*

  (e) (i) Sodium is soft compared to most other metals *(1 mark)*.

     (ii) Sodium has a low melting and boiling point compared to most other metals *(1 mark)*.

3 (a) a scum *(1 mark)*

  (b) C *(1 mark)*

  (c) A. Boiling removes temporary hardness but not permanent hardness *(1 mark)*. Water from source A still needed more soap to create a lather after boiling than the soft water *(1 mark)*. Therefore it must contain permanent hardness *(1 mark)*.

  (d) Adding washing soda/sodium carbonate/Na_2CO_3 *(1 mark)* — the calcium and magnesium ions are precipitated out of solution as insoluble carbonates *(1 mark)*.

    Using an ion exchange column *(1 mark)* — the calcium and magnesium ions are replaced by sodium ions or hydrogen ions, making the water soft *(1 mark)*.

  (e) E.g. using hard water can increase costs as more soap will be needed to make a lather *(1 mark)*. Scale can build up in kettles and heating systems, reducing their efficiency *(1 mark)*.

4 (a)

Solution A	Solution B	Description of test	Observations Solution A	Observations Solution B
Iron(II) chloride	Iron(III) chloride	Add sodium hydroxide (NaOH) solution	Green precipitate	Brown precipitate
Sodium chloride	Sodium iodide	Add dilute nitric acid (HNO₃) followed by silver nitrate (AgNO₃) solution	White precipitate	Yellow precipitate

(1 mark for each test, 1 mark for each set of observations)

  (b) sodium carbonate *(1 mark for identifying the sodium ion and 1 mark for identifying the carbonate ion)*

5 (a) Bonds broken $(2 \times 436) + 498 = +1370$ *(1 mark)*

    Bonds formed $(4 \times 464) = -1856$ *(1 mark)*

    Total change $+1370 - 1856 = -486$ (kJ/mol) **or** 486 kJ/mol released *(1 mark)*

    Energy change $= -486$ kJ/mol *(1 mark)*

  (b) Exothermic *(1 mark)*. The energy released from forming new bonds is greater than the energy needed to break the existing bonds *(1 mark)*.

6 (a) E.g. methyl orange / phenolphthalein *(1 mark)*.

  (b) $H_2SO_4(aq) + Ca(OH)_2(aq) \rightarrow CaSO_4(aq) + 2H_2O(l)$ *(1 mark)*

  (c) (i) $(8.8 \div 1000) \times 0.05 = 0.00044$ moles *(1 mark)*

     (ii) 0.00044 moles *(1 mark)*

    From the equation you can see that there is one molecule of H_2SO_4 to every one of $Ca(OH)_2$. Therefore the number of moles of each that react will be the same.

    (iii) $0.00044 \times (1000 \div 10) = 0.044$ mol/dm³ *(1 mark)*

    (iv) $0.044 \times 74 = 3.26$ g/dm³ *(1 mark)*

7 (a) A hydrogen fuel cell is an electrical cell that's supplied with hydrogen and oxygen and uses energy from the reaction between them to generate electricity *(1 mark)*.

  (b) hydrogen + oxygen $\rightarrow$ water *(1 mark)*

  (c) How to grade your answer:

    0 marks: There is no evaluation of the use of hydrogen fuel cells.

    1-2 marks: There is a brief description of either at least one advantage or at least one disadvantage of the use of hydrogen fuel cells.

    3-4 marks: There is some evaluation of the use of hydrogen fuel cells. The answer has a logical structure and spelling, grammar and punctuation are mostly correct.

    5-6 marks: There is a clear, balanced and detailed evaluation of the use of hydrogen fuel cells. The answer has a logical structure and uses correct spelling, grammar and punctuation.

  Here are some points your answer may include:

  Hydrogen fuel cell vehicles don't produce any conventional pollutants — no greenhouse gases, no nitrogen oxides, no sulfur dioxide, no carbon monoxide.

  The only by-products are water and heat. This would be a major advantage in cities, where air pollution from traffic is a big problem.

  Hydrogen fuel cells could eventually help countries to become less dependent on crude oil, as less petrol and diesel would be needed.

  Hydrogen is a gas so it takes up a lot more space to store than liquid fuels like petrol.

  Hydrogen is very explosive so it's difficult to store safely.

  Hydrogen fuel is often made either from hydrocarbons (from fossil fuels), or by electrolysis of water, which uses electricity (and that electricity's got to be generated somehow — usually this involves fossil fuels).

8 (a)

(1 mark)

  (b) By using oxidising agents or microbes like yeast *(1 mark)* to oxidise ethanol *(1 mark)*.

  (c) ethanoic acid + ethanol $\rightarrow$ ethyl ethanoate + water *(1 mark)*

  (d) -COO- / *(1 mark)*

  (e) E.g. in perfumes / in flavourings *(1 mark)*.

Index

Index

Index